SLIDE
RULE
simplified

Third Edition

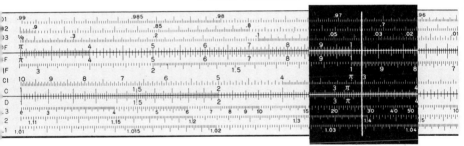

Charles O. Harris

Director of Faculty Development
General Motors Institute

Formerly Head, Department of Applied Mechanics
Michigan State University

Formerly Professor of Engineering Mechanics,
University of Notre Dame

Formerly Assistant Professor of Mechanics,
Illinois Institute of Technology

AMERICAN
TECHNICAL  CHICAGO 60637
SOCIETY

Copyright ©, 1943, 1961, 1972 by
AMERICAN TECHNICAL SOCIETY

Library of Congress Number 78-183979
ISBN: 0-8269-2342-9
FIRST EDITION

1st Printing 1943
2d Printing 1944
3d Printing 1945
4th Printing 1946
5th Printing 1949
6th Printing 1951
7th Printing 1952
8th Printing February, 1953
9th Printing October, 1953
10th Printing 1954
11th Printing 1955
12th Printing 1956
13th Printing 1957
14th Printing 1958
15th Printing 1959
16th Printing January, 1960
17th Printing July, 1960

SECOND EDITION (REVISED)

18th Printing 1961
19th Printing 1961
20th Printing March, 1962
21st Printing August, 1962
22d Printing 1963
23rd Printing 1964
24th Printing 1966
25th Printing 1968
26th Printing 1969
27th Printing 1970

THIRD EDITION (REVISED)

28th Printing 1972

PUBLISHER'S NOTES
ON THIRD EDITION

Since the first publication of *Slide Rule Simplified* in 1943, a number of important changes have taken place in the requirements of students, users, and teachers of the slide rule. The Mannheim type of rule, popular in those days, has been largely replaced by relatively inexpensive rules with more scales and better arrangements of scales. Because of extended use of dimensionally stable PVC and ABS plastics, really fine slide rules are available for a fraction of the price of earlier rules with like scales. Even log log slide rules of acceptable quality are available at reasonable prices.

Coupled with these facts, growing technology in many areas has required much greater numbers of workers capable of performing technical calculations.

The second edition, published in 1961, updated the book somewhat by recognizing the use of log log scales (six of them) in an Appendix. This expanded the original 9 scales to 15, with the main instruction still based on the older Mannheim type slide rule—a fact that limited its usefulness for more advanced calculations.

The third edition breaks away from this limitation while still retaining instructions for using the older slide rules as well as the more desirable types now widely used by persons who could not previously afford them.

The more modern slide rules do not merely add scales to those previously used. Some of the changes are radical. For example, most slide rules of *all* types have two scales designated as **S** and **T**. They are really *angle scales* for finding sines, cosines and tangents of given angles. However, the designations are misleading. Older scales designated as **S** and **T** were calibrated in angles divided into minutes or minutes and seconds. They were keyed to work with other slide rule scales based on a different system than the decimal trig rules with angles calibrated decimally. The "decimal trig" slide rules (including log log rules) always have an **ST** scale to complete the ranges of angles. The two systems are incompatible and therefore require separate instructions.

Counting the three "decimal trig" **S**, **T**, and **ST** scales, the **CF**,

CIF and **DF** folded scales, the R_1 and R_2 split scales and the 15 scales covered by the second edition expands the total to 23 scales—an increase of nearly 54% over the second edition and over two and one-half times the number of scales originally explained by the book.

The word "simplified" in the title is still justified, however, in the sense that this book deals only with finding numbers and the mechanics of numerical calculation to eliminate the drudgery and fatigue of "longhand" methods. It is now, as originally, confined to arithmetical operations, not attempting to teach algebra, trigonometry, calculus, etc.

While Dr. Harris is correct in saying that many practical calculations can be made on the slide rule by persons without basic knowledge of logarithms, exponents, powers and roots of numbers, or trigonometry, it is also true that the real expert in slide rule operation is knowledgeable in such matters. Accordingly, the basis of each process is explained for the benefit of those seeking further knowledge.

Of at least equal importance to the use of additional scales is new Chapter 16, entitled "The Powers of 10 Method for Locating the Decimal Point." This chapter presents an alternative to the Digit Count system that is still retained in the new edition. For many years the American School, while using *Slide Rule Simplified* as the basic text, has taught "powers of 10" in preference to Digit Count for this purpose.

Because of the expansion of international trade in recent years, many United States firms must convert from U.S. to metric measurements. For this reason the author has added Appendix B covering the most common conversions of length, volume, force, and temperature by slide rule. This is appropriate because the ordinary slide rule is ideally suited for such calculations. It is calibrated decimally, and the results of slide rule computation are in decimal form. In the event the United States changes to the SI system of units, nothing now learned about the slide rule will be obsoleted by the change. Direct calculations in metric measurements are, in fact, considerably simpler than those in the present U.S. measurements.

THE PUBLISHERS

iv

PREFACE

The slide rule is a valuable aid to anyone who has to make numerical calculations—estimator, merchant, accountant, and many others—and is an indispensable tool to the engineer and scientist. It is a tremendous timesaver to all of these people.

Many people who would like to use the slide rule are frightened away from it by the feeling that its operation is difficult to master. One of the primary aims of this book is to dispel this idea, and replace it with the certain knowledge that anyone who will study and practice can learn to use the slide rule with ease and confidence.

The instructions are presented in a manner that recognizes the usual difficulties of the learner and overcomes them. An unusual feature of the book is the complete instruction on how to read the different scales of the slide rule accurately and precisely, and thus avoid serious errors. Each type of calculation—multiplication, division, combinations of multiplication and division, the square and square root, the cube and cube root—all are discussed so thoroughly that they can be mastered by the reader who studies alone, as well as by those who study in the classroom. The treatment of each operation in the first eight chapters is so complete that it can be followed by anyone who has studied arithmetic and can multiply two numbers and divide one number by another, even though he has never before seen a slide rule.

On the other hand, Chapters 9 through 15 will be of value to people who need to make technical and advanced calculations. These chapters cover sines and cosines, the tangent of an angle, logs and antilogs, the split scales for square and square root, the reciprocal scales, the folded scales, and the log log scales.

A special feature of the 3rd edition of this book is Chapter 16, which presents and explains a method which uses powers of 10 in locating the decimal point in an answer.

Only a small percentage of those who own slide rules are well enough acquainted with them to use them to full advantage. One object of this book is to present such a thorough treatment of the slide rule that anyone who studies all of it will be able to perform a great variety of numerical calculations easily, accurately, and with confidence.

METHOD OF EXPLANATION. The method of explanation is, in general, the same throughout the book.

1. The operation, for instance multiplication, is carefully described, step by step, logically.

2. Each process is illustrated by a number of Illustrative Examples. Each of these examples was carefully chosen, so that the explanations are unusually complete. In many cases, sketches provide a picture of each step taken in the solution of a given example.

3. A great many Practice Problems are furnished for the student. It is especially important that these problems be solved, since it is only by practice that the correct use of the slide rule is mastered and real skill acquired. An important feature of these Practice Problems is the fact that they follow the form used in practical work; this means that the type of problems studied is exactly the same type that the reader might have to solve with the slide rule. Answers to these problems are given in the back of the book so that the solutions may be checked.

4. Rules are given for locating the decimal point by means of a system of "digit counts."

5. At the end of most chapters, there are Review Problems. No answers are given for Review Problems. Instructors will find these Review Problems useful as Examinations for classes; students working alone should use them as self tests.

6. The basis of each fundamental operation is explained by means of logarithms, since the slide rule is based on logarithms. Study of these explanations of the basis of the process is optional. They are given for the benefit of those who enjoy mathematics for its own sake, or who want to know just why the slide rule manipulations give the correct results.

Special attention is called to a brief discussion of Negative Numbers and the Law of Signs which has been put in the back of the book as a review for those who have forgotten.

The first edition of this text was written especially for the 10-inch Mannheim slide rule, because that was the most widely used slide rule in those days. Since that time, duplex slide rules and especially the log log slide rule have come into such common use that the treatment has been modified and expanded to cover all types of straight slide rules.

The author wishes to express his thanks and appreciation to Mr. Arthur E. Burke, Art Director of the American Technical Society, for excellent work in preparing the drawings and illustrations which appear throughout the book. Gratitude is also due to Mr. Dal Fitts for his careful and excellent editing of the third edition.

CHARLES O. HARRIS

HOW TO USE THIS BOOK

It is suggested that the book be studied in the following manner:

1. Study the chapters in the order given, at least through Chapter 8.

2. Learn each point thoroughly before going on to the next.

3. Read the explanations given and follow the Illustrative Examples carefully. Many of these examples have been suggested by common mistakes of other learners, and careful study will help you to avoid these, or similar, mistakes.

4. Work all the problems, both Practice and Review. A great deal of practice is necessary in order to become proficient in the use of the slide rule.

5. If interested in the basis of the slide rule, read the sections headed "Basis of the Process." However, it is not necessary to know the basis in order to use the slide rule. In any case, do not read the basis of an operation until you have learned the operation.

6. For convenient, ready reference, the fundamental rules have been assembled and put in the back of the book. You will also find there a review of negative numbers and the law of signs.

Practice. Practice as much as you can. As soon as you learn its operation, use the slide rule in your work whenever possible.

Decimal Point. A great deal of attention has been given to rules for locating the decimal point in the answer. This is an especially important consideration since an answer ten or one hundred times too large, or ten or one hundred times too small, is not only worthless, but can cause much harm. A system of "digit counts" is explained, which makes it possible to state exact and concise rules for locating the decimal point, and give them in terms of the digit counts for the numbers, rather than in terms of the characteristics of the logarithms. This is simple and more direct, and enables the learner to use the slide rule without any knowledge of logarithms.

Also, Chapter 16 is an explanation of another method of locating the decimal point is an answer. This method makes use of powers of 10.

Anyone who wants to use the slide rule for unusual or advanced calculations will find the basis for his work in this textbook.

Continued practice will bring skill in setting and in reading the slide rule and will give one confidence in the results obtained.

TABLE OF CONTENTS

CHAPTER 1

INTRODUCTION

WHAT THE SLIDE RULE IS. The slide rule is an instrument for performing certain arithmetical calculations. It is used widely by engineers, architects, businessmen, shopmen, and others who wish to make these arithmetical calculations quickly and accurately. The most important feature of its use is the saving of time and energy that it makes possible. The slide rule consists of three parts: the fixed part, called *the stock; the slide,* or movable part in the center; and *the runner.* The runner is a piece of glass or transparent plastic with a scratch or hairline in the center. Fig. 1-1 is

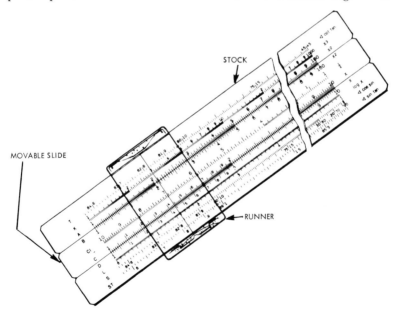

Fig. 1-1. Shortened view of a modern all-plastic slide rule with ten scales, all on the front.

an illustration of a slide rule with the different parts labeled. The slide rule is similar to many other instruments, in that, by its use, work can be done more quickly and accurately than by hand. However, unlike many instruments, its use can be learned easily. Anyone who will devote a reasonable amount of time to practice can learn to use the slide rule with ease and confidence.

WHAT YOU CAN DO WITH THE SLIDE RULE. Any calculation in arithmetic except addition and subtraction can be performed with the slide rule. The most common operations are multiplication, division, and combinations of these; to find the square of a number or its square root; the cube of a number or its cube root; and operations involving the trigonometric functions such as the sine, cosine, and tangent, although it is not necessary to know trigonometry in order to use the slide rule.

ADVANTAGES OF THE SLIDE RULE. The greatest advantage of the use of a slide rule is the saving of time and energy. In most problems, the labor of making the calculations in longhand requires much more time than the determination of just what calculations to make. When the slide rule is used, it is often possible to save 90 per cent of the time otherwise devoted to calculation. For example, to find the result of

$$\frac{436 \times 76 \times 362}{372 \times 52 \times 172}$$

longhand would require making two multiplications to find the numerator, then two more to find the denominator, and finally, dividing the numerator by the denominator. It would be necessary to write down many numbers in the intermediate steps of the process. With the slide rule, each of the six numbers would be located on the rule at the proper time in the operation, and the only number to write, besides setting down the original numbers,

$$\frac{436 \times 76 \times 362}{372 \times 52 \times 172}$$

would be the answer: The calculation could be made in 15 seconds, which represents a great saving of time. The energy consideration is equally important. Work done longhand results in the expenditure of much more mental and physical effort than the same amount of work done with the slide rule. This leads to fatigue and nervous strain, which in turn lead to errors; all this can be largely eliminated by using the slide rule. An important feature of industrial development is the requirement that workers of each generation accomplish more in a day than those of the previous generation. This places a premium on speed and accuracy. Hence, laborsaving devices become more and more important. Time and concentration that can be saved for any part of the task that really demands them, are too valuable to waste.

Compilation of tables usually leads to a certain type of calculation (for example, the division of the product of two numbers by the product of two others) which must be performed separately for each of many combinations of numbers. For doing such work, the slide rule offers methods which eliminate a great deal of unnecessary labor.

With the slide rule it is as easy to work with one number as another. The multiplication of 268 by 341 is as easy as 300 by 200. Multiplication with the slide rule involves only writing the operation, 268 × 341, a quick manipulation of the rule and writing the answer. In making this particular multiplication longhand, ten extra numerals must be written down during the process, and at least eleven mental steps are necessary. If made with the slide rule, calculations involving large numbers are no more difficult than those involving small ones. It is as easy to divide 23,700 by 198 as to divide 39 by 7.

When calculations require the use of the sine, cosine, or tangent of an angle, the function can be obtained from the slide rule. This releases the operator from the inconvenience of consulting a book of tables when in the middle of a problem, and also saves time. In an emergency when a set of tables is not available, the advantage of being able to determine the sine of an angle with the slide rule becomes most apparent.

Further advantages of the slide rule are compactness and cheapness. An eight- or ten-inch slide rule can be carried in a pocket, notebook, or brief case. Other devices for rapid calculation are either bulkier or less flexible in operation. Other mechanical calculators which compare in efficiency are far more expensive.

SUGGESTIONS FOR LEARNING. It is easy to learn to use the slide rule. A knowledge of logarithms will be found helpful but is not essential. The fundamental operations can be learned through study, and with practice soon become automatic.

The material in this book should be read with the slide rule in hand. The Illustrative Examples should be studied in detail and the problems worked carefully. There are enough problems so that anyone who works them all will become skilled in the use of the slide rule.

Speed in manipulating the slide rule will soon be acquired but should not be forced. The time saved by substituting the slide-rule method for the longhand method is far more important than the time saved by hasty operation of the rule itself.

A feeling of confidence in the results obtained by slide-rule calculation will develop rapidly. With experience will come the realization that the use of the slide rule actually reduces the number of errors.

WHAT SLIDE RULE TO USE. The slide rule shown in Fig. 1-1 is satisfactory for learning purposes, and for many practical uses. It is simple and its operation is easy to learn; yet it is sufficient for all types of calculations. It is the 10-inch length, which is the most common and the most practical.

As you acquire skill and progress in understanding of the slide rule, you may feel that your knowledge and requirements justify the purchase of a better slide rule. Advantages of the better rules include:

1. Better construction, which makes manipulation easier.

2. Freedom from shrinking and warping, so that the slide rule remains accurate

3. Clearer marking, which prevents eyestrain

Slide rules are available in a wide range of prices; but any slide rule, no matter what its cost, is a good investment.

In purchasing a new slide rule it is well to consider the conditions under which it will be used. It is obviously unwise to subject an expensive slide rule to dirt or mechanical hazards.

A slide rule of 8- or 10-inch length is the most convenient for general use. The scales are long enough for precision and the rule is not too long to be carried handily in a brief case or notebook. The 20-inch slide rule gives greater precision but is not so easy to carry around and is awkward to use in the classroom.

The scope of the book has been expanded in this third edition so that it now covers all of the slide rules in common use, from the old Mannheim rules to the most elaborate log log rules.

CHAPTER 2

HOW TO HOLD THE SLIDE RULE

If the slide rule is to be used efficiently, it is necessary for the operator to be able to adjust the slide and runner to the proper numbers with speed and precision. This requires that the slide move easily in the stock. The slide should fit just tightly enough so that its own weight will not cause it to drop from the stock when the rule is held vertically. If the slide sticks, it can usually be made to move easily by lubricating with graphite from a soft lead pencil. Fig. 2-1 shows how the pencil is to be applied to the slide. In addition to providing lubrication, this process removes dirt from the

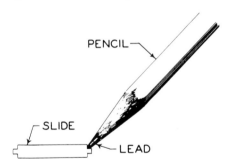

Fig. 2-1. Lubricating slide rule with graphite.

corners of the slide. Lubrication in this manner is not recommended for plastic slide rules, however. Usually the plastic material, such as PVC or ABS, has no tendency to bind and is resilient enough to remain in adjustment indefinitely.

ADJUSTING THE RUNNER. Most slide rule operations commence with the location of a number by means of the hairline of the runner. Fig. 2-2 shows the proper position of the hands on the rule for this maneuver. The rule should be held lightly and the palms of the hands should not be in contact with it. Of the front of each hand, only the cushion at the base of the little finger should

5

Fig. 2-2. Proper position of hands for adjusting the runner.

touch the slide rule. This affords sufficient purchase for holding the rule and leaves the thumbs free to adjust the runner. A slight pressure on the runner and stock by each thumb will hold the runner in full control and allow it to be adjusted quickly. Most beginners hold the rule too tightly. Any tendency toward this must be overcome.

When the number with which the calculation commences is near the end of the slide rule, the same spacing of the hands should be maintained as they move along the rule. As one hand moves off the rule, its forefinger may be used to assist the thumb in controlling the runner. A little practice in sliding the runner back and forth will help you to understand and follow these directions.

ADJUSTING THE SLIDE. The user of the slide rule must be able to adjust the slide to its proper position for each calculation. Fig. 2-3 shows the proper position of the hands on the rule

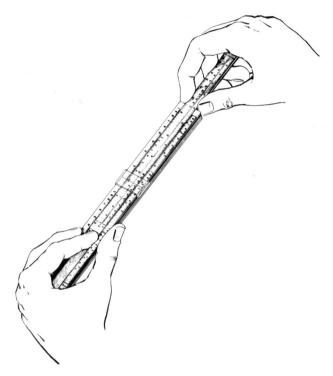

Fig. 2-3. Adjusting the slide when the right end projects from the stock.

when the right end of the slide projects from the stock. The left hand holds the stock lightly and the forefinger pushes against the slide. The right hand grips the slide with the forefinger pressing against the stock. The palms of the hands should not touch the slide rule. When the slide rule is held in this manner, the slide can be adjusted quickly and precisely.

When the left end of the slide projects from the stock, the positions of the hands are interchanged.

Any scales on the back of the slide are read by turning the rule over and extending the slide to the right. For this, the left hand should be held as in Fig. 2-2 and the right hand as in Fig. 2-3.

CHAPTER 3

THE BASIC SCALES
OF THE SLIDE RULE

All slide rule calculations, multiplication, division, etc., involve locating, in their proper positions on the rule, the numbers with which the operation is to be performed; and reading, on the slide rule, the number which is the answer. In order to multiply 16 × 13, for instance, you must know exactly how and where the numbers 16 and 13 are to be located on the slide rule, and where the answer will be found and how to read it. The first step in learning to use the slide rule is to become familiar with all parts of it so that locating a number or reading an answer can be done quickly and accurately. The purpose of this chapter is to describe and explain the different parts of the slide rule so that you will be able to do this. The chapter should be read with the slide rule at hand. All examples should be followed on your own rule.

Work carefully and be sure that you understand each topic before going on to the next. Nothing can be gained by skipping around.

SCALES. Fig. 1-1 shows the front of one type of slide rule. The fixed part, or frame, is called the *stock,* the movable part in the center is called the *slide,* and the glass or clear plastic is called the *runner.* The scratch or hairline on the runner is used to locate and read numbers on the slide rule. Each of these parts is labeled.

The slide rule in Fig.1-1 has ten rows of marks, each row extending along, and parallel to, the rule. Each row is called a scale and bears the name of the letter at its left end. Thus the **A** scale, with the letter **A** at its end, is on the upper part of the stock; the **B, CI** (pronounced see-eye) and **C** scales are on the slide; the **D** scale is on the lower part of the stock, while the **K** scale is on the upper part of the stock. These are the basic scales and the ones used the most. They are explained in this chapter to provide a foundation for the most common slide rule operations. Various other scales are each explained in the chapters which show how to use them.

8

THE DIGITS OF A NUMBER. Numbers consist of various sequences of the numerals *0* to *9* inclusive. For example, the numbers *3495, 2.16,* and *0.00948* are sequences of numerals. For the purpose of the discussions which follow in this book, *the first digit of a number is defined as the first numeral (other than zero) as the number is read from left to right.* In determining the first digit, any zeros at the extreme left of the number are passed over. In each of the following numbers, the first digit appears in bold-face type: 0.000**3**78; **7**.85; **4**3200; 0.0**2**09; **5**76; **1**,000,000; 0.**1**003. The first digit cannot be zero. The second digit is the numeral immediately after the first digit and the second digit can be zero. The third, fourth, fifth digits, etc., are the numerals in order as they follow the second digit of the number. Any digit except the first can be zero. The following examples will illustrate this.

ILLUSTRATIVE EXAMPLES

1. *In the number 0.9083, the first digit is 9, the second digit is 0, the third is 8, and the fourth is 3.*

2. *In the number 12.06, the first digit is 1, the second digit is 2, the third is 0, and the fourth is 6.*

3. *In the number 35000, the first digit is 3, the second digit is 5, and the third, fourth, and fifth digits are each zero.*

4. *In the number 1.933, the first digit is 1, the second digit is 9, and the third and fourth digits are each 3.*

5. *In the number 0.00628, the first digit is 6, the second digit is 2, and the third digit is 8. The zeros to the left of 6 are not counted as digits.*

6. *In the number 1.0004, the first digit is 1, the second, third, and fourth digits are each 0, and the fifth digit is 4.*

THE C AND D SCALES

The **C** and **D** scales, which are identical, appear below the center of the front of the slide rule. (See Fig. 1-1.) The **C** scale is on the slide, or movable part in the center, and the D scale is on the fixed part or stock.

USE OF THE C AND D SCALES. The C and D scales are used together for multiplication and division. In using the slide rule, multiplication and division are the most important operations because they are those most frequently performed. The C and D scales are also used with the **A** and **B** scales for finding the square or square root of a number; with the **K** scale for finding the cube or cube root of a number; with the tangent scale for finding the tangent of an angle or arctangent of a number; and with the log scale for finding the log or antilog of a number. The **C** and **D** scales are used more than any of the other scales on the slide rule.

MARKING OF THE C AND D SCALES. The number *1* at the left end of each scale is called the *left index,* see Fig. 3-1. The number *1* at the right end is called the *right index.* Between the two indices are the divisions, numbered *2* (about three-tenths of the total length from the left index), *3, 4, 5, 6, 7, 8,* and *9.* Hereafter the word *division* will mean one of these marks. Each length

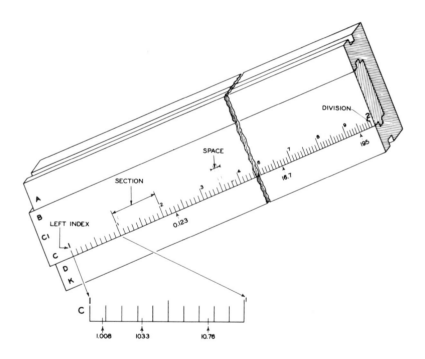

Fig. 3-1. Lefthand portion of the C scale, showing locations of numbers 1.008, 1033, and 10.76 in enlarged section; also numbers 0.123, 16.7 and 195.

between two consecutive divisions, for example between the divisions *4* and *5*, is divided into ten *sections* and each section is subdivided into *spaces*. Between the left index of the scale and the division marked 2, each section has ten spaces. This portion of the scale is shown in Fig. 3-1 where the terms *division, section,* and *space* are illustrated. Between the divisions marked *2* and *4*, there are only five spaces to each section, and to the right of the division marked *4*, there are only two spaces to each section.

DECIMAL POINT. The position of the decimal point of a number has nothing to do with the location of the number on the C or D scales of the slide rule. No matter where the decimal point is, the number will have the same location on the C or D scale. The only thing that influences the location of the number is the sequence of digits in the number. Thus the numbers *0.000348; 0.348; 3.48; 348; 34,800,* would all be the same on these scales.

HOW TO LOCATE A NUMBER ON THE C AND D SCALES. When the First Digit is 1. Fig. 3-1 shows the portion of the C scale between the left index and the division marked 2. Any number which has *1* for its first digit is located here. The second digit of the number determines in which one of the ten sections the number is to be located, and the third digit locates the number in the proper space of the section. Any digit except the first may be zero. The first cannot be zero, but is defined as the first numeral of the number which is not zero. Correct locations for the numbers *0.123, 16.7* and *195* are shown in Fig. 3-1. Detailed instructions for locating these numbers follow:

ILLUSTRATIVE EXAMPLES

7. *To locate the number 16.7.*
1) Since the first digit is *1*, the number is located in the portion of the scale shown in Fig. 3-1.
2) The second digit is *6*, so count off six sections from the left index. Note that the mark at the right of the sixth section bears the number *6*.
3) From this mark, count off seven spaces, since the third digit is 7. The number is located at the right end of the seventh space.

8. *To locate the number 195.*
1) The fact that the first digit of the number is *1* shows that the

number is to be located between the left index and the division marked *2*.

2) Count nine sections from the left index since the second digit is *9*.

3) From here count five spaces to the right. The number is located at the end of the fifth space beyond nine sections.

   9. *To locate the number 0.123.*

1) The first digit of the number is *1* so the number is located in the portion of the scale between the left index and the division marked *2*.

2) The second digit is *2*, so count two sections from the left index.

3) From here, count three spaces to the right. This is the location of the number.

   Numbers having more than three digits. Any number which has *1* for its first digit is located between the left index of the scale and the division marked *2*. If the number has no more than three digits it can be located exactly, that is, it will fall on a mark between two spaces. This was the case in each of the three foregoing examples. A number having four digits must be located approximately, since it will be between the marks. The first three digits locate the number in the proper space. The fourth digit is the number of tenths of a space between the left end of the space and the location of the number. For example, if the fourth digit is *6,* the number is to be located six-tenths of the space from the left side of the space, and this six-tenths of the space must be estimated. Fig. 3-1 also shows a larger view of the section at the extreme left of the scale with correct locations for the numbers *1.008, 1033* and *10.76*. The method of locating these numbers is described in the following examples:

ILLUSTRATIVE EXAMPLES

   10. *To locate 1.008.*

1) Since the first digit is *1,* the number is located between the left index of the scale and the division marked *2*.

2) The second digit is *0,* so the number lies in the first section.

3) The third digit is also *0,* so the number lies in the first space of this section.

4) Last, estimate eight-tenths of this space, since the fourth digit is *8*. This number is located here.

11. *To locate 10.76.*

1) The first digit is *1*, so the number lies between the left index of the scale and the division marked *2*.

2) Since the second digit is *0*, the number lies in the first section.

3) The third digit is *7*, so count off *7* spaces from the left index.

4) Since the fourth digit is *6*, estimate six-tenths of a space beyond this and locate the number there.

12. *To locate 1033.*

1) The first digit is *1*, which shows that the number lies between the left index and the division marked *2*.

2) The second digit is *0*, so the number lies in the first section.

3) The third digit is *3*, so count three spaces from the left index.

4) Since the fourth digit is *3*, estimate three-tenths of a space from the left side of the space in which the number belongs.

For any number which has *1* for its first digit, only the first four digits can be considered in locating the number on the C and D scales. If there are more than four digits, those after the fourth are treated as though they were zeros. For example, the number *157836* would be set as *157800* on the slide rule. This is an approximation, but the error involved is less than one part in one thousand. There are few engineering or shop calculations in which such an error would be serious. In many cases it would be necessary to increase the fourth digit when treating those after it as zeros in order to get the best approximation. For instance, the number *11389* is closer to *11390* than it is to *11380*, so *11390* would be used. When the fifth digit is *5* or greater, the fourth digit should be increased by one when replacing the digits after it by zeros; when the fifth digit is less than *5*, the fourth digit should be left unchanged.

When the First Digit is 2. Any number having *2* for its first digit is located between the division marked *2* and the division marked *3*. This portion of the scale is shown in Fig. 3-2 with illustrations of a section and a space. The second digit shows in which section the number lies. Since there are only five spaces in each section, each space has a value of two in the third digit. Thus the third digit of a number located in this portion of the scale can be set precisely only if it is even. The numbers *204*, *0.246* and *26800*

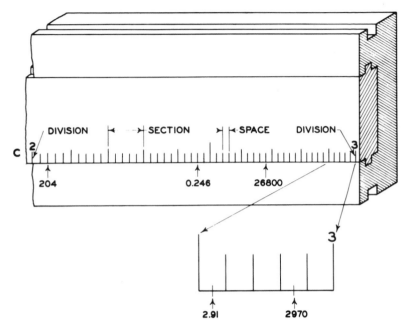

Fig. 3-2. Numbers 204, 0.246, and 26800 properly located between first digits 2 and 3; also numbers 2.91 and 2970 shown in enlarged section at right.

are shown in their proper locations in Fig. 3-2. The process of locating each of these numbers is shown in the following examples.

ILLUSTRATIVE EXAMPLES

13. *To locate 204.*

1) Since the first digit is *2,* the number is located between the divisions marked *2* and *3.*

2) The second digit is *0,* so the number is located in the first section of this portion of the scale.

3) The third digit is *4,* but since each mark on the scale has a value of two in the third digit, you count only two spaces from the left of the section to locate the number.

14. *To locate 0.246.*

1) The first digit of the number is *2,* so the number is located between the divisions marked *2* and *3.*

2) The second digit is *4*, so count four sections from the division marked *2*.

3) From here count three spaces since the third digit is *6* and each space has a value of two in the third digit.

   15. *To locate 26800.*

1) The number is located between the divisions marked *2* and *3* since the first digit is *2*.

2) Since the second digit is *6*, count six sections from the division marked *2*.

3) From here count four spaces since the third digit is *8* and each space has a value of two in third digit.

   Since the fourth and fifth digits are zero, they are not used in locating the number.

   If the third digit of the number is odd, it can be located by estimating one-half of a space. A larger view of the section at the extreme right of this portion of the scale is also shown in Fig. 3-2 with the proper locations for the numbers *2.91* and *2970*. The procedure for locating each of these numbers is given in the examples.

ILLUSTRATIVE EXAMPLES

   16. *To locate 2.91.*

1) The first digit of the number is *2*, so the number is located between the divisions marked *2* and *3*.

2) Since the second digit is *9*, count *9* sections from the division marked *2*.

3) From here, estimate one-half of a space to the right. This locates the number, since the third digit is *1* and each space has a value of two in the third digit.

   17. *To locate 2970.*

1) The number is located between the divisions marked *2* and *3* since the first digit is *2*.

2) Count nine sections from the division marked *2*, since the second digit of the number is *9*.

3) Since the third digit is *7*, count three and one-half spaces from the left of the section. Each space has a value of two in the third digit.

Since the fourth digit is zero, it is not used in locating the number.

Numbers having more than three digits. Only the first three digits of any number which has 2 for its digit can be represented on the C and D scales. If the number has more than three digits, those after the third do not affect the location of the number, but are treated as though they were zeros. Thus, the number *25342* would be located as *25300* on the slide rule. In any case in which the fourth digit is less than *5*, the third digit is left unchanged; in any case in which the fourth digit is *5* or greater, the third digit is increased by one in order to get a better representation of the number. For example, the number *2768* is closer to *2770* than to *2760*, so *2770* would be used in locating the number on the C or D scale.

Likewise, in the portion of the C scale to the right of the division marked *3*, only three digits of a number can be used in locating the number. If there are more than three digits, those after the third are treated as though they were zeros.

When the First Digit is 3. Any number which has *3* for its first digit is located between the divisions marked *3* and *4*. This portion of the scale is similar to that between divisions *2* and *3*. There are ten sections between divisions *3* and *4*, and each section is divided into five spaces. Each space then has a value of two in the third digit of the number. As before, the second digit indicates in which section the number lies, and the third digit gives the number of spaces from the left end of the section. The following example will illustrate.

ILLUSTRATIVE EXAMPLE

18. *To locate 31.5.*

1) Since the first digit of the number is *3*, the number is located between the divisions *3* and *4*.

2) The second digit is *1*, so count one section from division *3*.

3) From here count two and one-half spaces to locate the number. The third digit is *5* and each space has a value of two in the third digit.

When the First Digit is 4. Fig. 3-3 shows the portion of the C scale between the divisions *4* and *5*. Any number which has *4* for its first digit is located here. The second digit of the number determines the proper section. The number can be located precisely only if the third digit is 5 or 0. There are only two spaces in each section in this portion of the scale, and consequently each space must have a value of five in the third digit of the number. Correct locations for the numbers *0.0430* and *475* are shown in Fig. 3-3. The manner of locating them is described in the following examples.

ILLUSTRATIVE EXAMPLES

19. *To locate 0.0430.*
1) The first digit of the number is *4.* Hence the number is located between divisions *4* and *5.*
2) The second digit is *3,* so count three sections from division *4.*
3) Since the third digit is *0,* no spaces are counted from here. The number is located at the right end of the third section.

20. *To locate 475.*

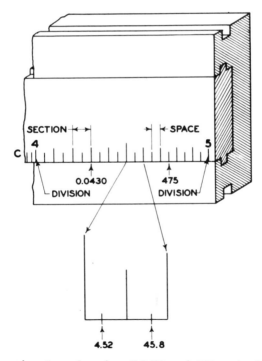

Fig. 3-3. Proper locations of numbers 0.0430 and 475 on the C scale; also numbers 4.52 and 45.8 shown in enlarged spaces below slide rule scales.

1) Since the first digit of the number is *4*, the number is located between divisions *4* and *5*.
2) Count seven sections from division *4*, since the second digit is 7.
3) From here count one space, because the third digit of the number is *5*, and each space has a value of five in the third digit.

If the third digit of the number is neither *5* nor *0*, its location may be determined approximately by estimating to the proper one-fifth of a space. Fig. 3-3 also shows a larger view of one section of this portion of the scale with correct locations for the numbers *4.52* and *45.8*. The following examples demonstrate the procedure used in locating them.

ILLUSTRATIVE EXAMPLES

21. *To locate 4.52.*
1) The first digit of the number is *4*, so the number is located between divisions *4* and *5*.
2) Since the second digit is *5*, count *5* sections from division *4*.
3) The third digit is 2, but each space on the scale has a value of five in the third digit. Hence, estimate two-fifths of a space beyond the fifth section and locate the number here.

22. *To locate 45.8.*
1) The number is located between divisions *4* and *5* since the first digit of the number is *4*.
2) The second digit is *5* so count *5* sections from division *4*.
3) From here estimate one and three-fifths spaces from the fifth section. Each space has a value of five in the third digit and the third digit is *8*.

Only the first three digits of any number beginning with *4* can be represented on the **C** or **D** scale. If there are more than three digits, the remainder does not affect the location of the number. Thus the number *4832* would be set as *483*.

When the First Digit Is 5, 6, 7, 8, or 9. Marks in portions of the scale to the right of division *5* are similar to the portion between divisions *4* and *5*. The following examples will show how such numbers are located.

ILLUSTRATIVE EXAMPLES

23. *To locate 504.*
1) Since the first digit of the number is *5*, the number is located between divisions *5* and *6*.

2) The second digit is *0,* so the number lies in the first section of this portion of the scale.

3) The third digit is *4,* but each space has a value of five in the third digit. Hence estimate four-fifths of a space from division *5.*

24. *To locate 0.66738.*

1) The number is located between divisions *6* and *7* since the first digit is *6.*

2) Count 6 sections from division *6* since the second digit is *6.*

3) The third digit is *7* so estimate one and two-fifths spaces from the end of the sixth section.

4) You cannot show the fourth and fifth digits of the number so ignore them.

25. *To locate 7.85.*

1) The first digit of the number is *7.* Hence the number is located between divsions *7* and *8.*

2) Since the second digit is *8,* count eight sections to the right of division *7.*

3) The third digit is *5* so count exactly one space to the right from this point.

26. *To locate 8190.*

1) Any number beginning with *8* must be located between divisions *8* and *9.*

2) The second digit is *1* so count one section to the right from division *8.*

3) Since the third digit is *9,* estimate one and four-fifths spaces from the right of the first section. The number is located here.

27. *To locate 0.00936.*

1) Since the first digit is *9,* the number is located between division *9* and the right index of the scale.

2) From division *9,* count three sections since the second digit is *3.*

3) From here estimate one and one-fifth spaces. The third digit is *6* and each space has a value of five in the third digit.

THE CI SCALE

The **CI** inverted scale, also called the reciprocal scale, is on the front of the slide and is marked by the letters *CI* at its left end. The **CI** scale can be seen in Fig. 1-1. It can be used with the **C** and **D** scales for multiplication and division and is especially useful for calculations which involve several operations of multiplication and division in sequence, such as,

$$\frac{47.3 \times 0.652 \times 5.3}{3.17 \times 158}$$

The **CI** scale has exactly the same markings as the **C** scale but is read from right to left. Hence, one who is familiar with the **C** scale can locate a number readily on the **CI** scale. An example will show how the scale is read from right to left.

ILLUSTRATIVE EXAMPLE

    28. *To locate 37.7 on the CI scale.*

1) The first digit of the number is *3* so the number is located between the divisions *3* and *4*.
2) Since the second digit is *7,* count seven sections to the left from division *3.*
3) From here, estimate three and one-half spaces to the left. The third digit is *7* and in this portion of the scale each space has a value of two in the third digit.

THE A AND B SCALES

    The **A** and **B** scales are the identical scales which are located on the upper portion of the front of the slide rule. They are shown in Fig. 1-1. The **A** scale is on the upper part of the stock and the **B** scale is on the slide.

    USE OF THE A AND B SCALES. The **A** and **B** scales are used with the **C** and **D** scales for finding the square or square root of a number. They can be used together for multiplying and dividing in the same manner as the **C** and **D** scales. Also, on some slide rules, they are used with the sine scale for finding the sine of an angle or the arc sine of a number.

    MARKING OF THE A AND B SCALES. Each scale is divided into two identical parts by the *1* at the center which is called the center index. The *1* at the extreme left of each scale is called the left index and the *1* at the extreme right is called the right index. Each half of the scale is similar to the **D** scale in that it offers the same numerical range. The divisions marked *2, 3, 4, 5, 6, 7, 8* and *9* occur in each half of the **A** scale, just as they occur in the **C** scale and there are still ten sections between each pair of consecutive divisions. However, because the scale has been compressed, there is a smaller number of spaces in each section than on the **C** scale. Between the left index and the division marked *2*, there are five spaces in each section; in the portion of the scale between the divisions marked *2* and *5*, there are two spaces in each section; and between the division marked *5* and the center index, the sections are not divided, that is, a space occupies a whole section.

HOW TO LOCATE A NUMBER ON THE A AND B SCALES. Since the right half of each scale is a duplicate of the left half, a given number could be located in either half. The question of which half is to be used in each problem is discussed in later chapters and the remarks in this section can be taken as applying to either half. The manner of locating a number is much the same as on the **C** and **D** scales. The first digit of the number locates the proper division mark, the second digit tells you how many sections to count to the right from the division mark, and the third digit indicates the number of spaces to be counted to the right from the section mark. The only new type of marking occurs between the division marked *5* and the right end of each half of the scale. Here a space is the same as a section, so the third digit must be set approximately by estimating to the tenth of a section. The portion of the **A** scale between divisions *6* and *8* is shown in Fig. 3-4, where the numbers *0.0675* and *70.7* are shown in their correct locations. The manner of locating each is given in the examples which follow.

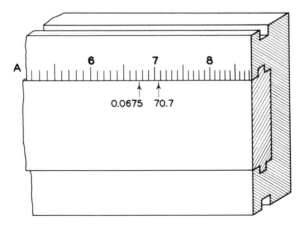

Fig. 3-4. Numbers 0.0675 and 70.7 are shown in correct locations on one portion of the A scale.

ILLUSTRATIVE EXAMPLES

29. *To locate 0.0675.*

1) The first digit is *6* so the number lies between divisions *6* and *7*.
2) The second digit is *7,* so count 7 sections to the right from the division marked *6.*
3) From here estimate five-tenths of the section, since the third digit is *5.*

30. *To locate 70.7.*

1) Since the first digit is *7,* the number is located between divisions *7* and *8.*
2) The second digit is *0,* so the number lies in the first section.
3) Since the third digit is *7,* the number is located at seven-tenths of the section from the left end of the section, that is from division *7.* You must estimate the seven-tenths.

Since there are fewer spaces to each section, a number cannot be located as precisely on the **A** and **B** scales as on the **C** and **D** scales. For this reason, the use of the **A** and **B** scales for multiplication and division is not recommended, although it is possible. Only the first three digits of a number can be used in locating it on the **A** or **B** scale. The remainder must be treated as though each were zero. Thus, the number 7363 would be located the same as 7360, and in any case in which the fourth digit is less than *5,* the third digit is left unchanged. If the fourth digit is *5* or greater, the third digit is increased by one. For example, the number 5827 would be set as 5830.

THE K SCALE

The **K** scale is located on the upper part of the front of the slide rule. See Fig. 1-1.

USE OF THE K SCALE. The **K** scale is used with the **D** scale for finding the cube or cube root of a number. For this reason it is often called the cube scale.

MARKING OF THE K SCALE. The **K** scale is a triple scale in that it consists of three scales exactly alike, each occupying one-third of the total length. Each of the three parts is similar to the **C** scale, since it has the same numerical range and since it has the same division marks as the **C** scale. However, because the scale has been compressed, there are not as many sections and spaces between consecutive division marks as on the **C** scale. From the left end of each third to the division marked *3,* there are ten sections between consecutive division marks and each section is divided into two spaces. From the division marked *3* to the division marked *6,* there are ten sections between consecutive division marks but the sections are not divided. In the remainder of the scale there are only five sections between consecutive division marks.

HOW TO LOCATE A NUMBER ON THE K SCALE. The **K** scale consists of three similar lengths and a given number can be located in any one of the lengths. Which to use in the specific problem will be discussed later. The manner of locating a number in a particular one of the three lengths is much the same as that of locating a number on the **B** or **C** scale. There are three types of marking on the **K** scale. They are:

1. Between the left end of each third and the division marked *3,* where there are ten sections between division marks and each section is divided into two spaces.

2. Between divisions *3* and *6* where there are ten sections between division marks and the sections are not divided.

3. In the remainder of the scale where there are only five sections between division marks.

The first two types of markings have been considered already in the discussions of the **A, B, C,** and **D** scales. In the portions of the scale where the third type occurs, the first digit of the number locates the number between the proper division marks. The second digit of the number determines how many sections are to be counted from the division mark. Since there are only five sections between division marks, each section must have a value of two in the second digit of the number. Hence the number can be located precisely only if the second digit is even. If it is odd, the number must be located approximately by estimating one-half of a section. Fig. 3-5 shows a portion of the **K** scale with correct locations of the numbers 63000 and 7.8. The following examples show how these numbers are located.

If the first digit of the number is *5* or less, the first three digits of the number can be used in locating it on the **K** scale. The remainder must be treated as though each were zero. If the first digit is *6* or greater, only the first two digits can be represented in locating the number on the **K** scale.

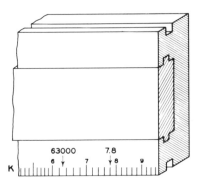

Fig. 3-5. One of the three portions of the K scale with correct locations of the numbers 63000 and 7.8.

ILLUSTRATIVE EXAMPLES

31. *To locate 63000.*

1) The fact that the first digit is *6* shows that the number lies between divisions *6* and *7*.

2) The second digit is *3*, so the number is located one and one-half sections to the right of division *6*. Each section has a value of two in the second digit.

32. *To locate 7.8.*

1) The first digit is *7*, so the number is located between divisions *7* and *8*.

2) The second digit is *8*, so count four sections to the right from division *7*. This locates the number.

REVIEW QUESTIONS

If you have studied the material of this chapter carefully, you should be able to answer the following questions.

1. What is a scale on the slide rule?
2. Where on the slide rule is the left index of the **D** scale?
3. What is the first digit of a number?
4. Which digits of a number can be zero?
5. What is a section? What is a space?
6. Which is larger, a section or a space?
7. Would the numbers *1.457* and *145.7* be located the same on the **C** scale?

8. On the **C** scale, which digit of a number determines the section in which the number lies, and which digit determines the space in which it lies?

9. How many digits of the number *19.3721* can be represented in locating the number on the **D** scale?

10. Can any number, no matter what its size, be located on the **D** scale?

11. What is the center index on the **B** scale?

12. How many digits of the number *978.42* can be used in locating the number on the **B** scale?

13. What is a division mark on the **C** scale?

14. Which scale reads from right to left?

15. Can the same number be located in more than one place on the **C** scale?

CHAPTER 4

MULTIPLICATION WITH THE
C AND D SCALES

THE PROCESS OF MULTIPLICATION. Multiplication is ordinarily accomplished with the **C** and **D** scales. The simplest operation is that of multiplying one number, the *multiplicand,* by another number, the *multiplier.* The process is carried out in the following steps:

STEPS IN THE PROCESS OF MULTIPLICATION

1) The first number, or multiplicand, is located on the **D** scale by adjusting the slide so that one index of the **C** scale coincides with the number.
2) The runner is then placed in such a position that the hairline coincides with the second number, or multiplier, on the **C** scale.
3) The answer is read on the **D** scale under the hairline. These steps can be stated as a rule. It is:

Rule 1. Multiplication. *Set one index of the C scale to the multiplicand on the D scale. Next, set the hairline of the runner to the multiplier on the C scale. Finally, read the answer on the D scale under the hairline.*

ILLUSTRATIVE EXAMPLES

Read the following examples carefully, and check each operation on your own slide rule.

1. *To multiply 11.7 × 136.* Fig. 4-1 shows the correct positions of the slide and runner for this operation. Only the **C** and **D** scales are shown in detail, since they are the only ones used in this multiplication. The operation should be performed in the following steps:

1) Move the slide until the left index of the **C** scale is over the number *11.7,* the multiplicand, on the **D** scale.

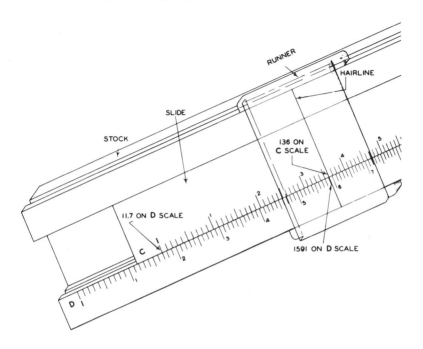

Fig. 4-1. Multiplication of 11.7 × 136.

2) Place the runner so that the hairline coincides with the number *136*, the multiplier, on the **C** scale.

3) Read the answer, *1591*, on the **D** scale under the hairline*.

2. *To multiply 4.23 × 224.* The correct positions for the slide and runner are shown in Fig. 4-2. The steps in the process are:

1) Set the left index of the **C** scale to *4.23* on the **D** scale.

2) Place the hairline of the runner on *224* on the **C** scale.

---

*It is necessary to estimate one-tenth of a space in order to determine the fourth digit in this answer. Slight inaccuracies in setting the multiplier, *136*, and the multiplicand, *11.7*, might cause you to read the answer as *1590* or *1592*. However, the probable error is limited to one point in the fourth digit in this example. There are very few problems in which such an error would be serious.

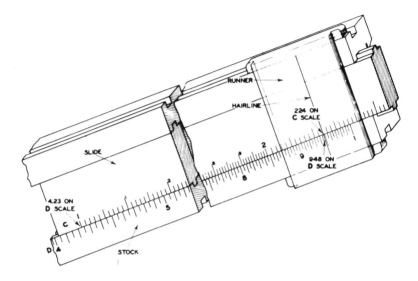

Fig. 4-2. Correct positions for the slide and runner are shown to multiply 4.23 × 224.

3) Read the answer, *948,* on the **D** scale under the hairline. Here of course, the third digit is estimated, but the maximum error, with careful work, is one point in the third digit.

Not all multiplications can be performed by starting with the left index of the **C** scale and moving the slide to the right. In many cases the multiplier on the **C** scale would be beyond the right end of the stock. You can demonstrate by trial that this is true for the multiplication *72 × 93.* However, in any case in which the operation cannot be completed by starting with the left index of the **C** scale, it can be accomplished by starting with the right index of the **C** scale and moving the slide to the left. The following examples demonstrate this.

ILLUSTRATIVE EXAMPLES

3. *To multiply 9.4 × 78.6.* Fig. 4-3 shows the correct position of the slide and runner for this calculation. The procedure is:
1) Place the right index of the **C** scale on *9.4* on the **D** scale.

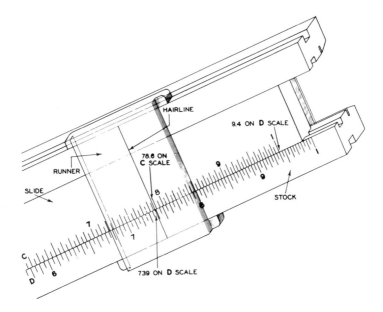

Fig. 4-3. Correct positions for the slide and runner are shown to multiply 9.4 × 78.6.

2) Set the hairline of the runner on *78.6* on the **C** scale.

3) Read the answer, *739,* on the **D** scale under the hairline.

    4. *To multiply 834 × 1.55.* The steps in the process are as follows:

1) This multiplication must be performed with the slide extending to the left, so place the right index of the **C** scale on the number *834* on the **D** scale.

2) Set the hairline of the runner on *1.55* on the **C** scale.

3) Read the answer, *1293,* on the **D** scale under the hairline.

    5. *To multiply 49.9 × 20.2.* The steps in this operation are described below:

1) A trial will show that the slide must move to the left. Hence, place the right index of the **C** scale on *49.9* on the **D** scale.

2) Set the hairline of the runner on *20.2* on the **C** scale.

3) Read the answer *1005* on the **D** scale under the hairline.

Any multiplication can be performed on the slide rule, but there is never a choice as to whether to move the slide to right or left.* Only one will work. The judgment of the experienced operator will indicate which to use in most cases; in the remainder, the fact that the multiplier is located beyond the end of the stock on the **C** scale is a definite indication that the slide must go the other way.

Multiplication can be done in any order; it makes no difference which factor is the multiplicand and which the multiplier. However, the runner will go in the same direction no matter which order of manipulation is used.

PRACTICE PROBLEMS

1. Do each of the foregoing examples by reversing the order, that is, interchange the multiplicand and multiplier.

Solve all of the following problems; (*a*) using the first number as the multiplicand; (*b*), using the second number as the multiplicand. Then check your answers with those given in the back of the book.

    2. $159 \times 5.8 = ?$ **4.** $3.3 \times 296 = ?$

    3. $243 \times 1.97 = ?$ **5.** $31.7 \times 32.2 = ?$

                6. $10.3 \times 95.5 = ?$

7. What is 27 per cent of 1680? (*Hint:* 27 per cent of a number is 27 hundredths of the number.)

8. How many square feet are contained in a rectangular room 18.3 feet wide and 85 feet long?

9. A carpenter drives screws at the rate of 87 per hour. How many does he drive in a 40-hour week?

10. How far will an automobile traveling at 68 miles per hour go in 3.75 hours?

---

*There is one exception to this rule. If the product of two numbers is a number of which the first digit is *1* and all other digits are zero, the multiplication can be made either way. Examples of such numbers are *1, 10, 100,* and *1000.*

11. The operator of a turret lathe can finish 33 machine parts in one hour. How many can he finish in an 8-hour shift?

12. Steel weighs 0.283 pounds per cubic inch. How much does a cubic foot weigh? (1 cu. ft. = 1728 cu. in.)

13. A certain type of garden hose costs 12 cents per foot. How much will 66.7 feet cost?

14. A steel bar is to be loaded at the rate of 1600 pounds per square inch. How much will a bar having an area of 0.785 square inches carry?

15. A certain type of bearing requires 1.45 pounds of bearing metal. How much will 540 bearings require?

When you have reached this point, you know how to multiply one number by another. Next you should work many problems. Make up your own, or if problems arise in your work or study, work them with the slide rule. This will give practice in placing the index of the **C** scale at the proper number on the **D** scale, and in setting the hairline of the runner on a number, with the result that you will be able to perform these operations quickly and with confidence. You will find that you can multiply one number by another very rapidly and that the motions become automatic so that very little mental effort is required. The more you use the slide rule, the more effective it will be as a tool.

Problem 6, in the foregoing list, can be used to illustrate a point in connection with multiplication. When the multiplication is performed with *10.3* as the multiplicand, nearly all of the slide remains within the stock. This makes for precision since the stock holds the slide in alignment and keeps it from wobbling. When *95.5* is used as the multiplicand, nearly all of the slide projects from the stock. In such a position the slide is loose in the stock and is liable to move while the runner is brought into position, thus causing an error. This will be easy to understand if you set your own slide rule in the positions described. In deciding which number to use for the multiplicand it is best to select the one which will cause most of the slide to remain within the stock.

ILLUSTRATIVE EXAMPLES

6. *To multiply 86.6 × 11.5.*

1) Try this with *86.6* as the multiplicand.

2) Try it with *11.5* as the multiplicand. Notice how much easier it is this way and how the slide is held firmly in the stock.
3) The answer is *996*.

   7. To multiply 9.8 × 103.
1) Try it with *103* as the multiplicand.
2) Try it with *9.8* as the multiplicand. Notice that the stock holds the slide firmly.

   The slide cannot wobble and is not likely to slip out of position while the runner is being adjusted.
3) The answer is *1009*.

PRACTICE PROBLEMS

After you have worked all of the following problems, check your answers with the correct answers shown in the back of the book.

$$1. \ 1.001 \times 998 = ?$$
$$2. \ 940 \times 1.05 = ?$$
$$3. \ 106.3 \times 9.65 = ?$$
$$4. \ 12.56 \times 88.3 = ?$$
$$5. \ 8.56 \times 130.5 = ?$$

Locating the Decimal Point in the Answer. Digit Count.* For purposes of this book, and to simplify the placing of the decimal point after the use of the slide rule, the decimal point is located in the answer by means of the *digit count.*

The digit count for 1 or a number greater than 1 is the number if digits to the left of the decimal point in the number. This means that for 1 or for numbers greater than 1 each digit to the left of the decimal point is considered a plus, or positive, digit; any numerals to the right of the decimal point are ignored. For example, in the number *672.94* there are three positive digits, hence the digit count is three ($+3$); those numerals to the right of the decimal point are ignored. When the number is a decimal fraction, there

---

*Another method of locating the decimal point makes use of powers of ten. This method is explained in Chapter 16.

will never be digits to the left of the decimal point. If the first digit of such a number is immediately to the right of the decimal point, there are zero digits to the left of the decimal point and the digit count is zero; for example, the digit count for *0.612* is zero.

The *digit count* for any number less than 0.1 is a negative number, and is numerically equal to the number of zeros at the right of the decimal point and between the decimal point and the first digit of the number. Each such zero is, for purposes of this book, counted as a minus, or negative, digit. For example, for the number *0.036* the digit count is one negative digit, or minus one (-1); for *0.00061* the digit count is three negative digits, or minus three (-3).

The following table is presented to help you understand how to make the digit count in the process of locating the decimal point.

TABLE 4-1. DIGIT COUNTS	
Number	Digit Count
400,000.	$+6$
40,000.	$+5$
4,000.	$+4$
400.	$+3$
40.	$+2$
4.	$+1$
.1	0
.01	-1
.001	-2
.0001	-3
.00001	-4
.000001	-5

Remember that all numerals are assumed to be positive when no sign is used, therefore the plus sign is not always used.

Two positive rules can be stated for locating the decimal point in the answer when multiplying one number by another.

1. Multiplication. *When the slide extends to the left, the sum of the digit count for the multiplicand and the digit count of the multiplier equals the digit count for the answer.*

If the digit count for the answer is plus, you will know it indicates the number of places to the left of the decimal point in the answer, because you will remember that in making the digit count each digit to the left of the decimal is counted as plus.

If the digit count for the answer is zero, you will know that there are no digits to the left of the decimal point in the answer and that the first digit is immediately to the right of the decimal.

If the digit count for answer is a minus number, you will know that there are that number of zeros immediately to the right of the decimal point.

ILLUSTRATIVE EXAMPLES

8. *To multiply 97.3 × 84.5.* The sequence of numbers in the answer is read as *823*. There are two digits to the left of the decimal point in each number, or a digit count of two, giving a total of four for the two numbers. Since the slide of the rule projects to the left of the stock, the digit count in the answer is the same as this sum, namely four (+4). This means that in the answer there will be four digits to the left of the decimal point. Hence a zero is added to the sequence of numbers to make it four digits, they are placed to the left of the decimal point, and the answer is *8230*.

9. *To multiply 0.866 × 19,700.* The sequence of numbers in the answer is read as *1707*. There are zero digits to the left of the decimal point in *0.866*, making a digit count of zero, and five digits to the left of the decimal point in *19700*, making a digit count of +5. The sum of zero and five is five. The slide of the rule extends to the left of the stock so the digit count for the answer is +5; there are five digits, then, to the left of the decimal point in the answer and it is *17,070*.

10. *To multiply 0.0635 × 0.00217.* The sequence of numbers in the answer is read as *1378*. The digit count for *0.0635* is minus one, and the count is minus two for *0.00217*. The sum of minus one and minus two is minus three. Since the slide projects to the left of the stock in this operation, the digit count for the answer is equal to this sum, minus three (−3). Therefore we know there are three zeros to the right of the decimal and the answer is *0.0001378*.

PRACTICE PROBLEMS

After you have worked all of the following problems, check

your answers with the correct answers shown in the back of the book.

1. $0.00475 \times 0.0730 = ?$
2. $18300 \times 0.0276 = ?$
3. $9.75 \times 0.000540 = ?$
4. $0.0172 \times 863 = ?$
5. $6280 \times 356 = ?$
6. What is 8.7% of 0.397?

7. An automobile travels at the rate of 73 feet per second. How far does it go in 92 seconds?

8. One gallon contains 231 cubic inches. How many cubic inches in 8.33 gallons?

9. Sand weighs 125 pounds per cubic foot. How much would 93 cubic feet of sand weigh?

10. One foot is equal to 12 inches. How many inches in one mile? One mile is equal to 5,280 feet.

11. What is 83% of 952?

12. A certain machine gun can fire 350 bullets per minute. How many can it fire in 7.5 minutes?

2. **Multiplication.** *When the slide extends to the right, subtract one from the sum of the digit count for the multiplicand and the digit count for the multiplier to get the digit count for the answer.*

Remember that if the digit count for the answer is plus, it indicates the number of digits to the left of the decimal point in the answer; if it is zero, the first digit of the answer is immediately to the right of the decimal point; if it is minus, it gives the number of zeros immediately to the right of the decimal point.

ILLUSTRATIVE EXAMPLES

11. *To multiply 12.6 × 0.318.* The sequence of numbers in the answer is read as *401*. There are two digits to the left of the decimal point in the multiplicand, *12.6,* making a digit count of plus two, and zero digits to the left of the decimal point in the multiplier, *0.318,* making a digit count of zero. The sum of two and zero is two. Since the slide extends to the right of the stock in this operation, the digit count for the answer is one less than two, or one. Hence, the answer is *4.01*.

12. *To multiply 2120 × 384.* The sequence of numbers in

the answer is read as *814*. The digit count is +4 for *2120** and +3 for *384*. The sum of four and three is seven. The slide projects to the right of the stock in this operation, so the digit count for the answer is one less than seven, or six. Hence, the answer is *814,000*.

13. *To multiply 0.000242 × 0.00308.* The sequence of numbers in the answer is read as *745*. The digit count is minus three for *0.000242* and minus two for *0.00308*. The sum of minus three and minus two is minus five. Since the slide extends to the right, the number of negative digits in the answer is one less than minus five, or minus six: † − 5 − (+1) = −6. Hence, the answer has six zeros immediately following the decimal point and is *0.000000745*.

14. *To multiply 1240 × 0.000473.* The sequence of numbers in the answer is read as *586*. Since there are four digits to the left of the decimal point in *1240* the digit count is four, and it is minus three for *0.000473*. The sum of plus four and minus three is one, 4 + (−3) = 1. Since the slide projects to the right of the stock, the digit count for the answer is one less than one, or zero. Hence, the answer is *0.586*.

PRACTICE PROBLEMS

After you have worked all of the following problems, check your answers with the correct answers shown in the back of the book.

1. 33000 × 0.0000216 = ?   **3.** 1.008 × 93.4 = ?
2. 0.0195 × 0.456 = ?   **4.** 13.3 × 0.00067 = ?
5. 0.0045 × 0.0208 = ?

6. The unit elongation of a bar of steel, for a rise in temperature of 1° F., is 0.0000065. What is the unit elongation for a rise in temperature of 139° F.?

7. A certain automobile requires 0.047 gallons of gasoline per mile. How much gasoline will it use in 114 miles?

---

*When a number is written without any decimal point, as *2120*, is is always understood that the decimal point follows the last digit. Here the decimal point follows the zero. The number could have been written as *2120.00*.

†A brief review of addition and subtraction with negative numbers is given in Appendix A.

8. A certain casting requires 218 pounds of malleable iron. How much will 37 such castings require?

9. An acre of ground is equivalent to 43560 square feet. How many square feet are contained in 0.017 acre?

10. How many square feet are there in 220 acres?

MULTIPLICATION OF EACH OF MANY NUMBERS BY ONE NUMBER. In calculating percentages, compiling tables, and similar operations, it is often necessary to multiply each of many numbers by a single number. Much time can be saved in such problems by using the single number as the multiplicand in each separate multiplication. In this way the slide needs to be set only once and can then remain fixed in the same position for all of the multipliers. The rules previously given for locating the decimal point hold here.

ILLUSTRATIVE EXAMPLE

15. *Compute 82% of each of the following numbers:* 983, 764, 712, 636, 603, 577, 432, 333. Since 82 per cent of a number is equal to *0.82* times the number, each number in the list must be multiplied by *0.82*. In each case the slide will project to the left of the stock. To start then, the slide is placed so that the right index of the **C** scale is at *82* on the **D** scale. The runner is placed so that its hairline is in turn at each of the numbers *983, 764, 712,* etc. on the **C** scale. For each the answer is read on the **D** scale under the hairline. During all of the operation the slide remains fixed. The answers are, respectively: 805; 626; 584; 522; 494; 473; 354; 273.

In many such problems, part of the multiplications will require the slide to move to the right and the remainder will require the slide to move to the left. This can be treated as two separate problems, one including the multiplications which require the slide to move to the right and the other including those which require the slide to move to the left. The rules given previously for locating the decimal point hold here.

ILLUSTRATIVE EXAMPLES

16. *Multiply each of the following numbers by 5.23:* 1.04, 1.69, 1.85, 2.76, 3.58, 4.65.

1) Place the left index of the **C** scale on *5.23* on the **D** scale. Set the runner so that the hairline is in turn on *1.04, 1.69,* and *1.85*

on the **C** scale. Read the answers on the **D** scale under the hairline, respectively: 5.44; 8.84; 9.68.

2) The rest of the problem must be done with the slide extending to the left. Place the right index of the **C** scale on *5.23* on the **D** scale. Set the runner so that the hairline is in turn on *2.76, 3.58* and *4.65* on the **C** scale. Read the answers on the **D** scale under the hairline, respectively: 14.44, 18.72; 24.3.

17. *Aluminum weighs 165 pounds per cubic foot. Calculate the weight of each of the following volumes of aluminum.* Each volume is given in cubic feet. 0.12, 0.375, 0.540, 0.648, 0.813, 0.950.

1) Place the left index of the **C** scale on *165* on the **D** scale. Set the hairline of the runner successively on *0.12, 0.375* and *0.540* on the **C** scale. Read the answers on the **D** scale under the hairline, respectively: 19.8 lb.; 61.8 lb.; 89.1 lb.

2) Place the right index of the **C** scale on *165* on the **D** scale. Set the hairline of the runner on *0.648, 0.813* and *0.950* in turn on the **C** scale. Read the answers on the **D** scale under the hairline, respectively: 106.9 lb.; 134.1 lb.; 156.8 lb.

PRACTICE PROBLEMS

After you have worked all of the problems, check your answers with the correct answers shown at the back of the book.

1. Calculate 89.5% of each of the following numbers: 0.915, 0.812, 0.767, 0.663, 0.533.

2. Convert each of the following volumes in cu. ft. into the equivalent volume in cu. in. 1.65, 3.76, 10.6, 15.8, 23.2, 39.5, 102.5, 133. (*Hint:* 1 cu. ft. = 1728 cu. in. so each number must be multiplied by 1728.)

3. The wholesale price for each of a number of articles is, respectively: $0.83, $0.96, $1.08, $1.17, $1.35, $1.62. The retail price for each is to be 120% of the wholesale price. Calculate the retail price of each to the nearest cent.

4. A speed of one mile per hour is equivalent to 1.467 feet per second. Convert each of the following speeds in miles per hour into feet per second. 22, 29, 30, 45, 50, 60, 72, 85, 95.

5. A series of circles has the following diameters, in feet: 35, 68.5, 104.5, 163, 216, 385. Calculate the circumference of each. (*Hint:* The circumference of a circle is 3.14 times the diameter.)

6. A bar of steel 1 inch square and one foot long weighs 3.4 pounds. Calculate the weight of each of the following lengths of 1 inch square steel bar: 0.78, 1.043, 2.17, 3.56, 5.22, 6.63, 8.2. Each length is given in feet.

MULTIPLICATION OF THREE OR MORE NUMBERS. There are many occasions on which it is necessary to multiply three or more numbers. In such cases, the operation can be carried all the way through without writing down any intermediate results. The first number is set on the **D** scale by placing the proper index of the **C** scale in coincidence with it. This is multiplied by the second number by setting the hairline of the runner to the second number on the **C** scale. This locates the product of the first two numbers on the **D** scale under the hairline. This product is then multiplied by the third number. In this process, the runner is left in position while the proper index of the **C** scale is brought into coincidence with the hairline. Then the runner is placed so that the hairline coincides with the third number on the **C** scale. The final answer is read on the **D** scale under the hairline. Obviously, this process could be extended to any number of multiplications.

In order to locate the decimal point in the answer, the digit counts for the original numbers are added. For each part of the operation in which the slide extends to the right of the stock, the number one is subtracted from this sum. The resulting number is the digit count for the answer. You may find it convenient to make a mark on the paper for each part of the operation in which the slide extends to the right of the stock. The number of marks can then be subtracted from the sum of the digit counts for the multiplicand and multipliers to give the digit count for the answer.

ILLUSTRATIVE EXAMPLES

18. *Multiply 157 × 32.3 × 0.636.* The operation is performed in the following steps:
1) Place the left index of the **C** scale on *157* on the **D** scale. Note that the slide extends to the right of the stock.
2) Set the hairline of the runner on *32.3* on the **C** scale. This locates the product of the first two numbers on the **D** scale under the hairline.
3) Leave the runner fixed and move the right index of the **C** scale

until it is under the hairline. Note that the slide moves to the left beyond the stock.

4) Place the hairline of the runner on *0.636* on the **C** scale.
5) Read the final answer as the sequence of numbers *323* on the **D** scale under the hairline.
6) Add:

$$
\begin{aligned}
\text{Digit count for } & \quad 157 = 3 \\
\text{Digit count for } & \quad 32.3 = 2 \\
\text{Digit count for } & \ 0.636 = 0 \\
\hline
\text{Sum } \ldots\ldots\ldots\ldots & \quad = 5
\end{aligned}
$$

Since the slide of the rule extended to the right of the stock once during the operation, subtract one from five, leaving four. The digit count is $+4$, hence there are four digits to the left of the decimal point in the final answer, and the answer is *3230*.

19. *Multiply 0.236 × 1.93 × 0.00205*. The process is as follows:

1) Set the left index of the **C** scale to *0.236* on the **D** scale.
2) Place the hairline of the runner on *1.93* on the **C** scale, noting that the slide moves to the right of the stock.
3) Leave the runner fixed while placing the left index of the **C** scale under the hairline. Note that the slide again projects to the right of the stock.
4) Move the hairline of the runner to *0.00205* on the **C** scale.
5) Read *934* as the sequence of numbers in the final answer on the **D** scale under the hairline.
6) Add:

$$
\begin{aligned}
\text{Digit count for } 0.236 \ \ & = \quad\ \ 0 \\
\text{Digit count for } 1.93 \ \ & = \quad\ \ 1 \\
\text{Digit count for } 0.00205 \ & = -2 \\
\hline
\text{Sum } \ldots\ldots\ldots\ldots \ & = -1
\end{aligned}
$$

The slide extended to the right of the stock twice during the operation, so subtract two from minus one, leaving minus three, $-1 - (+2) = -3$, the digit count for the answer. This means there are three zeros to the right of the decimal point in the final answer, which is *0.000934*.

20. *Multiply 938 × 0.775 × 0.462*. The multiplication is performed in the following steps:

1) Place the right index of the **C** scale on *938* on the **D** scale. Note that the slide extends to the left of the stock.
2) Place the hairline of the runner on *0.775* on the **C** scale.
3) Leave the runner in place while moving the right index of the **C** scale into coincidence with the hairline. Note that the slide projects to the left of the stock.
4) Move the hairline to *0.462* on the **C** scale.
5) Read the sequence of numbers in the final answer as *336* on the **D** scale under the hairline.
6) Add:

$$\begin{aligned}
\text{Digit count for } 938 &= 3 \\
\text{Digit count for } 0.775 &= 0 \\
\text{Digit count for } 0.462 &= 0 \\
\hline
\text{Sum} \quad \ldots\ldots\ldots\ldots &= 3
\end{aligned}$$

The slide did not extend to the right of the stock at all during the operation so there is nothing to be subtracted from *3*. Hence the digit count for the answer is 3. There are three digits to the left of the decimal point in the final answer and it is *336*.

PRACTICE PROBLEMS

After you have worked all of the following problems, check your answers with the correct answers shown at the back of the book.

1. 0.0000123 × 248 × 12 = ? **3.** 0.866 × 685 × 3.2 = ?
2. 45.4 × 0.495 × 356 = ?   **4.** 3.14 × 1.76 × 0.93 = ?
5. 790 × 12.3 × 0.707 = ?

6. A room is 18.3 ft. long, 12.5 ft. wide and 8.2 ft. high. How many cubic ft. does it contain?

7. An automatic screw machine can make 6 fittings per second. How many can it make in 8.3 minutes?

8. A certain type of heavy truck uses 0.187 gallons of gasoline per mile traveled. How must gasoline will a fleet of 16 trucks use in traveling 42 miles?

9. What is 37 per cent of 728 × 0.0055?

10. The bucket of a steam shovel has a capacity of 1.4 cubic yards. The shovel can lift 38 bucketfuls of dirt in one hour. How many cubic yards of dirt can it move in a 39-hour week?

Anyone who wishes to become skilled in the use of the slide rule must work many problems. Those given in this book are a beginning and can serve to acquaint you with the use of the rule. However, if you continue to use the slide rule and obtain more and more practice by solving more and more problems, you will develop speed and accuracy to such an extent that the rule will become a valuable tool for use in your work. A real mastery of the slide rule is one of the most valuable things that a technician or engineer can possess.

The review problems at the end of each chapter should be worked carefully. If any difficulty arises in doing them, you may have to read part of the chapter again.

Basis of the Process of Multiplication. This section is for the benefit of two classes of readers:

1. Those who must do unusual or advanced problems.

2. Those interested because of a liking for mathematics. It is possible to operate the slide rule efficiently without knowing or understanding the basis upon which this operation depends.

Slide rule operations are based on logarithms. The logarithm of a number to the base 10 is the power to which 10 must be raised to equal the number. Thus the logarithm of 100 is 2 since 10 must be raised to the power 2 to equal 100, the logarithm of 1000 is 3 since 10 must be raised to the power 3 to equal 1000, etc. The logarithm of 257 is 2.4099 since 10 must be raised to the power 2.4099 to equal 257.

The part of a logarithm to the left of the decimal point is called the *characteristic*. In general the characteristic is one less than the digit count for the number. Thus, the characteristic of the logarithm of 257 is 2 since the digit count of 257 is 3.

The part of the logarithm to the right of the decimal point is called the *mantissa*. The mantissa of the logarithm of 257 is 4099. The mantissa is ordinarily obtained from a table of logarithms but can often be found more efficiently with the slide rule. (See the discussion of "The Log Scale.") No matter where the decimal point of a number is located, the mantissa of its logarithm to the base 10 is always the same. Thus the mantissa of the sequence of numbers 257 is 4099 whether the number is 0.000257; 25700; etc.

Multiplication with the slide rule is based on the fact that the logarithm of the product of two numbers is equal to the sum of the logarithms of the two numbers. An example, the multiplication of *107* by *15.3*, will illustrate this. Using logarithms to the base 10,

$$\text{Logarithm of 107} = 2.0294$$
$$\text{Logarithm of 15.3} = \underline{1.1847}$$
$$\text{Sum} \ldots \ldots \ldots = \overline{3.2141}$$

The sum of the logarithms of *107* and *15.3* is *3.2141*. Hence, 3.2141 is the logarithm of the product of *107* and *15.3*. The mantissa, *2141*, gives the sequence of numbers in the answer as *16374* (from a table of logarithms*). The characteristic of the logarithm of the answer is *3* so the digit count for the answer is 4. Thus the product of *107*, and *15.3* is *1637.4*. It is to be noted that the mantissa, *2141*, of the logarithm of the answer, determined the sequence of numbers in the answer. The characteristic, *3*, served only to locate the decimal point.

This example would be done on the slide rule by using the **C** and **D** scales. The settings of the slide and runner are shown in Fig. 4-4. The steps in the operation are:

1) Place the left index of the **C** scale on *107* on the **D** scale.
2) Set the hairline of the runner to *15.3* on the **C** scale.
3) Read the answer, *1637*, on the **D** scale under the hairline.

Since the distance from the left end of each scale to a particular number represents, not the number, but the mantissa of the logarithm of the number, this operation actually adds the mantissa of the logarithm of the multiplicand, *107*, to the mantissa of the logarithm of the multiplier, *15.3*, to give the mantissa of the logarithm of the answer, *1637*. The mantissa for a number does not depend upon the location of the decimal point of the number, so the position of the hairline on the **D** scale gives only the sequence of numbers in the answer and does not locate the decimal point. The location of the decimal point can usually be estimated satisfactorily, but the operator need not rely upon this; a precise rule can be formulated, based on characteristics. If the mantissa is regarded as a decimal fraction, the addition of two mantissae would

---

*These figures can of course be found by use of the log scale of the slide rule; however only three digits can be read accurately.

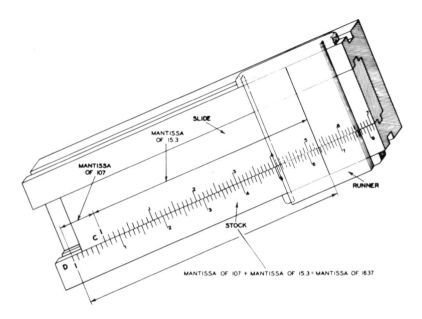

Fig. 4-4. In multiplying 107 × 15.3 with the C and D scales, we are in reality adding the mantissa of log 15.3 to the mantissa of log 107, as shown here.

give either a number less than one or a number between one and two. If less than one, say *.2141,* the characteristics of the two numbers to be multiplied would add without any "carry-over" from the mantissae, so the characteristic of the answer would be just the sum of the characteristics of the two numbers of the operation. For example:

$$
\begin{aligned}
\text{Logarithm of } 128 &= 2.1072 \\
\text{Logarithm of } 35.6 &= \underline{1.5514} \\
\text{Sum} \ldots\ldots\ldots\ldots &= 3.6586
\end{aligned}
$$

This rule applies to all cases in which the slide projects to the right of the stock and can be put into a more convenient form as an equation:

Characteristic of multiplicand + characteristic of multiplier = characteristic of answer

The characteristic is one less than the digit count for a number; that is,

Digit count for multiplicand — 1 = characteristic of multiplicand
Digit count for multiplier   — 1 = characteristic of multiplier
Digit count for answer   — 1 = characteristic of answer

Substituting these in the foregoing equation gives:
(digit count for multiplicand — 1) + (digit count for multiplier — 1) = (digit count for answer — 1)
Canceling a — *1* on each side,
(digit count for multiplicand + digit count for multiplier) — 1 = digit count for answer

Thus, in all multiplications in which the slide extends to the right of the stock, the digit count for the answer is one less than the sum of the digit count for the multiplicand and the digit count for the multiplier.

If the sum of the mantissae of the multiplicand and multiplier is greater than one, say *1.6893,* there is a "carry-over" of one from the mantissae to the characteristics, so the characteristic of the answer is one more than the sum of the characteristics of the two numbers of the operation. For example:

$$\begin{array}{l} \text{Logarithm of } 8.33 \ \ = 1.9206 \\ \text{Logarithm of } 0.642 = 0.8075 \\ \hline \text{Sum } \ldots\ldots\ldots\ldots = 2.7281 \end{array}$$

This applies to all cases in which the slide extends to the left of the stock. As an equation:
Characteristic of multiplicand + characteristic of multiplier + 1 = characteristic of answer
Putting this in terms of digit count, and remembering that the characteristic of a number is one less than its digit count,
(digit count for multiplicand — 1) + (digit count for multiplier — 1) + 1 = (digit count for answer — 1).
The — 1's and the + 1 cancel, so,
digit count for multiplicand + digit count for multiplier = digit count for answer
Thus, in any multiplication in which the slide extends to the left of the stock, the digit count for the answer is equal to the sum of

the digit count for the multiplicand and the digit count for the multiplier.

Use of the rules for locating the decimal point is illustrated in the discussion on location of the decimal point.

PRACTICE PROBLEMS

After you have worked all of the following problems, check your answers with the correct answers shown at the back of the book.

1. $37.3 \times 0.612 = ?$
2. $9.19 \times 4.72 = ?$
3. $1.032 \times 0.566 = ?$
4. $0.273 \times 3.14 = ?$
5. $328 \times 256 = ?$
6. $0.00637 \times 29.7 = ?$
7. $15.7 \times 1.83 = ?$

8. $0.755 \times 96 = ?$
9. $11.54 \times 13,000 = ?$
10. $2.16 \times 8.92 \times 0.495 = ?$
11. $385 \times 0.06 \times 3.07 = ?$
12. $7.77 \times 1.02 \times 128 = ?$
13. $525 \times 0.071 \times 0.95 = ?$
14. $99 \times 88 \times 77 = ?$

15. $0.344 \times 4.83 \times 0.61 \times 20.1 = ?$

16. Gravel weighs 120 pounds per cubic foot. There are 27 cubic feet in one yard. How much does a cubic yard of gravel weigh?

17. A certain automobile can travel 18.3 miles on a gallon of gasoline. How far can it go on 7.5 gallons?

18. On a certain streetcar line, the average number of passengers per trip is 96. How many are carried in 63 trips?

19. If 26 pounds of paper are purchased at 85 cents per pound, what is the total cost?

20. Calculate 93 per cent of each of the following numbers: 1150; 1670; 527; 393; 67.5; 254.

21. One gallon of paint will cover 450 square feet of surface. How many square feet will 25 gallons cover?

22. A certain tank truck has a capacity of 8700 gallons. How many gallons in 17 truckloads?

23. The pressure due to a one-foot depth of water is 0.433 pounds per square inch. What is the pressure due to a depth of 34 feet?

24. $92 \times 56 = ?$
25. $75.5 \times 0.123 = ?$
26. $2.95 \times 4.78 = ?$

27. $0.307 \times 69.5 = ?$
28. $0.0587 \times 1.765 = ?$
29. $100.6 \times 0.626 = ?$

30. $8.33 \times 25.6 = ?$

31. $52.5 \times 0.444 = ?$

32. $23.7 \times 4.15 \times 0.642 = ?$

33. $1.87 \times 3.93 \times 77.3 = ?$

34. $2.02 \times 534 \times 0.065 = ?$

35. $78 \times 89 \times 0.00235 = ?$

36. $29,600,000 \times 0.000471 \times 1.25 = ?$

37. $16,700 \times 0.87 \times 2.4 = ?$

38. $0.143 \times 7.02 \times 55.5 = ?$

39. $9.75 \times 0.94 \times 0.89 \times 78.5 = ?$

40. $27.6 \times 5280 \times 0.169 \times 3.7 = ?$

OTHER METHODS OF MULTIPLICATION

All slide rules have **C** and **D** scales located on the front, and multiplication can be done in the same way on all. However, many slide rules also have the folded scales (**CF** and **DF**), and the inverted scales (**CI** and **CIF**) and these scales can be used for multiplication. The use of the **CI** scale is explained in Chapter 13 and the use of the folded scales is explained in Chapter 14.

REVIEW PROBLEMS

You should use these problems to check your knowledge of this chapter. If you cannot solve them, you must study the chapter more carefully. Answers to Review Problems are not given in the back of the book. Readers who are working alone may check their answers by working the problems in reverse order or by doing the problems longhand.

1. How do you adjust the slide rule in order to locate the multiplicand?

2. On which scale is the answer read?

3. What is the product of 2.5×3.14?

4. Multiply $0.866 \times 0.707 \times 80$.

5. On which scale is the multiplier located?

6. $69.5 \times 1256 = ?$

7. $18000 \times 32.4 = ?$

8. $10.08 \times 99 = ?$

9. $1.23 \times 1.234 = ?$

10. $49.8 \times 20.2 = ?$

11. $14.3 \times 7 = ?$

12. $37.5 \times 2.67 = ?$

13. $528 \times 3070 = ?$

14. $0.00021 \times 939 = ?$

15. $25 \times 0.0067 = ?$

16. $3.14 \times 4.4 \times 2.86 = ?$

17. $0.043 \times 842 \times 0.072 = ?$

18. $2.06 \times 34.6 \times 18.5 = ?$

19. $0.785 \times 570 \times 4.8 \times 45.2 = ?$

20. $8.01 \times 0.693 \times 93 \times 0.0101 = ?$

21. An automobile driver maintains an average speed of 38 miles per hour. How far does he go in 8.5 hours?

22. A bagging machine can bag 23 bags of coffee in one minute. How many can it bag in 9 hours?

23. Multiply each of the following numbers by 0.866: 20; 28.7; 323; 41.4; 0.560; 7.85; 845.

24. Water weighs 62.4 pounds per cubic foot. Calculate the weight of each of the following volumes of water. Each is given in cubic feet. 0.333; 488; 51.5; 0.0624; 6.65; 9150.

25. A certain type of machine screw costs $0.00162 to make. Calculate the cost, to the nearest cent, of each of the following numbers of screws: 12; 144; 1728; 192; 48; 72; 84; 96.

26. Which number do you set with the hairline of the runner, the multiplicand or the multiplier?

27. State the rules for locating the decimal point in the product of two numbers.

28. A certain shaper in a machine shop makes 58 cutting strokes per minute. How many strokes does it make in one hour?

29. One gallon of water weighs 8.35 pounds. How much will 26 gallons weigh?

30. Steel plate one-fourth of an inch thick weighs 10.2 pounds per square foot. How much does a square piece of plate, 6.2 feet by 5.3 feet, weigh?

31. An assembly line produces 840 units per day. How many units will it produce in 46 days?

32. A testing machine operator can test 11 steel specimens in one hour. How many can he test in 6 seven-hour days?

33. A certain type of steel spring costs 3.6 cents to manufacture. Calculate the cost of 12 dozen springs to the nearest cent.

34. A steel cable, 382 ft. long, is stretched 0.000537 inch per inch. What is the total stretch?

35. Along a riveted joint, 29 rivets are to be equally spaced. The pitch (spacing center to center) is to be 3.21 inches. Find the distance from the center of the rivet on one end to the center of the rivet on the other end.

CHAPTER 5

DIVISION WITH THE C AND D SCALES

THE PROCESS OF DIVISION. Two numbers are involved in the ordinary process of division. The first number is the *dividend,* the number which is divided. The second number is the *divisor,* the number which divides into the dividend. For example, in dividing *39* by *7, 39* is the dividend and the *7* is the divisor. This operation can also be symbolized as *39 ÷ 7* or *39/7.* The answer is called the *quotient.*

STEPS IN THE PROCESS OF DIVISION

1) In dividing one number by another, the hairline of the runner is set to coincide with the first number, or dividend, on the **D** scale.
2) Then the slide is moved to such a position that the second number, or divisor, on the **C** scale is under the hairline.
3) In this setting only one index of the **C** scale can be between the ends of the **D** scale. The answer, or quotient, is read on the **D** scale, under this index of the **C** scale.

Rule 2. Division. *Set the hairline of the runner to the dividend on the **D** scale. Then slide the divisor on the **C** scale under the hairline. Finally, read the answer on the **D** scale under one index of the **C** scale.*

ILLUSTRATIVE EXAMPLES

1. *To divide 167 by 1.16.* Fig. 5-1 shows the proper setting of the slide and runner for this problem. It should be done in the following steps:

1) Set the hairline of the runner to *167,* the dividend, on the **D** scale.

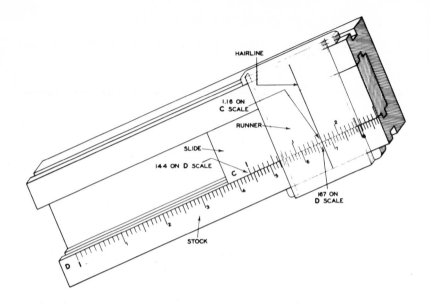

Fig. 5-1. Division of 167 by 1.16.

2) Move the slide so that *1.16,* the divisor, on the **C** scale is under the hairline.
3) The left index of the **C** scale remains between the ends of the **D** scale. Read the answer, *144,* on the **D** scale under the left index of the **C** scale.

    2. *To divide 748 by 0.89.* The correct setting of the slide and runner is shown in Fig. 5-2. The steps in the problem are:

1) Set the hairline of the runner to the dividend, 748, on the **D** scale.
2) Place the slide so that the divisor, *0.89,* on the **C** scale is under the hairline.
3) Read the answer, 841, on the **D** scale under the right index of the **C** scale.

    3. *To divide 632 by 1.43.* Fig. 5-3 shows how the slide and runner should be set for this problem. The procedure is:

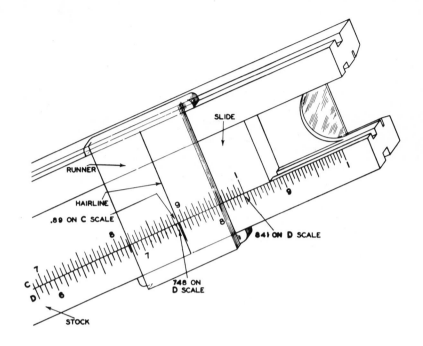

Fig. 5-2. Division of 748 by 0.89.

1) Locate the dividend, *632,* on the **D** scale by means of the hairline on the runner.
2) Adjust the slide so that the divisor, *1.43,* on the **C** scale is under the hairline.
3) Read the answer, *442,* on the **D** scale under the left index of the **C** scale.

There is never a question as to which index of the **C** scale locates the answer. Only one index can give a reading on the **D** scale at one time and this is the proper index to use.

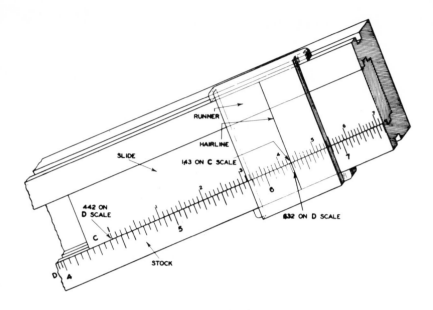

Fig. 5-3. Division of 632 by 1.43.

PRACTICE PROBLEMS

These problems are furnished for you to practice division. What you have just read is very simple, but you will forget it quickly unless you do many problems. Work only for the sequence of numbers, ignoring the decimal.

After you have worked all of the following problems, compare your answers with the correct answers shown at the back of the book.

1. $390 \div 0.7 = ?$ 3. $69.3 \div 0.08 = ?$
2. $299 \div 1.73 = ?$ 4. $283 \div 2.08 = ?$
5. $97 \div 0.13 = ?$

6. An engine runs at 4320 revolutions per minute. How many revolutions is this per second?

7. A certain type of steel drill is listed at $8.33 per dozen. Calculate the price of one drill to the nearest cent.

8. Divide 17,000 by 47.

9. A core molder, working at piece rates, earned $30.10 in a 35-hour week. In cents, what was his average hourly earning?

10. Assume that 655 is 82 per cent of a number x. Find x. (*Hint:* Divide 655 by 0.82.)

11. A small plot of ground, with 16.5-foot frontage, sells for $528. How much is this per front foot?

12. A bar of cast iron, with cross-sectional area of 1.62 square inches is subjected to a load of 1,100 pounds. How much is this in pounds per square inch?

13. The total load on a steel cable is to be 86,000 pounds. The cable is to be made of steel wires, each of which can carry 112 pounds. How many wires are required for the cable?

14. The circumference of a given circle is 735 inches. What is the diameter? (*Hint:* The circumference is 3.14 times the diameter.)

15. A rectangular room is 16.5 feet long and has an area of 198 square feet. Find the width of the room.

Location of the Decimal Point in Division.** Two positive rules can be stated for locating the decimal point in the answer when dividing one number by another.

1. Division. *When the slide extends to the right of the stock, the digit count* for the answer is one more than the digit count for the dividend minus the digit count for the divisor.*†

When the slide projects to the right of the stock, the answer, or quotient, is read on the **D** scale under the left index of the **C** scale. Remember that, in a number which is smaller than one, any zeros immediately following the decimal point are counted as negative digits. For example, in the number *0.00263* there are two negative digits, and the digit count is − 2. The following examples will demonstrate the method of locating the decimal point in dividing one number by another.

**Another method of locating the decimal point makes use of powers of ten. This method is explained in Chapter 16.

*Digit counts are explained in the chapter on Multiplication.

†There is one exception to this rule. When the dividend is *1, 10, 100, 1,000,* etc. the digit count for the answer is always equal to the digit count for the dividend minus the digit count for the divisor, no matter which way the slide extends. The slide could go either way because you could use either the left or right index of the D scale for the dividend in such a case.

ILLUSTRATIVE EXAMPLES

4. *To divide 6200 by 150.*

1) The sequence of numbers in the answer is read as *413.*
2) The digit count for the dividend, *6200,* is four; the digit count for *150* is three. Four minus three is one.
3) The slide extends to the right of the stock so add one to this difference. The result is two. Hence, the digit count for the answer is two, and it is 41.3.

5. *To divide 0.00428 by 0.026.*

1) The sequence of numbers in the answer is read as *1647.*
2) The digit count is two negative digits (-2) for the dividend, *0.00428,* and one negative digit (-1) for the divisor, *0.026.* Minus one subtracted from minus two is minus one,* $-2 - (-1) = -1$.
3) The slide extends to the right of the stock in this operation. Therefore, you should add one to minus one. This gives zero as the digit count for the answer, which means that there are zero digits to the left of the decimal point in the answer and it is 0.1647.

6. *To divide 746 by 0.000535.*

1) The sequence of numbers in the answer is read as *1395.*
2) The digit count is three for the dividend, *746,* and minus three (-3) for the divisor, *0.000535.* Minus three subtracted from three is six,* $3 - (-3) = 6$.
3) Add one to six since the slide extended to the right of the stock. This gives a digit count of seven for the answer. Hence, there are seven digits to the left of the decimal point in the answer and it is 1,395,000.

7. *To divide 0.864 by 1268.*

1) The sequence of numbers in the answer is read as *682.*
2) The digit count is zero for the dividend, *0.864,* and four for the divisor, *1268.* Zero minus four is minus four, $0 - 4 = -4$.
3) Since the slide extended to the right beyond the stock, you add one to minus four, $-4 + 1 = -3$, the digit count for the

---

*For an explanation of negative numbers see Appendix A.

answer. Hence there are three zeros to the right of the decimal point in the answer, and it is 0.000682.

PRACTICE PROBLEMS

After you have worked all the following problems, check your answers with the correct answers at the back of the book.

1. $1.21 \div 1.006 = ?$
2. $0.932 \div 4.77 = ?$
3. $0.00817 \div 0.0000123 = ?$
4. $70.7 \div 388 = ?$
5. $3,160,000 \div 201 = ?$

6. $648 \div 0.0509 = ?$
7. $54.1 \div 0.353 = ?$
8. $0.427 \div 32.3 = ?$
9. $0.0067 \div 0.0586 = ?$
10. $9.8 \div 0.866 = ?$

2. Division. *When the slide extends to the left of the stock, the digit count for the answer is equal to the digit count for the dividend minus the digit count for the divisor.* In such a case, the answer is read on the **D** scale under the right index of the **C** scale. As before, in a number which is less than one, the zeros immediately following the decimal point are counted as negative digits.

ILLUSTRATIVE EXAMPLES

8. *To divide 28.3 by 4.61.*

1) The sequence of numbers in the answer is read as *614*.
2) The digit count is two for the dividend, *28.3*, and one for the divisor, *4.61*. Two minus one is one: $2 - 1 = 1$.
3) The slide extends to the left of the stock during the operation; therefore, nothing is added to this. Hence, the digit count for the answer is one; which means there is one digit to the left of the decimal point in the answer, and it is 6.14.

9. *To divide 0.00143 by 37.5.*

1) The sequence of numbers in the answer is read as *381*.
2) The digit count for the dividend, *0.00143*, is minus two; for the divisor, *37.5*, the digit count is plus two. Two subtracted from minus two is minus four: $-2 - (+2) = -4$.
3) Since the slide extended to the left of the stock in this operation, nothing is to be added to minus four. Hence, the digit count for the answer is -4, there are four zeros to the right of the decimal point, and the answer is 0.0000381.

10. *To divide 0.217 by 0.000624.*

1) The sequence of numbers in the answer is read as *348*.
2) The digit count for the dividend, *0.217,* is zero, and minus three is the digit count for the divisor, *0.000624.* Minus three subtracted from zero is three, thus: $0 - (-3) = 3$.
3) The slide extended to the left of the stock. Therefore, nothing is added to three. Thus the digit count for the answer is three, and it is 348.

PRACTICE PROBLEMS

After you have worked all of the following problems, check your answers with the correct answers at the back of the book.

1. $1.008 \div 256 = ?$
2. $878 \div 95.3 = ?$
3. $0.560 \div 0.667 = ?$
4. $0.000417 \div 0.00745 = ?$
5. $0.0362 \div 57.5 = ?$
6. $1728 \div 0.0977 = ?$
7. $0.0722 \div 8.42 = ?$
8. $60,000 \div 815 = ?$
9. $0.0109 \div 99 = ?$
10. $27.5 \div 0.0631 = ?$

DIVISION OF ONE NUMBER BY EACH OF MANY NUMBERS. Many problems arise in which it is necessary to divide one number by each of many others. In this process the first number is always the dividend while each of the others is in turn the divisor. The dividend can be located on the **D** scale by means of the hairline on the runner. Then each divisor is, in its turn, brought under the hairline by moving the **C** scale. For each the answer is read under that index of the **C** scale which remains between the ends of the **D** scale. The dividend need be located only once.

ILLUSTRATIVE EXAMPLE

11. *To divide 89 by each of the following numbers:* 93.5; 82.1; 68.5; 51.7; 44.8; 37.3; 23.5; 17. The procedure is:

1) Set hairline of runner to the dividend, *89,* on the **D** scale.
2) Move the slide so that the first divisor, *93.5,* on the **C** scale is under the hairline. Read the answer for this part of the problem on the **D** scale under the right index of the **C** scale as *0.953.*
3) Leave the runner in its position, while moving the slide so that the second divisor, *82.1,* on the **C** scale is under the hairline.

Read the second part of the answer under the left index of the **C** scale as *1.082*.

4) Use the remainder of the divisors in a similar manner. The answers, respectively, are: 1.297; 1.721; 1.986; 2.39; 3.78; 5.23.

PRACTICE PROBLEMS

After you have worked all of the following problems, check your answers with the correct answers shown in the back of the book.

1. Express each of the following common fractions as a decimal fraction:

$$\frac{7}{11} \quad \frac{7}{13} \quad \frac{7}{15} \quad \frac{7}{17} \quad \frac{7}{19}$$

2. Convert each of the following common fractions to a decimal fraction:

$$\frac{1}{7} \quad \frac{1}{13} \quad \frac{1}{15} \quad \frac{1}{21} \quad \frac{1}{31}$$

3. Divide 68400 by each of the following numbers: 1875; 2520; 3125; 4420; 6010.

DIVISION OF EACH OF MANY NUMBERS BY A SINGLE NUMBER. In calculating percentages, compiling tables, converting common fractions to decimal fractions, etc., it is often necessary to divide each of several numbers by a single number. The dividend changes for each part of the problem, but the divisor is always the same. Each part of the problem can be symbolized as $\frac{dividend}{divisor}$. But this can also be written as $\frac{1}{divisor} \times$ dividend. (1)

The value of $\frac{1}{divisor}$ can be obtained by dividing *1* by the *divisor*. Either index of the **D** scale can be used as the *1* in this case, and the value of $\frac{1}{divisor}$ is located on the **D** scale under the proper index of the **C** scale. Then if $\frac{1}{divisor}$ is regarded as a multi-

plicand and the dividend as a multiplier, $\dfrac{1}{divisor}$ is located properly to be multiplied by the dividend. This is done by (2) setting
the hairline of the runner to the dividend on the **C** scale. Then the
answer is read on the **D** scale under the hairline. Each part of
the problem is worked in the same way. Once the slide is set to
the value of $\dfrac{1}{divisor}$, several numbers can be used in turn as dividends without moving the slide.

ILLUSTRATIVE EXAMPLES

12. *Divide each of the following numbers by 972:* 112; 195.3;
220; 394; 487.

1) Obtain the value of $\dfrac{1}{972}$. Do this by using the right index of
   the **D** scale as *1*; that is, place *972* on the **C** scale over the right
   index of the **D** scale. The value of $\dfrac{1}{972}$ is then located on the
   D scale under the left index of the **C** scale. However, you need
   not trouble to write down the value of $\dfrac{1}{972}$.

2) Multiply $\dfrac{1}{972}$ by each of the other numbers. This requires
   setting the hairline of the runner to each of the dividends in
   turn on the **C** scale. Read the answer for each number in its
   turn on the **D** scale under the hairline. The answers, respectively, are: 0.1152; 0.201; 0.227; 0.406; 0.502.

13. *Convert each of the following common fractions to a*
decimal fraction: $\dfrac{11}{108}$ $\dfrac{15}{108}$ $\dfrac{24}{108}$ $\dfrac{29}{108}$ $\dfrac{37}{108}$. This requires that each
numerator be divided by *108*.

1) Divide *1* by *108* to get $\dfrac{1}{108}$. Use the left index of the **D** scale
   as *1* and bring *108* on the **C** scale over it. The value of $\dfrac{1}{108}$
   is located on the **D** scale under the right index of the **C** scale.

2) Multiply each of the above numerators by $\frac{1}{108}$. Locate each numerator in turn on the **C** scale by setting the hairline of the runner to it. When a particular numerator is set, read the answer for it on the **D** scale under the hairline. The answers, respectively, are: 0.1018; 0.1389; 0.222; 0.269; 0.343.

You observe that the right index of the **D** scale was taken as *1* to divide *1* by *972* in Example 12. The left index of the **D** scale was taken as *1* to divide *1* by *108* in Example 13. Of course, each index of the **D** scale can be read as *1,* so each division could be made with either index and the result would be the same. However, when you are ready to multiply such a quotient, $\frac{1}{972}$ or $\frac{1}{108}$, etc., by the dividends of the problem, the **C** scale must be in such a position that you can locate the multipliers on it and read answers on the **D** scale. An example will illustrate the point.

ILLUSTRATIVE EXAMPLE

14. *Divide 443 and 518 by 71.*

1) Obtain $\frac{1}{71}$ by using the left index of the **D** scale as *1*. Divide it by *71*.

2) Try to multiply by *443* or *518*. You cannot do this since the part of the **C** scale you need to use is to the left of the stock.

3) Now obtain $\frac{1}{71}$ by using the right index of the **D** scale as *1*. Divide it by *71*.

4) Multiply this by *443* and *518*. The answers are 6.24 and 7.30.

You can always multiply $\frac{1}{divisor}$ by any dividend. However, you must use the proper index of the **D** scale as *1* in obtaining $\frac{1}{divisor}$. A good rule is: If the sequence of numbers (without re-gard for the decimal point) in the dividend is smaller than the sequence of numbers (without regard for the decimal point) in the divisor, use the right index of the **D** scale; if larger, use the left index of the **D** scale. In some problems, as in the following example, you may have to use the right index of the **D** scale for part of the calculations and the left index of the **D** scale for the remainder.

ILLUSTRATIVE EXAMPLE

15. *Divide each of the following numbers by 5.28:* 1.18; 18.52; 322; 59.8; 716; 9.27.

1) Obtain $\dfrac{1}{5.23}$ by using the right index of the **D** scale as *1*. Divide it by *5.23*.

2) Multiply this result by *1.18; 18.52;* and *322* in turn. The answers are 0.226; 3.54; and 61.6, respectively.

3) Obtain $\dfrac{1}{5.23}$ by using the left index of the **D** scale as *1*. Divide it by *5.23*.

4) Multiply by *59.8; 716;* and *9.27* in turn. The answers are 11.42; 137; and 1.772, respectively.

PERCENTAGE CALCULATIONS. A very common type of calculation is that in which it is required to find what per cent a given number x is of another number, y. To do this, you divide x by y and multiply the result by *100*. Multiplication by *100* does not require any manipulation of the slide rule. You simply write down the value of $\dfrac{x}{y}$ and set the decimal point two places to the right of the normal location. Then you have the per cent which x is of y.

16. *What per cent is 68 of 94?*

1) Divide *68* by *94*. The result is *0.723*.

2) To change this to per cent, multiply by *100*. This only requires that you move the decimal point two places to the right. The answer is 72.3 per cent.

Many of the problems in which it is necessary to divide each of many numbers by a single number are percentage calculations.

PRACTICE PROBLEMS

After you have worked all of the following problems, check your answers with the correct answers shown at the back of the book.

1. Convert each of the following common fractions to a decimal fraction:

$$\frac{11}{66} \qquad \frac{17}{66} \qquad \frac{23}{66} \qquad \frac{31}{66} \qquad \frac{47}{66} \qquad \frac{57}{66} \qquad \frac{65}{66}$$

2. The numbers 202; 287; 413; 562; and 833, represent volumes in cubic inches. Convert each to cubic feet. (*Hint:* There are 1728 cubic inches in one cubic foot.)

3. The cost of one dozen of each of a number of articles is, respectively, $1.90; $3.50; $6.80; $8.30; $9.20; and $11.60. Calculate the cost of a single article of each kind to the nearest cent.

4. Find what per cent each of the following numbers is of 616: 12; 208; 317; 493; 654; 76.5; 8.43.

5. A speed of 1 mile per hour is equivalent to 1.467 feet per second. Convert each of the following speeds in feet per second to miles per hour: 20; 28; 39; 46; 63; 88; and 110.

6. Each of the following numbers is 63 per cent of a certain other number: 101.5; 234; 501; 67.3; 786; 8.27. Find the other number for each. (*Hint:* Divide each number by 0.63.)

7. Divide each of the following numbers by 86.3: 2.77; 946; 62.4; 9.03; 10.78; 87.5.

8. Convert each of the following common fractions to a decimal fraction:

$$\frac{12}{17} \qquad \frac{5}{17} \qquad \frac{7}{17} \qquad \frac{8}{17} \qquad \frac{14}{17} \qquad \frac{16}{17}$$

9. Find what per cent each of the following numbers is of 42.7; 4.95; 16.06; 8.8; 26.2; 3.95; 9.48.

10. Convert each of the following common fractions to a decimal fraction:

$$\frac{3}{7} \qquad \frac{11}{70} \qquad \frac{47}{700} \qquad \frac{8}{70} \qquad \frac{90}{7,000} \qquad \frac{92}{700} \qquad \frac{63}{70} \qquad \frac{5}{7}$$

DIVISION OF ONE NUMBER BY THE PRODUCT OF TWO NUMBERS. Many engineering and shop formulae lead to the division of one number by the product of two others. For example, suppose you want the result of $\dfrac{7{,}200}{3.14 \times 14.8}$. It is very convenient to be able to obtain such a result by continuous manipulation of the slide rule without writing down any intermediate answer. The numbers in such a problem can be designated as the *dividend,* the *first divisor* (in the foregoing example the first divisor is *3.14*), and the *second divisor* (in this example the second divisor is *14.8*). The calculation is started by (1) setting the hairline of the runner to the dividend on the **D** scale. (2) The first divisor on the **C** scale is brought under the hairline by moving the slide. The result of this part of the calculation can be read on the **D** scale under the proper index of the **C** scale. There is no need, however, to write it down; simply (3) move the runner so that the hairline is on this index of the **C** scale. (4) Next adjust the slide so that the second divisor on the **C** scale is under the hairline, and (5) the final answer is read on the **D** scale under the index of the **C** scale that is between the ends of the **D** scale. In the following examples, work only for the sequence of numbers, ignoring the decimal.

ILLUSTRATIVE EXAMPLES

17. *Find the result of* $\dfrac{7{,}200}{3.14 \times 14.8}$.

1) Locate the dividend, *7,200,* on the **D** scale by means of the hairline of the runner.
2) Move the slide so that the first divisor, *3.14,* on the **C** scale is under the hairline.
3) Leave the slide in this position while moving the hairline of the runner to the left index of the **C** scale.
4) Adjust the slide so that the second divisor, *14.8,* on the **C** scale is under the hairline.
5) Read the answer, *155,* on the **D** scale under the left index of the **C** scale.

18. *Find the result of* $\dfrac{18{,}560}{550 \times 1.3}$.

1) Set the hairline of the runner to the dividend, *18,560,* on the **D** scale.
2) Slide the first divisor, *550,* on the **C** scale under the hairline.
3) Let the slide remain in its position. Move the runner so that its hairline coincides with the right index of the **C** scale.

4) Bring the second divisor, *1.3,* on the **C** scale under the hairline of the runner.

5) Read the final answer, *26,* on the **D** scale under the left index of the **C** scale.

PRACTICE PROBLEMS

In the following problems, work only for sequence of numbers, ignoring the decimal point. *After* you have worked all of them, check your answers with the correct answers shown in the back of the book.

1. $\dfrac{97}{38 \times 1.2} = ?$ 3. $\dfrac{5.45}{1.1 \times 1.05} = ?$

2. $\dfrac{2,730}{0.785 \times 745} = ?$ 4. $\dfrac{1,728}{220 \times 0.0216} = ?$

5. $\dfrac{0.866}{0.693 \times 0.707} = ?$

Location of Decimal Point. The procedure for locating the decimal point in the answer when dividing one number by the product of two others is:

1. Add the digit count for the first divisor to the digit count for the second divisor.

2. Subtract this sum from the digit count for the dividend.

3. Add one to this result for each part of the operation in which the slide extends to the right of the stock. You may find it desirable to make a mark on the paper for each time that the slide extends to the right during the problem.

ILLUSTRATIVE EXAMPLES

19. *Find the result of* $\dfrac{3,040}{18.7 \times 0.011}.$

The sequence of numbers in the answer is read as *1479.* Notice that the slide extended to the right of the stock twice, once during each part of the operation.

1) For the first divisor, *18.7,* the digit count is two; for the second divisor, *0.011,* it is minus one. The sum of two and minus one is one: $2 + (-1) = 1.$

2) The digit count for the dividend, *3,040*, is four. Subtract one from four, leaving three.

3) Add two to this, since the slide extended to the right of the stock during each of the two parts of the problem. The result is five, the digit count for the answer. Hence there are five digits to the left of the decimal point in the answer and it is 14,790.

20. *Calculate* $\dfrac{12,560}{29,000,000 \times 0.785}$.

The sequence of numbers in the answer is read as *551*. Notice that the slide did not extend to the right of the stock at all during the operation.

1) The digit count is eight for the first divisor; *29,000,000;* and zero for the second divisor, *0.785*. The sum of eight and zero is eight.

2) The digit count for the dividend, *12,560,* is five. Subtract eight from five, leaving minus three: $5 - (+8) = -3$.

3) Since the slide did not extend to the right of the stock, there is nothing to add to minus three. Hence, -3 is the digit count for the answer, there are three zeros to the right of the decimal point in the answer, and it is 0.000551.

21. *Find the result of* $\dfrac{0.00247}{0.0000083 \times 16.7}$.

The sequence of numbers in the answer is read as *1782*. Notice that the slide extended to the right of the stock during one part of the operation.

1) The digit count is minus five for the first divisor, *0.0000083,* and plus two for the second divisor, *16.7*. The sum of minus five and plus two is minus three. $-5 + 2 = -3$.

2) The digit count for the dividend, *0.00247,* is minus two. Subtract minus three from minus two, leaving plus one:* $-2 - (-3) = -2 + 3 = +1$.

3) Add one to this, since the slide extended to the right of the stock once during the problem. The result is two. So the digit count for the answer is $+2$, there are two digits to the left of the decimal point in the answer, and it is 17.82.

---

*For an explanation of negative numbers, see Appendix A.

PRACTICE PROBLEMS

After you have worked all of the following problems, check your answers with the correct answers shown at the back of the book.

1. $\dfrac{833}{0.442 \times 5} = ?$ 6. $\dfrac{0.244}{0.0045 \times 4,180} = ?$

2. $\dfrac{0.0128}{27.7 \times 0.00176} = ?$ 7. $\dfrac{9,400}{11,400,000 \times 0.379} = ?$

3. $\dfrac{4.12}{0.355 \times 9.6} = ?$ 8. $\dfrac{3.75}{21.5 \times 0.137} = ?$

4. $\dfrac{67.2}{7.24 \times 32.2} = ?$ 9. $\dfrac{0.000062}{0.00047 \times 0.0263} = ?$

5. $\dfrac{5,280}{3,600 \times 7.5} = ?$ 10. $\dfrac{296}{83.4 \times 1.020} = ?$

Basis of the Process of Division. This explanation is written for the benefit of those who wish a thorough knowledge of the slide rule and who may have occasion to make rather unusual types of calculations. Frequently, a complete understanding of the slide rule will make it possible to develop short cuts and individual timesavers. However, it is possible to divide one number by another without knowing the basis of the process.

Division with the slide rule is based on logarithms. It rests on the fact that the logarithm of the quotient of two numbers is equal to the logarithm of the dividend minus the logarithm of the divisor. In dividing *17.1* by *1.33,* for example, the logarithm of the quotient, or answer, is equal to the logarithm of the dividend, *17.1,* minus the logarithm of the divisor, *1.33.* Using a table of logarithms to the base 10,

$$
\begin{aligned}
\text{Logarithm of dividend, } 17.1 &= 1.2330 \\
\text{Logarithm of divisor, } 1.33 &= 0.1239 \\
\hline
\text{Difference} &= 1.1091
\end{aligned}
$$

The quotient is the number which has *1.1091* for its logarithm. With the aid of the tables, the quotient is found to be *12.86.* The setting of the slide rule for this division is shown in Fig. 5-4. In

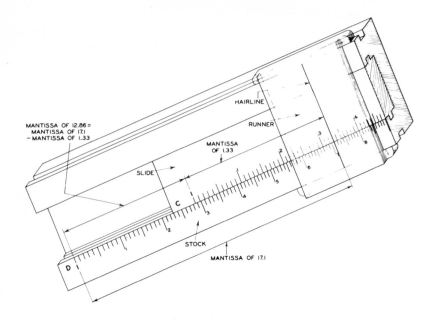

Fig. 5-4. Division of 17.1 by 1.33.

each case, the distance from the left end of the scale to the location of the number represents the mantissa of the logarithm to the base 10.

The mantissa of the logarithm is the part of the logarithm to the right of the decimal point. It gives the sequence of numbers and has nothing to do with the location of the decimal point of the number. The characteristic* of the logarithm, which is the part to the left of the decimal point, shows the location of the decimal point of the number. You will recall that the characteristic of the logarithm of a number is one less than the digit count for the number.

Fig. 5-4 shows that the slide rule operation actually subtracts the mantissa of the logarithm of the divisor, *1.33,* from the mantissa of the dividend, *17.1,* to give the mantissa of the quotient, *12.86.*

---

* See the explanation of characteristics on p. 42.

Thus the sequence of numbers in the answer is determined. Note that, as stated before, the mantissa gives only the sequence of numbers and does not locate the decimal point; that comes from the characteristic. If the slide of the rule extends to the right of the stock during the division, the mantissa of the divisor is less than that of the dividend. Hence, there is no "carryover" to the characteristics in subtraction, and the characteristics can be subtracted separately. The characteristic of the logarithm of the quotient is equal to the characteristic of the dividend minus the characteristic of the divisor. The logarithm of the quotient in this example is 1.1091 and its characteristic is *1*. This means there are two digits to the left of the decimal point in the answer, so it is *12.86*. The decimal point can be located by use of characteristics, but it is more convenient to use the digit counts for the dividend and divisor. As an equation,

characteristic of dividend — characteristic of divisor =
characteristic of quotient

Remembering that,

characteristic of a number = digit count for the number — 1

the foregoing equation can be written,

(digit count for dividend — 1) — (digit count for divisor — 1) =
(digit count for quotient — 1)

Canceling a — 1 on each side,

(digit count for dividend — digit count for divisor) + 1 =
digit count for quotient

Hence when the slide extends to the right during the division, the digit count for the quotient is one more than the digit count for the dividend minus the digit count for the divisor.

If the slide extends to the left of the stock, the mantissa of the logarithm of the divisor is greater than the mantissa of the dividend. Hence in subtraction, there is a "carryover" to the characteristics, and the characteristic of the quotient is one less than the characteristic of the logarithm of the dividend minus the characteristic of the divisor. As an equation, this is,

characteristic of dividend — characteristic of divisor — 1 =
characteristic of quotient

When the equation is put in terms of digits, it becomes,

(digit count for dividend — 1) — (digit count for divisor — 1) — 1

= (digit count for quotient − 1)

Canceling all − 1's,

   digit count for dividend − digit count for divisor =
            digit count for quotient

Hence, when the slide extends to the left of the stock during the division, the digit count for the quotient is equal to the digit count for the dividend minus the digit count for the divisor.

PRACTICE PROBLEMS

After you have worked all of the following problems, check your answers with the correct answers shown at the back of the book.

1. $96.6 \div 38.3 = ?$
2. $278 \div 53.7 = ?$
3. $0.472 \div 11.7 = ?$
4. $301 \div 81.2 = ?$
5. $2.17 \div 1.93 = ?$
6. $34,700 \div 368 = ?$
7. $5280 \div 65.5 = ?$
8. $43.4 \div 48.2 = ?$
9. $1380 \div 21.3 = ?$
10. $0.866 \div 0.0589 = ?$

11. $1.682 \div 29.1 = ?$
12. $32.2 \div 5.7 = ?$
13. $7.25 \div 1.28 = ?$
14. $18,000 \div 2.42 = ?$
15. $989 \div 0.0765 = ?$
16. $112 \div 0.785 = ?$
17. $25.4 \div 8.67 = ?$
18. $0.346 \div 1.53 = ?$
19. $8320 \div 63.7 = ?$
20. $536 \div 28.1 = ?$

Convert the following fractions to decimals.

21. $\dfrac{3}{8} \quad \dfrac{3}{13} \quad \dfrac{3}{17}$

22. $\dfrac{5}{9} \quad \dfrac{5}{11} \quad \dfrac{5}{12}$

23. $\dfrac{4}{21} \quad \dfrac{5}{21} \quad \dfrac{11}{21}$

24. $\dfrac{11}{87} \quad \dfrac{24}{87} \quad \dfrac{31}{87}$

25. $\dfrac{14}{109} \quad \dfrac{19}{109} \quad \dfrac{23}{109}$

Work the following:

26. $\dfrac{64.7}{21 \times 0.317} = ?$

27. $\dfrac{135.7}{5.4 \times 9.2} = ?$

28. $\dfrac{0.195}{2.31 \times 0.415} = ?$

29. $\dfrac{15,600}{28.2 \times 0.813} = ?$

30. $\dfrac{888}{75.2 \times 1.62} = ?$

OTHER METHODS OF DIVISION

All slide rules have **C** and **D** scales on the front, and division can be performed in the same way on all. However, many slide rules also have inverted scales and folded scales, and these scales can be used efficiently in the process of division. Their use is explained in Chapters 13 and 14.

REVIEW PROBLEMS

Answers to Review Problems are not given in the back of the book. Readers who are working alone may check their answers by working the problems longhand.

1. A rectangular vat has floor dimensions of 7.5 feet and 6.2 feet. Its volume is 113 cubic feet. Find its height.

2. Convert $\dfrac{5}{12}$ to a decimal fraction.

3. A motorist travels 332 miles in 8.25 hours. What is his average speed?

4. Eighteen rivets are to be equally spaced in a row so that the distance from the center of the rivet on one end to the center of the rivet on the other end is 41.8 inches. What should be the distance between centers of adjacent rivets?

5. Steel plate 1 inch thick weighs 40.8 pounds per square foot. How thick is plate which weighs 7.65 pounds per square foot?

6. On what scale is the dividend located?

7. A mason can lay 820 bricks in an eight-hour day. What is the average number laid per minute?

8. There are 43,560 square feet in one acre. How many acres are there in 273,000 square feet?

9. Convert each of the following common fractions to a decimal fraction:

$$\frac{3}{128} \qquad \frac{7}{128} \qquad \frac{11}{128} \qquad \frac{19}{128} \qquad \frac{34}{128} \qquad \frac{63}{128} \qquad \frac{105}{128}$$

10. Find what per cent 117 is of 483.

11. What is $\dfrac{1}{24}$ of $\dfrac{1}{32}$?

12. Solve the following equation for x:
$$0.00824\,x = 153$$

13. A manufacturer pays $13,440 for 39,500 pounds of copper. What is the cost per pound?

14. On what scale is the divisor located?

15. The circumference of a certain circle is 484 feet. What is its diameter?

16. A certain pump has a rate of 96 gallons per minute. How long must it operate to fill a tank which has a capacity of 6,900 gallons?

17. Calculate $\dfrac{11}{29}$ of $\dfrac{1}{3}$

18. A trucking company's bill for 11,500 gallons of gasoline was $2,060. What was the cost per gallon?

19. Each of the following numbers is 28.5 per cent of another number: 1.38; 21.2; 3,430; 7.36; 0.991. Calculate each of the other numbers.

20. A manufacturer plans to build a storage bin with a capacity of 1,750 cubic feet. He has available space 19.7 feet wide and building regulations prohibit storing the particular material to a depth greater than 6 feet. How long a space does he need?

21. $\dfrac{7,300}{2,550,000 \times 4.3} = ?$

22. $\dfrac{16,550}{0.000573} = ?$

23. $\dfrac{97.5}{1,030} = ?$

24. $\dfrac{1.05}{0.932} = ?$

25. $\dfrac{30.4}{30.6} = ?$

26. $\dfrac{50,500}{70.7} = ?$

27. $\dfrac{895}{0.866 \times 0.693} = ?$

28. $\dfrac{0.299}{37.8 \times 0.00061} = ?$

29. $\dfrac{43}{3.14 \times 6 \times 9.3} = ?$

30. $\dfrac{0.000632}{0.0000123} = ?$

COMBINATIONS OF MULTIPLICATION AND DIVISION WITH THE C AND D SCALES

Most problems in science and technology can be solved by the use of formulae, formulae which can be found in handbooks, reference books and textbooks. The usual procedure is to find the proper formula and substitute in it those numbers which fit in the particular example. Then the answer is obtained by carrying out the calculations. Many formulae lead to calculations involving several operations of multiplication and division, for example,

$$\frac{5 \times 4750 \times 13,820,000}{384 \times 30,000,000 \times 133.5}$$

It is in this type of calculation that the slide rule appears to greatest advantage, since the calculation can be carried all the way through to the final answer without writing down any intermediate results. The savings in time and effort are enormous. Also, it is so much simpler to do it with the slide rule that you are less likely to make an error than if you do it longhand. General rules can be stated for performing such a calculation, but are apt to become complicated and long. For this reason, the procedure will be described by the use of examples. Follow them carefully with your own slide rule.

ILLUSTRATIVE EXAMPLES

1. Find the result of $\dfrac{5 \times 4750 \times 13,820,000}{384 \times 30,000,000 \times 133.5}$

In such a problem it is best to work from left to right and to perform alternately the processes of division and multiplication. The procedure is:

1) Set the hairline of the runner to the first number in the numerator, in this case *5,* on the **D** scale.
2) Divide this by the first number in the denominator, *384,* by bringing *384* on the **C** scale under the hairline.
3) Hold the result of this operation on the **D** scale under the left

index of the **C** scale, and multiply by the second number in the numerator, *4750*, by setting the hairline of the runner to *4750* **on the C** scale.

4) **The** result of this much of the problem is on the **D** scale under the hairline. Leave the runner where it is and divide by the **second** number of the denominator, *30,000,000* by bringing *30,000,000* on the **C** scale under the hairline.

5) Leave the slide fixed and multiply by the third number in the numerator, *13,820,000*, by setting the hairline of the runner to *13,820,000* on the **C** scale.

6) Let the runner stay where it is and divide by the third number in the denominator, *133.5*, by bringing *133.5* on the **C** scale under the hairline.

7) Read the final answer, *0.214*, on the **D** scale under the left index of the **C** scale.

Do not worry, at this time, about locating the decimal point in the answer. That comes later. Ignore it just now and concentrate on getting only the sequence of numbers in the answer. Be sure that no number is left out and that no number is used twice.

In Example 1 there are six separate numbers to be set on the slide rule. It is reasonable to expect a slight error in setting each one. These errors may accumulate so that your answer will differ from the one given here in the third digit. However, any such error should be less than one per cent. Experience in setting numbers will give increased precision and errors will be reduced.

2. *Find the result of* $\dfrac{225 \times 52 \times 32}{37 \times 29}$

1) Set the hairline of the runner on the first number of the numerator, *225*, on the **D** scale.

2) Divide by the first number in the denominator, *37*, by bringing *37* on the **C** scale under the hairline of the runner.

3) Multiply by the second number in the numerator, *52*, by setting the hairline of the runner to *52* on the **C** scale.

4) Divide by the second number of the denominator, *29*, by bringing *29* on the **C** scale under the hairline of the runner.

5) Multiply by the third number of the numerator, *32*, by setting the hairline of the runner to *32* on the **C** scale.

6) Read the answer, *349*, on the **D** scale under the hairline.

A problem of this sort can be done in much less time than is required to tell how to do it. This one, for example, can be worked in less than ten seconds by anyone who is familiar with the slide rule, and no strenuous mental activity is involved.

3. *Calculate* $\dfrac{98 \times 144 \times 1.25}{4 \times 0.375}$

1) Set the hairline of the runner to the first number of the numerator, *98*, on the **D** scale.
2) Divide by the first number of the denominator, *4*, by moving *4* on the **C** scale under the hairline of the runner.
3) Multiply by the second number of the numerator, *144*, by setting the hairline of the runner to *144* on the **C** scale.
4) Divide by the second number of the denominator, *0.375*, by bringing *0.375* on the **C** scale under the hairline of the runner.
5) Multiply by the third number of the numerator, *1.25*, by setting the hairline of the runner to *1.25* on the **C** scale.
6) Read the answer, *11,750*, on the **D** scale under the hairline of the runner.

Notice that each number of the numerator is located by moving the hairline of the runner while each number of the denominator is located on the **C** scale under the hairline by moving the slide.

It is time now to mention another important matter, that of checking the answer to be sure that it is right; because engineering and shop calculations *must* be right. The best way to check is to perform the calculations in reverse order, that is from right to left. You can do it and check it with the slide rule in much less time than you can do it longhand.

Not all problems go as smoothly as the foregoing. Occasionally, when you are ready to multiply by the second or third number of the numerator, you will find that this number on the **C** scale is beyond the end of the **D** scale. When this happens you must reverse the slide. This you can do by multiplying by one and dividing by one. Multiply by one by setting the hairline of the runner to that index of the **C** scale which is between the ends of the **D** scale. Then divide by one by sliding the other index of the **C** scale under the hairline. Multiplication or division by one does not change the answer; however, it does enable you to continue the process of getting the answer. The following examples demonstrate it.

ILLUSTRATIVE EXAMPLES

4. *Calculate* $\dfrac{34.8 \times 2.3}{97.5 \times 0.707}$

1) Set the hairline of the runner to the first number of the numerator, *34.8,* on the **D** scale.
2) Divide by the first number of the denominator, *97.5,* by bringing *97.5* on the **C** scale under the hairline.
3) You cannot multiply now by the second number of the numerator, *2.3,* because *2.3* on the **C** scale is beyond the end of the **D** scale. Hence, you must reverse the slide. Set the hairline of the runner to the right index of the **C** scale. Leave the runner in this position and bring the left index of the **C** scale under the hairline.
4) Now multiply by the second number of the numerator, *2.3,* by setting the hairline of the runner to *2.3* on the **C** scale.
5) Divide by the second number of the denominator, *0.707,* by bringing *0.707* on the **C** scale under the hairline of the runner.
6) Read the answer, *1.162,* on the **D** scale under the left index of the **C** scale.

When the last setting is for a multiplication, read the answer on the **D** scale under the hairline of the runner. When the last setting is for a division, read the answer on the **D** scale under the index of the **C** scale. Obviously, only one index of the **C** scale can be between the ends of the **D** scale at one time. The answer is always located on the **D** scale.

5. *Find the result of* $\dfrac{385 \times 0.707}{21.6 \times 5.45}$

1) Set the hairline of the runner to the first number of the numerator, *385,* on the **D** scale.
2) Divide by the first number of the denominator, *21.6,* by sliding *21.6* on the **C** scale under the hairline.
3) The next step is to multiply by the second number of the numerator, *0.707.* However, *0.707* on the **C** scale is beyond the end of the **D** scale. Therefore you must reverse the slide. Place the hairline of the runner over the left index of the **C** scale. Now move the slide so that the right index of the **C** scale is under the hairline.

4) Multiply by *0.707* by placing the hairline of the runner on *0.707* on the **C** scale.

5) Divide by the second number of the denominator, *5.45*, by sliding *5.45* on the **C** scale under the hairline.

6) Read the answer, *2.31*, on the **D** scale under the right index of the **C** scale.

6. Calculate $\dfrac{5.7 \times 1.25 \times 0.375}{8.63 \times 0.283 \times 95}$

1) Set the hairline of the runner to the first number of the numerator, *5.7*, on the **D** scale.

2) Divide by the first number of the denominator, *8.63*, by bringing *8.63* on the **C** scale under the hairline.

3) The second number of the numerator, *1.25*, is beyond the left end of the **D** scale. You must reverse the slide. Therefore, move the hairline of the runner to the right index of the **C** scale. Then slide the left index of the **C** scale under the hairline.

4) Multiply by *1.25* by moving the hairline of the runner to *1.25* on the **C** scale.

5) Divide by the second number of the denominator, *0.283*, by sliding *0.283* on the **C** scale under the hairline.

6) The third number of the numerator, *0.375*, is beyond the right end of the **D** scale, so you must reverse the slide. Set the hairline of the runner on the left index of the **C** scale. Then move the right index of the **C** scale under the hairline.

7) Now multiply by *0.375* by setting the hairline of the runner to *0.375* on the **C** scale.

8) Divide by the third number of the denominator, *95*, by sliding *95* on the **C** scale under the hairline.

9) Read the answer, *0.1152*, on the **D** scale under the right index of the C scale.

PRACTICE PROBLEMS

After you have worked all of the following problems, check your answers with the correct answers at the back of the book.

The problems are given to help you acquire skill in manipulation of the slide rule; work only for the sequence of numbers in the answer and do not worry about locating the decimal point.

1. $\dfrac{75 \times 20.2}{32.2} = ?$

2. $\dfrac{44 \times 44}{386 \times 16} = ?$

3. $\dfrac{13 \times 15 \times 17}{12 \times 14 \times 16} = ?$

4. $\dfrac{23 \times 5500 \times 10,550,000}{648 \times 14,000,000 \times 226} = ?$

5. $\dfrac{1950 \times 108 \times 32}{11,400,000 \times 3.14 \times 81} = ?$

6. $\dfrac{98.5 \times 62.4}{2.45 \times 33.1} = ?$

7. $\dfrac{1 \times 1 \times 1}{6.3 \times 5.1 \times 0.133} = ?$

8. $\dfrac{70.7 \times 0.495 \times 8.97}{59.5 \times 2.01} = ?$

9. $\dfrac{3.96 \times 41 \times 2.67}{1.005 \times 6.33 \times 2.18} = ?$

10. $\dfrac{139 \times 22.1 \times 1.708}{65 \times 93.6 \times 72} = ?$

11. $\dfrac{74.2 \times 81.9 \times 69.3}{3.1 \times 2.06 \times 1.55} = ?$

12. $\dfrac{8.66 \times 0.707}{5.77 \times 1.061} = ?$

13. $\dfrac{167000 \times 29 \times 4}{30,000,000 \times 3.14 \times 8.5} = ?$

14. $\dfrac{2.78 \times 43.2 \times 1.867}{0.798 \times 9.54 \times 8.02} = ?$

15. $\dfrac{555 \times 11.06 \times 4.93}{64.4 \times 1.05 \times 34.6} = ?$

Location of the Decimal Point.* By this time you should be able to make the slide rule settings for a calculation of this type and obtain the sequence of numbers in the answer. The next thing is to learn how to locate the decimal point in the answer. This is done by making a *digit summation.* There are two stages in this process and they will be designated as **A** and **B, A** to be completed during the manipulation of the slide rule, and **B** after the sequence of numbers in the answer has been written.

A. You multiply by each number of the numerator except the first. You divide by each number of the denominator. When multiplying, you set the hairline of the runner to the number on the **C** scale. When dividing, you slide the number on the **C** scale under the hairline. Then proceed as follows:

1) When multiplying by a number of the numerator, jot down $-$ 1 if the slide projects to the right of the stock. If the slide projects to the left, there is nothing to jot down. There is one exception to this. If you multiply by *1, 10, 100, 1000,* etc., (that is, in **a**

---

*Another method of locating the decimal point makes use of powers of ten. This method is explained in Chapter 16.

genuine multiplication and not just a reverasal of the slide) jot down — 1 no matter which way the slide projects.

2) When dividing by a number of the denominator, jot down + 1 if the slide projects to the right of the stock after the slide is in position. If the slide projects to the left, there is nothing to jot down. There is one exception to this rule. If you divide by *1, 10, 100, 1000,* etc., in a genuine division and not just a reversal of the slide, jot down + 1 no matter which way the slide projects from the stock.

3) Each reversal of the slide requires multiplication by one, for which you would jot down — 1, and division by one, for which you would jot down + 1. The — 1 cancels the + 1, so do not bother to jot anything down.

4) As you jot down the + 1's and — 1's, carry them in one horizontal row. A particular problem might yield this:

$$- 1 + 1 + 1$$

B. After writing down the sequence of numbers in the answer, continue the horizontal row of numbers by adding the digit count* for each number of the numerator and subtracting the digit count for each number of the denominator. The net result is the digit count for the answer. The following examples will illustrate this process. Follow them on your own slide rule and locate the decimal point in the answer.

The horizontal row of numbers will be referred to hereafter as *digit summation,* since it gives the digit count for the answer.

ILLUSTRATIVE EXAMPLES

7. *Calculate* $\dfrac{544 \times 12.73}{0.442 \times 3.86}$

Work from left to right, and multiply and divide in alternation.

1) Set the hairline of the runner to *544* on the **D** scale.

2) Divide by *0.442* by sliding *0.442* on the **C** scale under the hairline. You are dividing and the slide projects to the right of the stock, so jot down + 1. This is the start of the digit summation.

3) Multiply by *12.73* by setting the hairline of the runner to *12.73* on the **C** scale. You are multiplying and the slide pro-

---

*Digit counts are explained in Chapter 4.

jects to the right of the stock, so jot down -1 in the digit summation.

4) Divide by *3.86* by sliding *3.86* on the **C** scale under the hairline. You are dividing and the slide projects to the left of the stock. Hence, there is nothing to add or subtract from the digit summation.

5) Read the sequence of numbers in the answer as *406*. This is on the **D** scale under the right index of the **C** scale.

6) At this point you have in the digit summation,
$$+ 1 - 1$$

7) Add the digit count for the first number of the numerator, *544;* that is, add three, and you have,
$$+ 1 - 1 + 3$$

8) Add the digit count for the second number of the numerator, *12.73*. That is, you add two, and the digit summation is,
$$+ 1 - 1 + 3 + 2$$

9) Subtract the digit count for the first number of the denominator, *0.442*. Since this is zero, you now have,
$$+ 1 - 1 + 3 + 2 - 0$$

10) Subtract the digit count for the second number of the denominator, *3.86*. This is one, and the summation is,
$$+ 1 - 1 + 3 + 2 - 0 - 1$$

11) This completes the digit summation. Sum up:
$$+ 1 - 1 + 3 + 2 - 0 - 1 = 4$$

Then the digit count of the answer is four, so there are four digits to the left of the decimal point in the answer, and it is *4060*.

This may seem long, but the time required to work the problem is much less than that required to tell how to work it. Obviously, you will not need to write down the digit summation each time you add to it or subtract from it. You need to write each number of it only once.

8. *Find the result of* $\dfrac{21.8 \times 0.577 \times 3980}{1728 \times 3.14 \times 66.5}$

1) Set the hairline of the runner to *21.8* on the **D** scale.

2) Divide by *1728* by sliding *1728* on the **C** scale under the hairline. This is a division and the slide projects to the right of the stock so jot down $+ 1$. This is the start of the digit summation.

3) Multiply by *0.577* by setting the hairline of the runner to *0.577* on the **C** scale. This is a multiplication and the slide projects to the right of the stock so jot down — 1 in the digit summation.

4) Divide by *3.14* by sliding *3.14* on the **C** scale under the hairline. This is a division and the slide projects to the right of the stock, so add + 1 to the digit summation.

5) Multiply by *3980* by setting the hairline of the runner to *3980* on the **C** scale. This is a multiplication and the slide projects to the right of the stock so add — 1 to the digit summation.

6) Divide by *66.5* by sliding *66.5* on the **C** scale under the hairline. This is a division and the slide projects to the right of the stock, so add + 1 to the digit summation.

7) Read the sequence of numbers in the answer as *1390*. This is read on the **D** scale under the left index of the **C** scale.

8) At this point, the digit summation should be,

$$+ 1 - 1 + 1 - 1 + 1$$

9) Now add to the digit summation the digit count for each number of the numerator. For the numbers *21.8, 0.577* and *3980,* you add, respectively, two, zero, and four. This leaves the digit summation as:

$$+ 1 - 1 + 1 - 1 + 1 + 2 + 0 + 4$$

10) Next subtract the digit count for each number of the denominator. For the numbers, *1728, 3.14,* and *66.5,* you subtract, respectively, four, one, and two. This completes the digit summation as,

$$+ 1 - 1 + 1 - 1 + 1 + 2 + 0 + 4 - 4 - 1 - 2 = 0$$

11) Then the digit count for the answer is zero, hence there are zero digits to the left of the decimal point in the answer and it is *0.139.*

All that must be written in doing Example 8 is the problem, the answer, and the digit summation. Thus,

$$\frac{21.8 \times 0.577 \times 3980}{1728 \times 3.14 \times 66.5} = 0.139, \text{ and}$$

$$+ 1 - 1 + 1 - 1 + 1 + 2 + 0 + 4 - 4 - 1 - 2 = 0$$

As soon as you have completed the digit summation, put the decimal point in the answer. The sequence of numbers in the answer should be written as soon as you can read it.

Occasionally when you are ready to multiply by one of the numbers of the numerator, you find that this number on the **C** scale is outside the **D** scale. Then you must reverse the slide, that is, put the index of the **C** scale which is not within the stock in the place of the index which is. Then you can proceed to multiply. The operation of reversing the slide contributes nothing to the digit summation.

ILLUSTRATIVE EXAMPLES

9. *Calculate* $\dfrac{346 \times 15.62 \times 30.5}{85.5 \times 7.34}$

1) Set the hairline of the runner to *346* on the **D** scale.
2) Divide by *85.5* by sliding *85.5* on the **C** scale under the hairline. This is a division and the slide projects to the left of the stock so there is no contribution to the digit summation.
3) The second number of the numerator, *15.62,* is beyond the stock on the **C** scale. Hence, you must reverse the slide. Bring the hairline of the runner to the right index of the **C** scale. Then hold the runner fixed while sliding the left index of the **C** scale under the hairline. This sort of maneuver contributes nothing to the digit summation.
4) Multiply by *15.62* by setting the hairline of the runner to *15.62* on the **C** scale. This is multiplication and the slide projects to the right of the stock, so start the digit summation with — 1.
5) Divide by *7.34* by sliding *7.34* on the **C** scale under the hairline of the runner. This is a division and the slide projects to the left of the stock so there is nothing to add to the digit summation.
6) Multiply by *30.5* by setting the hairline of the runner to *30.5* on the **C** scale. This is a multiplication and the slide projects to the left of the stock so there is nothing to add to the digit summation.
7) Read the sequence of numbers in the answer on the **D** scale under the hairline of the runner. It is read as *2630.*
8) At this point the digit summation should be — 1.
9) Add to the digit summation the digit count for each number of the numerator. For the numbers *346, 15.62* and *30.5,* you

add, respectively, three, two, and two. The row of numbers is then,

$$- 1 + 3 + 2 + 2$$

10) Subtract the digit count for each number of the denominator. For the numbers *85.5* and *7.34,* subtract, respectively, two and one. This completes the digit summation and it is:

$$- 1 + 3 + 2 + 2 - 2 - 1 = 3$$

11) Then the digit count for the answer is three, hence there are three digits to the left of the decimal point in the answer, and it is *263.*

In some cases it is necessary to reverse the slide more than once. However, this adds very little to the amount of work in the problem.

10. *Find the result of* $\dfrac{3.14 \times 750,000 \times 29.3}{1,950,000 \times 0.462 \times 5.86}$

1) Set the hairline of the runner to *3.14* on the **D** scale.
2) Divide by *1,950,000* by sliding *1,950,000* on the **C** scale under the hairline. This is a division and the slide projects to the right of the stock, so start the digit summation with $+ 1$.
3) The second number in the numerator, *750,000,* on the **C** scale is beyond the end of the **D** scale. Hence you must reverse the slide. Move the hairline of the runner to the left index of the **C** scale and then leave the runner in this position while sliding the right index of the **C** scale under the hairline. There is no change in the digit summation.
4) Multiply by *750,000* by setting the hairline of the runner to *750,000* on the **C** scale. This is a multiplication, but since the slide projects to the left of the stock there is nothing to add to the digit summation.
5) Divide by *0.462* by sliding *0.462* on the **C** scale under the hairline. This is a division, but the slide projects to the left of the stock so it contributes nothing to the digit summation.
6) The third number of the numerator, *29.3,* on the **C** scale is beyond the end of the **D** scale, so you must reverse the slide. Do this by setting the hairline of the runner to the right index of the **C** scale and leaving the runner in this position while bringing the left index of the **C** scale under the airline. This adds nothing to the digit summation.
7) Multiply by *29.3* by setting the hairline of the runner to *29.3*

on the **C** scale. The slide projects to the right for this multi-plication, so add − 1 to the digit summation.

8) Divide by *5.86* by sliding *5.86* on the **C** scale under the hair-line. This is a division and the slide extends to the right of the stock, so add + 1 to the digit summation.

9) Read the sequence of the numbers in the answer as *1304*. This is read on the **D** scale under the right index of the **C** scale.

10) At this point you should have in the digit summation,

$$+ 1 - 1 + 1$$

11) Add to the digit summation the digit count for each number of the numerator. For the numbers *3.14*, *750,000*, and *29.3*, you add, respectively, one, six, and two, so the digit summation is,

$$+ 1 - 1 + 1 + 1 + 6 + 2$$

12) Subtract from the digit summation the digit count for each number of the denominator. For the numbers *1,950,000*, *0.462*, and *5.86* you subtract respectively, seven, zero, and one. This completes the digit summation as,

$$+ 1 - 1 + 1 + 1 + 6 + 2 - 7 - 0 - 1 = 2$$

13) Then the digit count for the answer is two, hence there are two digits to the left of the decimal point in the answer and it is *13.04*.

Many calculations involve very small numbers, such as *0.00635*, in which there are several zeros between the decimal point and the first digit of the number. In such a case, remember each zero between the decimal point and the first digit is counted as a negative digit. Example, the digit count for *0.00635* is minus two.

ILLUSTRATIVE EXAMPLES

11. *Calculate* $\dfrac{0.000781 \times 2730 \times 0.047}{0.0000092 \times 1.54 \times 1.732}$

1) Set the hairline of the runner to *0.000781* on the **D** scale.

2) Divide by *0.0000092* by sliding *0.0000092* on the **C** scale under the hairline. In this division, the slide projects to the left of the stock, so there is no contribution to the digit summation.

3) Multiply by *2730* by setting the hairline of the runner to *2730* on the **C** scale. Since the slide projects to the left of the stock, this gives nothing for the digit summation.

4) Divide by *1.54* by sliding *1.54* on the **C** scale under the hair-

line. In this division, the slide projects to the right of the stock, so start the digit summation with + 1.

5) Multiply by *0.047* by setting the hairline of the runner to *0.047* on the **C** scale. This is a multiplication and the slide projects to the right, so add − 1 to the digit summation.

6) Divide by *1.732* by sliding *1.732* on the **C** scale under the hairline. In this division, the slide projects to the right of the stock, so add + 1 to the digit summation.

7) Read the sequence of numbers in the answer on the **D** scale under the left index of the **C** scale. It is *408*.

8) At this point the digit summation should be,

$$+ 1 − 1 + 1$$

9) Add to the digit summation the digit count for each number of the numerator. For the numbers *0.000781, 2730,* and *0.047,* these are, respectively, minus three, four, and minus one. Hence the digit summation becomes,

$$+ 1 − 1 + 1 − 3 + 4 − 1$$

10) Complete the digit summation by subtracting the digit count for each number of the denominator. For the numbers *0.0000092, 1.54,* and *1.732,* subtract respectively, minus five, one, and one. This gives finally,

$$+ 1 − 1 + 1 − 3 + 4 − 1 − (− 5) − 1 − 1 = 4$$

11) Then the digit count for the answer is four, hence, there are four digits to the left of the decimal point in the answer, and it is *4080*.

12. *Calculate* $\dfrac{29,500,000 \times 0.00136 \times 0.0397}{0.00243 \times 7850 \times 0.922}$

1) Set the hairline of the runner to *29,500,000* on the **D** scale.

2) Divide by *0.00243* by sliding *0.00243* on the **C** scale under the hairline. In this division, the slide extends to the right so start the digit summation with + 1.

3) Multiply by *0.00136* by setting the hairline of the runner to *0.00136* on the **C** scale. This is a multiplication and the slide projects to the right of the stock, so add − 1 to the digit summation.

4) Divide by *7850* by sliding *7850* on the **C** scale under the hairline. This is a division and the slide projects to the left, so there is nothing to add to the digit summation.

5) The third number of the numerator, *0.0397,* on the **C** scale is

beyond the left end of the **D** scale. Therefore, you must reverse the slide. Move the hairline of the runner to the right index of the **C** scale. Then, leave the runner fixed and slide the left index of the **C** scale under the hairline. This adds nothing to the digit summation.

6) Multiply by *0.0397* by setting the hairline of the runner to *0.0397* on the **C** scale. In this multiplication, the slide projects to the right of the stock so add — 1 to the digit summation.

7) Divide by *0.922* by sliding *0.922* on the **C** scale under the hairline. Since the slide extends to the left there is nothing to add to the digit summation.

8) Read the sequence of numbers in the answer as *906* on the **D** scale under the right index of the **C** scale.

9) At this point the digit summation is,

$$+ 1 - 1 - 1$$

10) Add to the digit summation the digit count for each of the numbers of the numerator. For the numbers *29,500,000,* *0.00136* and *0.0397,* these are respectively, eight, minus two and minus one. The digit summation becomes,

$$+ 1 - 1 - 1 + 8 - 2 - 1$$

11) Subtract from the digit summation the digit count for each number of the denominator. For the numbers *0.00243, 7850* and *0.922,* you subtract, respectively, minus two, four, and zero. Hence, the digit summation when completed is,

$$+ 1 - 1 - 1 + 8 - 2 - 1 - (- 2) - 4 - 0 = 2$$

12) Then the digit count for the answer is two, so there are two digits to the left of the decimal point in the answer, and it is *90.6.*

The next example will show how to apply the rules when there are several numbers such as *1, 10, 100, 100,* etc. in the problem.

13. *Calculate* $\dfrac{10 \times 1 \times 100}{0.223 \times 384 \times 1.92}$

When the first number in the numerator is *1, 10, 100, 1000,* etc., always start by setting this number on the left index of the **D** scale.

1) Set the hairline of the runner to *10* at the left index of the **D** scale.

2) Divide by *0.223* by sliding *0.223* on the **C** scale under the hair-

line. In this division the slide projects to the left beyond the stock, so there is no contribution to the digit summation.

3) Multiply by *1* by setting the hairline of the runner to the right index of the **C** scale. Whenever you multiply by *1* jot down — *1* no matter which way the slide projects. This — 1 starts the digit summation.

4) Divide by *384* by sliding *384* on the **C** scale under the hairline. This is a division and the slide projects to the right of the stock so add + 1 to the digit summation.

5) Multiply by *100* by setting the hairline to the left index of the **C** scale. No matter which way the slide goes in this multiplication you should add — 1 to the digit summation.

6) Divide by *1.92* by sliding *1.92* on the **C** scale under the hairline. In this division, the slide extends to the left so there is nothing to add to the digit summation.

7) Read the sequence of numbers in the answer as *609*. This is read on the **D** scale under the right index of the **C** scale.

8) At this point the digit summation should be,

$$- 1 + 1 - 1$$

9) Add to the digit summation the digit count for each number of the numerator. For the numbers *10, 1* and *100*, these are, respectively, two, one and three; so the digit summation becomes.

$$- 1 + 1 - 1 + 2 + 1 + 3$$

10) Subtract from the digit summation the digit counts for each number of the denominator. For the numbers *0.223, 384* and *1.92,* you subtract respectively, zero, three and one. This completes the digit summation as,

$$- 1 + 1 - 1 + 2 + 1 + 3 - 0 - 3 - 1 = 1$$

11) Then the digit count for the answer is one; so there is one digit to the left of the decimal point in the answer, and it is *6.09.*

Some problems contain numbers from which you could cancel common factors. For instance the numerator might contain *81* and the denominator *24,* so you could cancel by dividing each by *3,* leaving *27* and *8,* respectively. Generally, however, it is a waste of time to cancel such numbers. In this case you would still have to set *27* and *8* on the slide rule and this is no easier than *81* and *24.*

In most problems you could complete the whole operation on the slide rule with the original numbers in less time than you would take to cancel the common factors. Many such cases arise in which the use of good judgment will save time.

Occasionally the problem will contain more numbers in the denominator than in the numerator, as

$$\frac{1152 \times 6.15}{33.9 \times 0.77 \times 21.8}$$

Here you should insert a one in the numerator so that there will be as many numbers in the numerator as in the denominator. The problem will then be,

$$\frac{1152 \times 6.15 \times 1}{33.9 \times 0.77 \times 21.8}$$

When it is in this form it can be done by the usual methods and the rules for locating the decimal point in the answer will apply. Whether you write down the one or not, you will use it in doing the problem, and if you do not write it down, you may leave it out of the digit summation. It has a digit count of one because it has one digit to the left of the decimal point, and that must be taken into account in locating the decimal point in the answer. If there are several more numbers in the denominator than in the numerator you must insert enough ones in the numerator so that it will contain as many numbers as the denominator. Thus you would change,

$$\frac{554}{3820 \times 0.295 \times 6.17 \times 19.8}$$

to,

$$\frac{554 \times 1 \times 1 \times 1}{3820 \times 0.295 \times 6.17 \times 19.8}$$

before making the calculation.

PRACTICE PROBLEMS

After you have worked all of the porblems, check your answers with the correct answers shown at the back of the book.

Check the location of the decimal point as well as the sequence of numbers. Carry out the digit summation for each problem. Do not worry if you miss on the third digit of the answer.

Write down the sequence of numbers in the answer as soon as you can read it. If you wait until you have completed the digit summation, you will have forgotten it and you will have to do the problem over. Also, do not lay the rule down and think that you will read the answer later. The slide or runner may slip, or you may forget whether to read the answer under the hairline of the runner or under an index of the **C** scale.

1. $\dfrac{10.66 \times 345}{2.78 \times 65.4} = ?$

2. $\dfrac{100 \times 10 \times 1000}{78 \times 9.6 \times 0.203} = ?$

3. $\dfrac{0.966 \times 0.707 \times 28}{0.577 \times 0.642} = ?$

4. $\dfrac{132000 \times 45.8}{29,800,000 \times 7.85} = ?$

5. $\dfrac{65 \times 0.0000067 \times 14,200,000}{7 \times 0.1945} = ?$

6. $\dfrac{1088 \times 576 \times 576}{386 \times 67} = ?$

7. $\dfrac{185 \times 192}{4 \times 0.375} = ?$

8. $\dfrac{23 \times 4980 \times 8000}{648 \times 11,400,000 \times 115} = ?$

9. $\dfrac{0.123 \times 0.0207 \times 3.24}{1.16 \times 0.201 \times 0.0317} = ?$

10. $\dfrac{34.5 \times 28.7}{16 \times 9.7} = ?$

11. $\dfrac{1.932 \times 0.59 \times 3.14}{0.92 \times 2.17} = ?$

12. $\dfrac{33 \times 33 \times 33}{21 \times 21 \times 21} = ?$

13. $\dfrac{3750 \times 6.28}{60} = ?$

14. $\dfrac{85 \times 5280}{3600} = ?$

15. $\dfrac{10,150 \times 24 \times 12}{154 \times 97.5} = ?$

16. $\dfrac{62,500 \times 1728}{48 \times 12,000,000 \times 78} = ?$

17. $\dfrac{0.382 \times 256}{18.5 \times 29} = ?$

18. $\dfrac{78.5 \times 157 \times 22}{85 \times 17 \times 18.3} = ?$

19. $\dfrac{6720 \times 0.0527}{216 \times 428} = ?$

20. $\dfrac{4.95 \times 34.7}{8.6 \times 6.67} = ?$

21. $\dfrac{1260 \times 0.427 \times 21.5}{32.7 \times 516} = ?$

22. $\dfrac{0.693 \times 14}{45.1 \times 9.7 \times 0.23} = ?$

23. $\dfrac{48.4 \times 62.5}{21.2 \times 57.3} = ?$

24. $\dfrac{2.77 \times 0.064}{1.97 \times 0.17} = ?$

25. $\dfrac{3460 \times 84.7}{16,000 \times 158} = ?$

26. $\dfrac{0.957 \times 4.15}{1.875 \times 0.015} = ?$

27. $\dfrac{267 \times 17.6}{15.2 \times 576} = ?$

28. $\dfrac{5.25 \times 88 \times 7.5}{22.5 \times 13} = ?$

29. $\dfrac{9600 \times 432}{25,600 \times 198} = ?$

30. $\dfrac{0.476 \times 8.43 \times 14.3}{2.75 \times 0.826} = ?$

OTHER METHODS FOR COMBINATIONS OF MULTIPLICATION AND DIVISION

All slide rules have C and D scales on the front. Combinations of multiplication and division can be performed with the C and D scales on all of them in the manner explained in this chapter. However, many slide rules also have inverted scales and folded scales, and these scales can be used quite effectively for this type of problem. Their use is explained in Chapters 13 and 14.

REVIEW PROBLEMS

Answers to Review Problems are not given in the back of the book. Readers who are working alone may check their answers by working the problems longhand.

1. $\dfrac{35.1 \times 26.2 \times 784}{128 \times 54.2 \times 98} = ?$

2. $\dfrac{7.48 \times 0.407 \times 323}{0.670 \times 92.5 \times 137} = ?$

3. $\dfrac{0.000573 \times 0.072}{0.418 \times 3.14} = ?$

4. $\dfrac{63 \times 56 \times 36}{24 \times 32 \times 15} = ?$

5. $\dfrac{4750 \times 51 \times 51}{32.2 \times 0.611} = ?$

6. $\dfrac{38 \times 38 \times 38}{35 \times 35 \times 35} = ?$

7. $\dfrac{0.1075 \times 23.6}{2730 \times 0.00391} = ?$

8. $\dfrac{0.00058 \times 7130}{0.000082} = ?$

9. $\dfrac{0.01 \times 10 \times 0.001}{11.76 \times 0.0591 \times 0.73} = ?$

10. $\dfrac{3.14 \times 1.826 \times 2.97}{4 \times 0.0342} = ?$

11. $\dfrac{178 \times 0.462}{15.2 \times 0.765} = ?$

12. $\dfrac{6820 \times 4.27}{5.25 \times 3.68 \times 37.5} = ?$

13. $\dfrac{1 \times 15,650 \times 5,420,000}{48 \times 28,900,000 \times 278} = ?$

14. $\dfrac{1673 \times 38.7}{17.32 \times 9.63 \times 0.804} = ?$

15. $\dfrac{4.34}{0.707 \times 1.32 \times 2.07} = ?$

CHAPTER 7

THE SQUARE AND SQUARE ROOT WITH THE A AND D SCALES

One of the easiest calculations with the slide rule is that of obtaining the square or square root of a number. It is convenient to be able to do this quickly in problems involving areas, solution of quadratic equations, triangles, etc.

THE SQUARE OF A NUMBER. The square of a number is defined as the product of the number multiplied by itself. The proper way to obtain it is (1) to set the hairline of the runner to the number on the **D** scale and (2) read the square of the number on the **A** scale under the hairline. A given number can be set in only one location on the **D** scale so there is no possibility of setting it in the wrong place. (Since the scales on the slide are not used in the calculation, the slide may be in any position.) (3) Locate the decimal.

Rule 3. (a) **The Square.** *Set the hairline of the runner to the number on the D scale. Read the square of the number on the A scale under the hairline.*

Location of the Decimal Point.** The problem of locating the decimal point in a number is just the problem of finding the digit count* of the number, then using it to count off the digits to the left or right of the decimal point, depending upon whether the digit count is plus or minus. You will remember from the discussion of the "Scales of the Slide Rule" that the digits of a number are the numerals of the number, with the limitation that the first digit is the first numeral other than zero. Any other digit than the first can be zero. Thus, in the decimal number *0.00377,* the first digit is *3* since *3* is the first numeral which is not zero. In the num-

---

** Another method of locating the decimal point employs powers of ten. It is explained in Chapter 16.

*For the explanation of Digit Counts, see Chapter 4.

ber *28.5*, the first digit is *2*, the second digit is *8*, and the third is *5*. In the case of a number such as *1572* in which no decimal point is shown, it is always understood that the decimal point follows the last numeral. The number *1572* could just as well be written *1572.0*.

The **A** scale is a double scale and this fact can be used in locating the decimal point in the square of a number.

Case 1. *When the square of the number is read in the left half of the **A** scale, multiply the digit count for the number by 2 and subtract 1. The result is the digit count for the square of the number.*

Case 2. *When the square of the number is read on the center index or in the right half of the **A** scale, multiply the digit count for the number by 2. The result is the digit count for the square of the number.* (The center index of the **A** scale is the number 1 in the center of the scale. It is read as *10, 1000*, etc.)

In the actual procedure of squaring a number, it is best to write down the digits in the square as soon as you can read them; then apply the rules for locating the decimal point. Leave the runner in position until you have placed the decimal point in the answer.

ILLUSTRATIVE EXAMPLES

1. *Square 1.84*. The correct setting of the runner for this problem is shown in Fig. 7-1. The steps in the problem are:
1) Set the hairline of the runner to *1.84* on the **D** scale.
2) Read the digits in the square of *1.84* on the **A** scale under the hairline. The numerals are *338*. Notice that this is read in the left half of the **A** scale, so the rule in Case 1 will apply for locating the decimal point.
3) The digit count for *1.84* is one, so multiply one by two, and subtract one from the result in accordance with Case 1. This gives *1*. Then the digit count for the square of *1.84* is one, so the square is 3.38.

2. *Square 45.7*.
1) Set the hairline of the runner to *45.7* on the **D** scale.
2) Read the digits in the square as *209*. This is read on the right half of the **A** scale under the hairline; hence the rule in Case 2 is to be used for locating the decimal point.
3) The digit count for *45.7* is two. Multiply two by two, obtaining

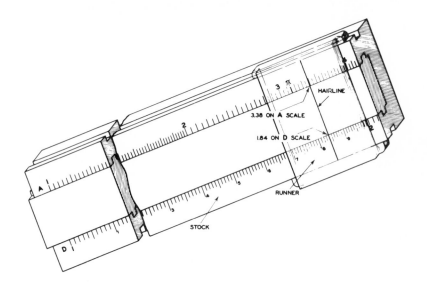

Fig. 7-1. Square of 1.84.

four, which in accordance with Case 2, is the digit count of the square; so there are four digits to the left of the decimal point in the square of *45.7* and it is *2090*.

3. *There are 320 rods in one mile. How many square rods in a square mile?* The answer is the square of *320*.

1) Set the hairline of the runner to *320* on the **D** scale. The number *320* is between the divisions marked *3* and *4*. (The divisions are the marks designated by the numbers *2, 3, 4, 5, 6, 7, 8* and *9*. Division *2* is about three-tenths of the way from the left index.) From the division marked *3*, count two sections to the right. In this portion of the scale, a section consists of five small spaces. The number *320* is located at the right end of the second section.

2) Read the digits in the square of *320* on the **A** scale under the hairline. The digits are *102* as far as they can be read. The first digit is *1* since the hairline is between the center index and the division marked *2*. It is in the first section to the right of the center index so the second digit is zero. Each small space

has a value of two in the third digit of the number, and since there is only one space between the center index and the hairline, the third digit is 2.

3) The digit count for *320* is three. Multiply three by two, obtaining six for the result. Since the square of *320* was read in the right half of the **A** scale, the rule in Case 2 holds; six is the digit count for the answer, so there are six digits to the left of the decimal point in the answer and it is *102,000*. There are 102,000 square rods in one square mile.

4. *A square wire is 0.016" on a side. What is the area of its cross section?* The answer is the square of *0.016.*

1) Set the hairline of the runner to *0.016* on the **D** scale. The first digit of *0.016* is *1* so the number is located between the left index and the division marked 2. (Notice that this 2 is the second 2 from the left index and is about three-tenths of the length from the left index.) The second digit is *6,* so count six sections from the left index. In this portion of the scale, each section contains ten spaces. Since there are only two digits in the number, it is located at the right edge of the sixth section. The hairline should coincide with the long mark by the number *6.*

2) Read the digits in the square of *0.016* as *256* on the **A scale** under the hairline. Notice that this is read in the left half of the **A** scale.

3) The digit count is minus one for *0.016.* Two times minus one is minus two. Since the square of *0.016* was read in the left half of the **A** scale, the rule in Case 1 for locating the decimal point applies, and you must subtract one from minus two. This gives minus three, which is the digit count for the answer. Hence there are three zeros to the right of the decimal point in the answer and it is *0.000256.* The area of the cross-section of the wire is *0.000256* square inches.

5. *Square 0.00579.*

1) Set the hairline of the runner to *0.00579* on the **D** scale. The first digit of *0.00579* is *5* so the number is located between the divisions marked *5* and *6.* Since the second digit is *7,* count seven sections to the right from division 5. Notice that each section has only two spaces in this portion of the scale. The third digit of the number is *9,* and each space has a value of

five in the third digit, so estimate one and four-fifths spaces from the right of the seventh section. This locates the number.

2) Read the digits in the square of *0.00579* as *336* on the right half of the **A** scale under the hairline.

3) The digit count is minus two for *0.00579*. Two times minus two is minus four. The square was read in the right half of the **A** scale, so there is nothing to subtract from minus four, and this is the digit count for the answer. This means that there are four zeros after the decimal point and before the first digit of the answer. Thus the answer is *0.0000336*.

PRACTICE PROBLEMS

After you have worked all of the following problems, check your answers with the correct answers in the back of the book.

1. A floor of a square room measures 17.5 feet on each side. Find its area.

2. The area of a circle is 3.14 times the square of its radius. Find the area of a circle of 6.5-inch radius.

3. One inch is equivalent to 2.54 centimeters. How many square centimeters are there in 1 square inch?

4. The strength of a rectangular beam is proportional to the square of its depth. How much stronger is a rectangular beam 8.3 inches deep than one 3.7 inches deep? Other factors are the same for the two beams. (*Hint:* Divide the square of 8.3 by the square of 3.7.)

5. Steel plate 1 inch thick weighs 0.283 pound per square inch. How much does a square plate 10.6 inches on a side weigh?

Square each of the following numbers:

6. 0.0737	**11.** 0.00444
7. 196.7	**12.** 8.66
8. 32.1	**13.** 204
9. 0.312	**14.** 0.0371
10. 5280	**15.** 633

THE SQUARE ROOT OF A NUMBER. The square root of a number is a second number which when multiplied by itself will give the original number. In order to obtain the square root of a number with the slide rule, you would set the hairline of the runner to the number on the **A** scale and read its square root on the **D** scale under the hairline.

Since the **A** scale is a double scale and a given number could be located in either half of it, the question arises as to which half to use in each particular problem. The answer is very simple. If the digit count is an odd number, locate the number in the left half of the **A** scale. If the digit count is an even number locate the number in the right half of the **A** scale. One special case must be mentioned. On the **A** scale there are three points that might be read as *1, 10, 1000,* etc. These points are the left index, the center index and the right index. In taking the square root of such a number, however, the correct index to be used depends upon where the decimal point of the number is located; and you must use the correct index. Numbers such as *10* and *1000* in which the digit count is even, are to be located on the center index of the **A** scale. When the digit count is odd (for example, 1 or 100) locate it on the left index of the **A** scale. A few simple examples will show how to deal with such numbers.

Rule 3. (b) The Square Root. *Set the hairline of the runner to the number on the A scale. Read the square root of the number on the D scale under the hairline.*

ILLUSTRATIVE EXAMPLES

6. *Where is the number 10 located on the A scale for the purpose of finding the square root?*

1) The digit count for *10* is two, and two is an even number so *10* is set on the center index of the **A** scale. The center index is the mark numbered *1* in the center of the scale.

7. *Where is the number 10,000 located on the A scale for the purpose of finding the square root?*

1) The digit count is five for *10,000,* and five is an odd number. Hence, *10,000* is located at the left index of the **A** scale.

Applying the rules to a decimal fraction, such as *0.0000123,* each zero between the decimal point and the first digit of the number is treated as a negative digit, and the digit count is minus four. Negative numbers, like positive numbers, are even or odd. Some decimal fractions, such as *0.707,* have no zeros between the decimal point and the first digit; these numbers are considered to have a digit count of zero. In applying the rules in such cases, zero is considered to be an even number. The following problems will give practice in dealing with numbers less than one.

PRACTICE PROBLEMS

Determine where in the A scale each of the following numbers should be located for the purpose of finding its square root. *After* you have written down which parts of the A scale you would use, check your answers with the correct answers at the back of the book.

1. 0.951	6. 0.0742
2. 0.0134	7. 0.1
3. 0.001	8. 0.00548
4. 0.000456	9. 0.0000242
5. 0.0001	10. 0.01

Location of the Decimal Point.* There are two rules for locating the decimal point in the square root of a number.

Case 1. *When the digit count for the original number is odd, add one to the digit count and divide by two. The result gives the digit count for the square root. This procedure is to be followed when the number is located in the left half of the A scale.*

Case 2. *When the digit count for the original number is even, divide the digit count by two. The result gives the digit count for the square root. This is the procedure when the number is located in the right half of the A scale.*

The following examples illustrate the method of finding the square root of a number and the process of locating the decimal point.

ILLUSTRATIVE EXAMPLES

8. *Find the square root of 152.*

1) The digit count for *152* is three. Three is an odd number, so set the hairline of the runner to *152* in the left half of the **A** scale.

2) Read the digits in the square root of *152* on the **D** scale under the hairline. The digits are *1234*.

---

*Another method of locating the decimal point employs powers of ten. It is explained in Chapter 16.

3. The digit count for *152* is odd, so add one to it, and divide by two, thus: $3 + 1 = 4$ and $4 \div 2 = 2$. Hence there are two digits to the left of the decimal point in the square root of *152* and it is *12.34*.

9. *Find the square root of 0.00663.*

1) The digit count for *0.00663* is minus two. Minus two is an even number, so set the hairline of the runner to *0.00663* on the right half of the **A** scale.

2) Read the digits in the square root of *0.00663* as *816* on the **D** scale under the hairline.

3) The digit count for *0.00663* is minus two. This is even, so divide by two, thus: $- 2 \div 2 = - 1$. Hence there is one zero to the right of the decimal point in the square root of *0.00663* and it is *0.0816*.

10. *Find the square root of 1000.*

1) The digit count for *1000* is four, and four is an even number, so set the hairline of the runner to the center index of the **A** scale.

2) Read the digits in the square root of *1000* as *316*. This is read on the **D** scale under the hairline.

3) Since the digit count for 1000 is even, divide it by two, thus: $4 \div 2 = 2$. Hence there are two digits to the left of the decimal point in the square root of *1000* and it is *31.6*.

11. *Find the square root of 79,600.*

1) The digit count for *79,600* is five, and five is an odd number. Therefore, set the hairline of the runner to *79,600* in the left half of the **A** scale.

2) Read the digits in the square root of *79,600* as *282* on the **D** scale under the hairline.

3) Since the digit count for *79,600* is odd, add one to the number of digits and divide by two, thus: $5 + 1 = 6$ and $6 \div 2 = 3$. Hence there are three digits to the left of the decimal point in the square root of *79,600* and it is *282*.

12. *Find the square root of 0.0327.*

1) The digit count is minus one, an odd number for *0.0327*, so set the hairline of the runner to *0.0327* on the left half of the **A** scale.

2) Read the digits in the square root of *0.0327* on the **D** scale under the hairline. The digits are *181*.

3) Minus one, the digit count for *0.0327*, is an odd number; therefore, add one and divide by two, thus: $-1 + 1 = 0$ and $0 \div 2 = 0$. Hence there are zero digits to the left of the decimal point in the square root of *0.0327*, and it is *0.181*.

PRACTICE PROBLEMS

After you have worked all of the following problems, check your answers with the correct answers in the back of the book.

1. A square bin is to have a floor area of 87 square feet. Find the length of one side.

2. There are 43,560 square feet in 1 acre. What is the length of one side of a square plot of ground that is 1 acre in area?

3. What is the radius of a circle that has an area of 3.89 square inches? (*Hint:* Divide 3.89 by 3.14 and take the square root.)

4. Solve for *x,* in the equation,

$$x^2 = 0.067$$

5. The area of an equilateral triangle is 0.433 times the square of the length of one side. Find the side of an equilateral triangle which has an area of 6.13 square feet.

Find the square root of each of the following numbers:

6. 22,400,000   **11.** 10

7. 2,240,000   **12.** 0.001

8. 0.000348   **13.** 577,000

9. 793   **14.** 29,500

10. 0.1943   **15.** 0.0000123

SUPPLEMENTARY REMARKS. Finding the square of a number is ordinarily only a part of the problem. Usually other operations such as multiplication or division form a part of it. You may be tempted to perform these other operations with the **A** and **B** scales and of course you could, since each half of the **A** and **B** scales offers the same range of numbers as the **C** and **D** scales. However, there are two good reasons for not doing this, both depending upon the fact that a given numerical range on the **A** scale is compressed to half the length that it occupies on the **D** scale. *First,* you can neither locate nor read a number on the **A** scale as precisely and quickly as you can on the **D** scale. *Second,* you are likely to experience eye strain in using the **A** and **B** scales for multiplication and division. The time saved by using the **A** and **B** scales instead of the **C** and **D** scales for multiplication and division is small in comparison with that saved by substituting the slide rule method for the longhand method. This last factor is the important one. To accomplish this saving is a considerable achievement; hence the **A** and **B** scales are not recommended for multiplication and division. The small amount of additional time that may be saved does not compensate for possible eye strain and loss of precision.

Basis of the Process. Like other slide-rule calculations, finding the square of a number is based on logarithms. The square of a number is the product of the number multiplied by itself. Hence the logarithm of the square of a number is equal to the logarithm of the number plus the logarithm of the number, or two times the logarithm of the number. By way of example, let us find the square of *15.62* by use of logarithms. From a table of logarithms* to the base 10,

$$\text{Logarithm of } 15.62 = 1.1937$$
$$2 \times 1.1937 = 2.3874$$

The logarithm of the square of *15.62* is 2.3874. In a table of logarithms, *2.3874* is found to be the logarithm of *244;* then the square of *15.62* is *244*. You will recall that there are two parts to a logarithm, the *characteristic,* or part to the left of the decimal point, and the *mantissa,* or part to the right of the decimal point. The characteristic of the logarithm of a number depends on the location of the decimal point of the number and is one less than the digit count for the number. The mantissa of the logarithm of a number depends only on the sequence of numbers and is independent of the location of the decimal point of the number. Only the mantissa of the number is represented on the slide rule. The distance from the left index of the **D** scale to the location of a number represents the mantissa of the logarithm of the number. Since a numerical range on the **A** scale occupies only half the length that it would on the **D** scale, the same number, say *2,* is only half as far from the left index of the **A** scale as from the left index of the **D** scale. Conversely, at the same distance from the left index, the number on the

---

*The log scale of the slide rule can be used; however, only three digits can be read accurately.

A scale has a mantissa twice as large as the number on the **D** scale. Hence, the number on the **A** scale is the square of the number directly below it on the **D** scale.

Location of the Decimal Point by Logarithms. If the mantissa of the logarithm of a number is less than *0.5000,* there is no "carryover" to the characteristic column in multiplying by two. Hence, the characteristic of the square of the number is just twice the characteristic of the number itself. This is the case when the square is read in the left half of the **A** scale. With the characteristic of the square of the number known, the decimal point can be located, since the characteristic is one less than the digit count. However, it is more convenient to have the relation directly in terms of digits. As an equation the characteristic relation is,

$$2 \times \text{characteristic of number} = \text{characteristic of square}$$

When this is put in terms of digits, it is:

$$2 \, (\text{digit count for number} - 1) = \text{digit count for square} - 1$$

or

$$2 \times \text{digit count for number} - 2 = \text{digit count for square} - 1$$

This reduces to,

$$2 \times \text{digit count for number} - 1 = \text{digit count for square}$$

In words, if the square is read on the left half of the **A** scale, the digit count for the square of a number is one less than twice the digit count for the number.

If the mantissa of the logarithm of a number is more than *0.5000,* there is a "carryover" of one to the characteristic column in multiplying by two. Therefore, the characteristic of the square of the number is one more than twice the characteristic of the number. This is the case when the square is read on the right half of the **A** scale. The equation which expresses the relation between characteristics is,

$$2 \times \text{characteristic of number} + 1 = \text{characteristic of square}$$

When this is expressed in terms of digits, it becomes,

$$2 \, (\text{digit count for number} - 1) + 1 = \text{digit count for square} - 1$$

or

$$2 \times \text{digit count for number} - 2 + 1 = \text{digit count for square} - 1$$

This reduces to,

$$2 \times \text{digit count for number} = \text{digit count for square}$$

That is, when the square is read in the right half of the **A** scale, the digit count for the square of a number is exactly twice the digit count for the number.

These results can be used to show where to locate a number on the **A** scale in order to read its square root on the **D** scale. If the square is located in the left half of the **A** scale,

$$2 \times \text{digit count for number} - 1 = \text{digit count for square}$$

or

$$\text{digit count for number} = \frac{\text{digit count for square} + 1}{2}$$

This can be rewritten for purposes of studying the square root. The relation of a number to its square is the same as the relation of the square root of a given number to the given number. Hence,

$$\text{digit count for square root} = \frac{\text{digit count for given number} + 1}{2}$$

The digit count for the square root must be an integer. Hence, the digit count for the given number must be an odd number so that when added to one and divided by two the result will be an integer. Conversely, if the digit count for a given number is odd, the number must be located in the left half of the **A** scale so that its square root can be read directly below on the **D** scale.

If the square of a number is located in the right half of the **A** scale,

$$2 \times \text{digit count for number} = \text{digit count for square}$$

or

$$\text{digit count for number} = \frac{\text{digit count for square}}{2}$$

This can be rewritten just as in the preceding case.

$$\text{digit count for square root} = \frac{\text{digit count for given number}}{2}$$

Again, the digit count for the square root must be an integer. Thus the digit count for the given number must be even, so that when it is divided by two the result will be an integer. Therefore, if the digit count for a given number is even, the number must be located in the right half of the **A** scale so that the square root can be read directly below on the **D** scale.

PRACTICE PROBLEMS

After you have worked all of the following problems, check your answers with the correct answers at the back of the book.

Square each of the following numbers:

1. 23
2. 1.954
3. 6.17
4. 384
5. 0.878
6. 5280
7. 41.7
8. 0.0718
9. 12.7
10. 56.5

Find the square root of each of the following numbers:

11. 1230
12. 93.5
13. 378
14. 2420
15. 163,000
16. 0.082
17. 1.67
18. 0.733
19. 21.5
20. 848

Solve the following:

21. $\sqrt{(24.5)^2 + (33.1)^2} = ?$
22. $(1.75)^2 + 2.92 = ?$
23. $\sqrt{3100 + (88)^2} = ?$
24. $\sqrt{(382)^2 + (256)^2} = ?$
25. $\sqrt{(9.43)^2 + (5.85)^2} = ?$

OTHER METHODS OF CALCULATING SQUARES AND SQUARE ROOTS

All calculations for square and square root can be made with the **A** and **D** scales, but not all slide rules have an **A** scale. Some have two split scales instead. On some slide rules, these split scales are designated as R_1 and R_2, and on others they just have the square root symbol $\sqrt{}$ in front of them. The use of these split scales is explained in Chapter 12.

REVIEW PROBLEMS

Answers to the Review Problems are not given in the back of the book. Readers who are working alone may check their answers by working the problems longhand.

Some of these Review Problems are more comprehensive than the earlier ones in the chapter and require other operations in addition to finding square and square root; however, most practical problems do.

1. The square of the hypotenuse of a right triangle is equal to the sum of the squares of the legs. Find the hypotenuse of a right triangle which has legs of 6 inches and 9 inches, respectively.

2. Solve for x.

$$x = \frac{13 + \sqrt{(13)^2 - 96}}{3}$$

3. The hypotenuse of a certain right triangle is 8.5 inches and one leg is 7.3 inches. Find the other leg.

4. Calculate $\frac{\pi}{4}(2.25)^2$ (Hint: $\pi = 3.14$)

5. On which scale do you locate a number when you want to square it?

6. The volume of a right circular cylinder is equal to 3.14 times the square of the radius times the altitude. Find the volume of a right circular cylinder which has a radius of 1.75 inches and an altitude of 2.75 inches.

7. The volume of a right circular cone is one-third times 3.14 times the square of the radius of the base times the altitude. Find the volume of a right circular cone which has a radius of 0.63 inches and an altitude of 0.31 inches.

8. On which scale is the square of a number read?

9. It is desired to build a cylindrical tank, 10 feet in diameter, to have a capacity of 1800 cubic feet. What altitude should the tank have?

10. Steel weighs 0.283 pounds per cubic inch. Find the weight of a circular steel bar 2.5 inches in diameter and 21 inches long.

11. The area of a circle is equal to $\frac{\pi}{4}d^2$ where d is the diameter. Find the area of a circle of 118-foot diameter.

12. What is the diameter of a circular wire that has a cross-sectional area of 0.013 square inches?

13. Solve for x.

$$x = \sqrt{(21.5)^2 - (14.3)^2}$$

14. Find the length of the diagonal of a rectangle which has sides of 27 and 33 feet, respectively.

15. A cylindrical tank is 60 feet in diameter and 36 feet high. How many gallons of water will it hold? One cubic foot is equivalent to 7.48 gallons.

In each of the following problems, perform the indicated operation.

16. $(384)^2$

17. $\sqrt{1942}$

18. $\sqrt{(138)^2 + (87.5)^2}$

19. $(0.0756)^2$

20. $(66.8)^2$

21. $(1.972)^2$

22. $\sqrt{3030}$

23. $(0.00373)^2$

24. $\sqrt{0.00373}$

25. $\sqrt{108,000,000}$

CHAPTER 8

THE CUBE AND CUBE ROOT
WITH THE K AND D SCALES

Many formulae require the use of the cube or cube root of a number. These operations are so easily and quickly done with the slide rule that everyone who owns one should know the processes.

The easiest way to find the cube or root of a number is to use the **K** scale with the **D** scale by a process in which no other scales are used.

THE CUBE OF A NUMBER. The cube of a number is the product of the number multiplied by itself twice. The cube of a number a is equal to $a \times a \times a$. In order to find the cube of a number by use of the **K** scale, set the hairline of the runner to the number on the **D** scale and read the cube on the **K** scale under the hairline. There is only one place to locate a given number on the **D** scale. Hence, you cannot go wrong here.

Rule 4. (a) The Cube. *Set the hairline of the runner to the number on the **D** scale. Read the cube of the number on the **K** scale under the hairline.*

Location of the Decimal Point.* The **K** scale is a triple scale, containing three identical lengths. The rules for locating the decimal point in the cube of a number depend upon where the cube is located on the **K** scale. They are:

Case 1. *If the cube of a number is located in the left part of the **K** scale, the digit count for the cube is equal to two less than three times the digit count for the number.*

Case 2. *If the cube of a number is read in the center part of the **K** scale, the digit count for the cube is one less than three times the digit count for the number.*

---

*Another method of locating the decimal point makes use of powers of ten. This method is explained in Chapter 16.

Case 3. *If the cube of a number is read in the right part of the K scale, the digit count for the cube is exactly three times the digit count for the number.*

The process of finding the cube of a number is demonstrated in the following examples.

ILLUSTRATIVE EXAMPLES

1. *Cube 13.5.*

1) Set the hairline of the runner to *13.5* on the **D** scale.
2) Read the digits in the cube of *13.5* on the **K** scale under the hairline. The digits are *247*. Notice that it is read in the left part of the **K** scale, so the rule in Case 1 applies.
3) The digit count for *13.5* is two. Multiply two by three. The result is six.
4) Since the cube was read in the left part of the **K** scale, subtract two from six. The result is four, the digit count for the answer.
5) Then there are four digits to the left of the decimal point in the cube of *13.5,* and it is *2470.*

It.is best to write down the sequence of numbers in the cube as soon as you can read it and then think about locating the decimal point.

2. *Cube 0.0427.*

1) Set the hairline of the runner to *0.0427* on the **D** scale.
2) Read the digits in the cube of *0.0427* as *78.* This is read on the **K** scale under the hairline. Notice that the cube is read in the center part of the **K** scale, so the rule in Case 2 applies.
3) The digit count for *0.0427* is minus one. Here the zero between the decimal point and the 4 is counted as a negative digit. Minus one multiplied by three is minus three.
4) Subtract one from minus three since the cube was read in the center part of the **K** scale; the result is minus four, the digit count for the answer.
5) Then there are minus four digits in the cube of 0.0427, which means that there must be four zeros to the right of the decimal point, between the decimal point and the 7, and the cube is 0.000078.

3. *Cube 0.742.*

1) Set the hairline of the runner to *0.742* on the **D** scale.

2) Read the digits in the cube of *0.742* on the **K** scale under the hairline as *41*. Notice that this is read in the right part of the **K** scale.

3) The digit count for *0.742* is zero. Zero multiplied by three is zero.

4) Since the cube of *0.742* was read in the right part of the **K** scale, there is nothing to subtract from zero.

5) There are zero digits to the left of the decimal point in the cube of *0.742* and it is *0.41.*

    4. *Cube 3.63.*

1) Set the hairline of the runner to *3.63* on the **D** scale.

2) Read the digits in the cube of *3.63* on the **K** scale under the hairline. This is read in the center part of the **K** scale and is *479.*

3) The digit count for *3.63* is one. One multiplied by three is three.

4) Subtract one from three since the cube was read in the center part of the **K** scale. The result is two.

5) Then there are two digits to the left of the decimal point of the cube of *3.63* and it is ***47.9.***

    5. *Cube 0.143.*

1) Set the hairline of the runner to *0.143* on the **D** scale.

2) Read the digits in the cube of *0.143* as *293* on the **K** scale under the hairline. Notice that the cube is located in the left part of the **K** scale.

3) The digit count for *0.143* is zero. Zero multiplied by three is zero.

4) Since the cube of *0.143* was read in the left part of the **K** scale, subtract two from zero. The result is minus two.

5) Then there are two zeros to the right of the decimal in the cube of *0.143,* and it is *0.00293.*

PRACTICE PROBLEMS

After you have worked all of the following problems, check your answers with the correct answers shown in the back of the book.

Cube each of the following numbers. Locate the decimal point in the answer.

1. 97.5	**3.** 128	**6.** 17.32	**9.** 0.203
2. 0.0866	**4.** 3.45	**7.** 39.6	**10.** 19.6
	5. 0.431	**8.** 0.915	

11. Find the volume of a cube that is 7.23 inches on a side.

12. The volume of a sphere is one-sixth times 3.14 times the cube of the diameter. Find the volume of a ball bearing that is one-fourth inch in diameter.

13. Find the volume of material required for a hollow sphere that has an outside diameter of 5.6 inches and an inside diameter of 3.9 inches.

14. Solve for x,

$$x = (9.4)^3 + 0.0341(17.2)^3$$

15. Find the cube of $\dfrac{0.707 \times 453}{66.8}$

THE CUBE ROOT OF A NUMBER. The cube root of a number, a, is a second number, b, such that $a = b \times b \times b$. The cube root of a number is found by reversing the process of finding the cube. The hairline of the runner is set to the number on the **K** scale and the cube root is read on the **D** scale under the hairline. The **K** scale is a triple scale and a given number can be located in three different places on it. This raises the question of which part of the scale to use in each problem. The answer to this question depends upon the digit count for the number. When the digit count is divided by three, the result must be an integer, an integer plus one-third or an integer plus two-thirds. The part over and above an integer is called the *remainder* and the integer must be expressed so that the *remainder is positive*. The rules are:

1) When the remainder is one-third, locate the number in the left portion of the **K** scale.
2) When the remainder is two-thirds, locate the number in the center portion of the **K** scale.
3) When the remainder is zero, locate the number in the right portion of the **K** scale. The remainder is zero if the digit count for the number is exactly divisible by three, or if the digit count is zero.

In applying these rules to numbers such as *0.00185*, each zero between the decimal point and the first digit of the number is counted as a negative digit. Thus the digit count for *0.00185* is minus two. Minus two divided by three is minus two-thirds, but in order to have a positive remainder, this should be expressed as minus one plus one-third. The remainder is one-third. As another axample consider *0.0000227*. There are four zeros between the decimal point and the first digit of the number. Hence the digit count for *0.0000227* is minus four. Minus four divided by three is minus one and one-third, but in order to have a positive remainder this would be expressed as minus two plus two-thirds. The remainder is positive and is two-thirds; it is absolutely necessary to have a positive remainder.

The numbers *1, 10, 100, 1000*, etc., require special attention. When you have determined which third of the **K** scale to use, locate the number at the left edge of that third. For example, the number *1000* has a digit count of four. Four divided by three is one and one-third. The remainder is one-third, so the number *1000* should be located in the left third of the **K** scale to find its cube root. Locate it at the left edge of the left third of the **K** scale.

Rule 4. (b) The Cube Root. *Set the hairline of the runner to the number on the* **K** *scale. Read the cube root of the number on the* **D** *scale under the hairline.*

Location of the Decimal Point.* The first step in locating the decimal point in the cube root of a number is to divide the digit count for the number by three. If the result is an integer, it is the digit count for the cube root. If the result is not an integer, then it should be increased to the next larger integer. This next larger integer is then the digit count for the cube root. Remember that to increase a negative number is to bring it closer to zero. Thus when minus two plus one-third is increased to the next larger integer, the result is minus one.

As usual the process will be illustrated with a few examples.

ILLUSTRATIVE EXAMPLES

6. *Find the cube root of 1210.*

1) Four is the digit count for *1210*. Four divided by three is one

---

*Another method of locating the decimal point makes use of powers of ten. This method is explained in Chapter 16.

and one-third. The remainder is one-third. Therefore, set the hairline of the runner to *1210* in the left portion of the **K** scale.

2) Read the digits in the answer on the **D** scale under the hairline. The digits are *1066.*

3) The result of dividing the digit count for *1210* by three was one and one-third. Increase this to the next larger integer which is two.

4) Then there are two digits to the left of the decimal point in the cube root of *1210* and it is *10.66.*

7. *Find the cube root of 0.0344.*

1) The digit count for *0.0344* is minus one. Minus one divided by three is minus one-third, but in order to have a positive remainder, this should be expressed as minus one plus two-thirds. The remainder is two-thirds, so set the hairline of the runner to *0.0344* in the center portion of the **K** scale.

2) Read the digits in the cube root of *0.0344* as *325* on the **D** scale under the hairline.

3) The digit count for *0.0344,* divided by three was minus one plus two-thirds. The next larger integer is zero.

4) The digit count for the answer is zero, there are zero digits to the left of the decimal point in the cube root of *0.0344,* and it is 0.325.

8. *Find the cube root of 468,000.*

1) The digit count for *468,000* is six. Six divided by three is two. The remainder is zero, so set the hairline of the runner to *468,000* in the right portion of the **K** scale.

2) Read the sequence of numbers in the cube root of *468,000* as *775* on the **D** scale under the hairline.

3) The result of dividing the digit count for *468,000* by three was exactly two, with a remainder of zero. Two is an integer and does not have to be increased.

4) Then the digit count for the cube root of *468,000* is two and it is 77.5.

9. *Find the cube root of 73,000.*

1) The digit count for *73,000* is five. Five divided by three is one and two-thirds. Since the remainder is two-thirds, the hairline of the runner should be set to *73,000* in the center portion of the *K* scale.

2) Read the sequence of numbers in the cube root of *73,000* as *417* on the **D** scale under the hairline.

3) When you divided the digit count for *73,000* by three, the result was one and two-thirds. Increase this to the next larger integer which is two.

4) Then there are two digits to the left of the decimal point in the cube root of *73,000* and it is *41.7*.

10. *Find the cube root of 0.0001.*

1) The digit count for *0.0001* is minus three. Minus three divided by three is minus one with a remainder of zero. Therefore, set the hairline of the runner to *0.0001* in the right portion of the **K** scale. This must be set at the left edge of the right portion.

2) Read the digits in the cube root of *0.0001* as *464* on the **D** scale under the hairline.

3) The remainder, after dividing the digit count for *0.0001* by three, was zero. Hence the integer minus one stands unchanged as the digit count for the answer.

4) Then there is one zero to the right of the decimal point in the cube root of *0.0001* and it is *0.0464*.

PRACTICE PROBLEMS

After you have worked all of the following problems, check your answers with the correct answers shown in the back of the book.

These problems will help you to remember what you have just learned.

Find the cube root of each of the following numbers:

1. 34.5	**3.** 3,450	**6.** 1,950,000	**9.** 0.431
2. 345	**4.** 0.00748	**7.** 5.240	**10.** 7,650
	5. 32,000	**8.** 288	

11. What is the largest cube that can be made from 30 pounds of steel? Steel weighs 0.283 pounds per cubic inch.

12. A spherical tank must be designed for a capacity of 1000 cubic feet. What must be the diameter? The volume of a sphere is one-sixth times 3.14 times the cube of the diameter.

13. Solve for *x*,

$$x^3 = 24.5 + (3.9)^2$$

14. Find the cube root of $\dfrac{15900}{32.2 \times 0.646}$

15. A hollow sphere is to have an external diameter of 1.25 inches and a volume of material of 0.834 cubic inches. Find the internal diameter.

Basis of the Process. Again we turn to logarithms and the fact that the logarithm of a product is equal to the sum of the logarithms of the numbers multiplied. The cube of a number is equal to the number multiplied by itself twice, so the logarithm of the cube is equal to the logarithm of the number plus the logarithm of the number plus the logarithm of the number. Or, the logarithm of the cube is equal to three times the logarithm of the number. The logarithm of *11.3* is *1.0531*. The mantissa, which is the part of the logarithm to the right of the decimal point depends only upon the sequence of numbers in the number *11.3*. The mantissa can be found from a set of tables of logarithms. The characteristic, which is the part of the logarithm to the left of the decimal point, depends only on the location of the decimal point in the original number. It is always one less than the digit count for the number. The cube of *11.3* can be found by means of logarithms. Thus,

$$\text{Logarithm of } 11.3 = 1.0531$$
$$3 \times \text{logarithm of } 11.3 = 3.1593$$

The logarithm of the cube of *11.3* is *3.1593*. A table of logarithms gives the sequence of numbers in the cube of *11.3* as *1443*. The characteristic is *3* so there are four digits to the left of the decimal point. Hence, the cube of *11.3* is *1443*.

On the slide rule this would be found by setting the hairline of the runner to *11.3* on the D scale. The distance from the left end of the **D** scale to *11.3* represents the mantissa of the logarithm of *11.3*. The cube of *11.3* is read on the **K** scale under the hairline, with the distance from the left end of the **K** scale to the cube representing the mantissa of the cube. The **K** scale is a triple scale and a given range of numbers occupies one-third as much space on it as on the **D** scale. Conversely, with the equal distances on the **K** scale and **D** scale, the distance on the **K** scale represents a mantissa three times as large as the distance on the **D** scale. Hence, the mantissa of the number on the **K** scale that is under the hairline is three times as large as the mantissa of the number on the **D** scale that is under the hairline. Therefore the number on the **K** scale is the cube of the number on the **D** scale, or the number on the **D** scale is the cube root of the number on the **K** scale.

Location of the Decimal Point by Logarithms. If the mantissa of the logarithm of the number that is to be cubed is less than *0.333,* there is no "carry-over" to the characteristic when multiplying by three. Hence the characteristic of the cube is exactly three times the characteristic of the number. If the mantissa of the number is less than *0.333,* the number will be located in the left one-third of the **D** scale and the cube will be read in the left portion of the **K** scale. As an equation the relation between characteristics in this case is,

$$3 \times \text{characteristic of number} = \text{characteristic of cube}$$

When this is expressed in terms of the digit count, it becomes,

$$3\ (\text{digit count for number} - 1) = \text{digit count for cube} - 1$$

or,

$$3 \times \text{digit count for number} - 3 = \text{digit count for cube} - 1$$

When the -1 is transposed to the left side of the equation, there results,

$$3 \times \text{digit count for number} - 2 = \text{digit count for cube}$$

In words this is: the digit count for the cube of a number is two less than three times the digit count for the original number. But this is true only when the cube is read in the left portion of the **K** scale. The relation between digits can be rewritten to show when to locate a number in the left portion of the **K** scale for the purpose of finding its cube root. After transposing the (-2) the equation is,

$$3 \times \text{digit count for number} = \text{digit count for cube} + 2$$

When the equation is divided by three, it becomes,

$$\text{digit count for number} = \frac{\text{digit count for cube}}{3} + \frac{2}{3}$$

or, rewording for use in finding the cube root of a number,

$$\text{digit count for cube root} = \frac{\text{digit count for number}}{3} + \frac{2}{3}$$

since the cube root of a number bears the same relation to the number as a given number bears to its cube. The digit count for the cube root must be an integer. Therefore, the right side of the equation must be an integer and if the two-thirds is exactly enough to increase

$$\frac{\text{digit count for number}}{3}$$

to the next larger integer, then,

$$\frac{\text{digit count for number}}{3}$$

must be an integer plus one-third. This is the basis for the rule that the digit count for the cube root is obtained by dividing the digit count for the original number by three and increasing the result to the next larger integer. This applies to all cases in which the number is located in the left portion of the **K** scale. After dividing the digit count by three, the remainder is one-third. Hence, whenever the remainder is one-third, the number should be located in the left portion of the **K** scale and its cube root should be read directly above it on the **D** scale.

If the mantissa of the logarithm of the number that is to be cubed is between *0.333* and *0.667*, the number is located in the middle one-third of the **D** scale, and the cube is read in the center portion of the **K** scale. Also, when the mantissa is multiplied by three, there is a carry-over of one to the characteristic. Hence, the characteristic of the cube of the number is one more than three times the characteristic of the original number. As an equation, this is,

3 × characteristic of number + 1 = characteristic of cube

Changing to digits,

3 (digit count for number − 1) + 1 = digit count for cube − 1

or,

3 × digit for number − 3 + 1 = digit count for cube − 1.

Simplifying,

3 × digit count for number − 1 = digit count for cube.

Thus, when the cube is read in the center portion of the **K** scale the digit count for the cube is one less than three times the digit count for the original number. The equation can be rewritten as,

3 × digit count for number = digit count for cube + 1

or, for use in finding the cube root of a number,

3 × digit count for cube root = digit count for number + 1

After dividing by three, this becomes,

$$\text{digit count for cube root} = \frac{\text{digit count for number}}{3} + \frac{1}{3}$$

Each side of this equation must be an integer. If the right side is an integer, then

$$\frac{\text{digit count for number}}{3}$$

must be an integer plus two-thirds. From this follows the rule that if the remainder is two-thirds when the digit count is divided by three, the number is to be located in the middle portion of the **K** scale for the purpose of finding the cube root. Also it is apparent that the digit count for the cube root is obtained by dividing the digit count for the original number by three and increasing this to the next larger integer.

If the mantissa of the logarithm of the number is between *0.667* and *1.000,* the number is located in the right one-third of the **D** scale and its cube is read in the right portion of the **K** scale. Also, when the logarithm is multiplied by three, there is a carry-over of two from the mantissa to the characteristic of the cube. Thus the characteristic of the cube of a number is two more than three times the characteristic of the original number, when the cube is read in the right portion of the **K** scale. As an equation, the characteristic relation is,

3 × characteristic of number + 2 = characteristic of cube

When this is expressed in terms of digit counts, it is,

3 (digit count for number − 1) + 2 = digit count for cube − 1

or,

3 × digit count for number − 3 + 2 = digit count for cube − 1

The integers cancel, leaving,

3 × digit count for number = digit count for cube

Thus, when the cube is read in the right portion of the **K** scale, the digit count for the cube is exactly three times the digit count for the original number. The equation can be rewritten as,

$$\text{digit count for number} = \frac{\text{digit count for cube}}{3}$$

or, rewording for use in finding the cube root of a number,

$$\text{digit count for cube root} = \frac{\text{digit count for number}}{3}$$

When the digit count for a number is exactly divisible by three, the number should be located in the right portion of the **K** scale for the purpose of finding its cube root. Also, the digit count for the cube root of the number is exactly one-third of the digit count for the number.

PRACTICE PROBLEMS

After you have worked all of the following problems, check your answers with the correct answers shown in the back of the book.

Find the cube of each of the following numbers:

1. 3.93	**3.** 0.71	**6.** 7.6	**9.** 1.76
2. 12.5	**4.** 21.4	**7.** 4.7	**10.** 28.7
	5. 0.532	**8.** 19.5	

Find the cube root of each of the following numbers:

11. 35	**13.** 152	**16.** 424	**19.** 1.78
12. 0.67	**14.** 9670	**17.** 87.5	**20.** 15,700
	15. 2.73	**18.** 0.055	

OTHER TYPES OF SLIDE RULES. The marking is usually the same for the **K** scale, no matter what the type of slide rule. However, the location of the **K** scale is not the same on all slide rules. With some, this scale is on the lower part of the stock as shown in Fig. 8-1. Here the mark on the lower edge of the runner locates a number on the **K** scale. The cube root of this number is read on the **D** scale under the hairline of the runner. In Fig. 8-1, the number *23.5* is located in the center third of the **K** scale by means of the mark on the runner. The cube root of *23.5* is *2.87* and so *2.87* on the **D** scale is under the hairline of the runner.

Frequently the **K** scale is located on the front of the stock, near the upper edge. In such a case, the hairline of the runner locates at one time a number on the **K** scale and also a number on the **D** scale. When the **K** scale is in such a location, it can be used in the manner described in this chapter.

On some types of slide rules, this scale is designated by another letter instead of **K**. This makes no difference in the use of the scale.

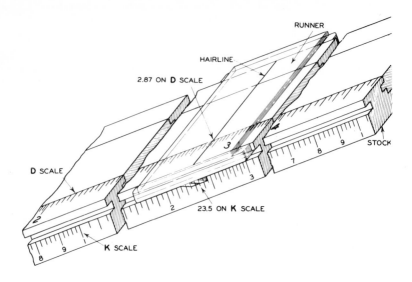

Fig. 8-1. Some slide rules are still to be found with the K scale marked on the edge.

REVIEW PROBLEMS

Answers to Review Problems are not given in the back of the book. Readers who are working alone may check their answers by working the problems longhand.

Find the cube of each of the following numbers:

1. 9.87	3. 0.0227	6. 1184	9. 5.84
2. 16.7	4. 0.473	7. 1.184	10. 0.00919
	5. 6.93	8. 37.2	

Find the cube root of each of the following numbers:

11. 29,600,000	15. 0.373	19. 0.0638	23. 115,600
12. 37.3	16. 4.52	20. 19.5	24. 758
13. 1672	17. 56.8	21. 2.84	25. 483
14. 0.00531	18. 0.0000785	22. 0.00177	

CHAPTER 9

THE SINE AND COSINE OF AN ANGLE

Many engineering and shop problems require the use of the sine or cosine of an angle. The quickest way to find one of these functions is to get it from the slide rule. You will find it very convenient to be able to do this and the value you get is precise enough for most practical calculations.

There are two distinct kinds of sine scales on slide rules. They are different in range and marking, even though both are designated by the letter **S**. First, we'll tell you how to determine which **S** scale is on your slide rule. Then, we'll tell you which sections of this chapter to read to learn how to use your **S** scale.

If your slide rule has both an **S** and **ST** scale, you have the first kind of **S** scale and you should read **Part A** of this chapter to learn how to use these two scales, and then read **Part C** to learn what to do with large angles and very small angles. The range of this **S** scale is from 5.7° to 90°, and the range of the **ST** scale is from 0.57° to 5.7°. Many of the modern slide rules, especially the large and expensive ones, have these two scales.

If your slide rule has an **S** scale but not an **ST** scale, you have the second kind of **S** scale and should read **Part B** of this chapter to learn how to use this **S** scale, and then read **Part C** to learn what to do with large angles and very small angles. The range of this **S** scale is from 34′ (the mark ′ means minutes; a minute is 1/60 of a degree) to 90°.

PART A–SLIDE RULES WHICH HAVE BOTH S AND ST SCALES.

Some slide rules, especially log log slide rules, have the **S** and **ST** scales on the slide, usually on the back of the rule. There is a

D scale on the same side, and the **S** and **ST** scales are keyed to this **D** scale.

Other slide rules, usually the less expensive ones, have the **S** and **ST** scales on the front of the stock. These scales are also keyed to the **D** scale.

THE S SCALE. The **S** scale is marked in degrees and decimal fractions of a degree. It has a range from about 5.7° at the lefthand end to 90° at the righthand end.

There are two sets of numbers on the **S** scale. One set is just to the left of a division and the other set is just to the right. The righthand numbers are the ones we are interested in now. We will explain the other set later.

Between 5.7° (at the lefthand end of the scale) and 10°, each space represents 0.05°. Fig. 9-1 shows the location of 7.33° on the **S** scale.

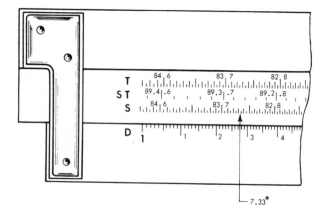

Fig. 9-1. Locating 7.33° on the righthand markings of the S scale on decimal trig. slide rule with both S and ST scales.

Between 10° and 20°, each space represents 0.1°. Fig. 9-2 shows the location of 12.8°.

Between 20° and 30°, each space represents 0.2°.

Between 30° and 60°, each space represents 0.5°.

Between 60° and 80°, each space represents 1°.

The mark just to the left of the last mark is 85°.

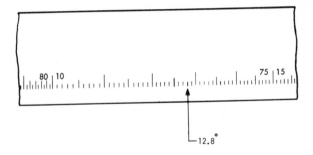

Fig. 9-2. Locating 12.8° on the righthand markings of the S scale of a decimal trig. slide rule.

THE SINE OF AN ANGLE. The way to obtain the sine of an angle with this type of slide rule is to line up the righthand end of the **S** scale with the righthand index of the **D** scale.* Then, set the hairline of the runner to the angle on the **S** scale, and read the sine of the angle on the **D** scale under the hairline. The **D** scale has a range from 0.1 to 1 for this purpose. Let's try this procedure.

> **Rule 5. (a) The Sine. (Applies only to slide rules with both the S and ST scales.)** *Set the hairline of the runner to the angle on the righthand markings of the **ST** or **S** scale. Read the sine of the angle on the **D** scale under the hairline.*

ILLUSTRATIVE EXAMPLES

1. *What is the sine of 6.7°?*

1) Line up the **S** scale with the **D** scale.
2) Set the hairline of the runner to 6.7° on the **S** scale.
3) Read the sine of 6.7° as 0.1166 on the **D** scale under the hairline.

2. *Determine the sine of 37.3°.*

1) Line up the **S** scale with the **D** scale.
2) Set the hairline of the runner to 37.3° on the **S** scale.
3) Read the sine of 37.3° as 0.606 on the **D** scale under the hairline.

---

*If the **S** scale is on the stock, it is already lined up with the **D** scale, so you can ignore this instruction. However, it will be repeated often for the benefit of those who have slide rules with the **S** scale on the slide.

3. *Obtain the sine of 72.5°.*

1) Line up the **S** scale with the **D** scale.
2) Set the hairline of the runner to 72.5° on the **S** scale.
3) Read the sine of 72.5° at 0.954 on the **D** scale under the hairline.

PRACTICE PROBLEMS

Do these problems for practice and then check your answers with the correct answers in the back of the book. What is the sine of each of these angles?

1. 42.5°	**2.** 21.4°
3. 10.8°	**4.** 63°
5. 36°	**6.** 51.2°
7. 7.75°	**8.** 33.6°
9. 18.6°	**10.** 27.5°

Basis of the Process. The **D** scale can be thought of as a scale ranging from 0.1 to 1.0, in which the distance from the lefthand index to a number represents the logarithm of the number. The **S** scale, which is of the same length as the **D** scale, is laid off to correspond with the **D** scale so that the distance from the lefthand end to an angle represents the logarithm of the sine of the angle. Thus, the relation between the number on the **D** scale and the angle on the **S** scale is,

*logarithm of number on **D** scale =*
*logarithm of sine of angle on **S** scale.*

If the logarithms of two numbers are equal, the two numbers must be equal. Thus,

*number on **D** scale = sine of angle on **S** scale.*

THE ST SCALE. The **ST** scale is used for small angles. It has a range from 0.573° at the lefthand end to 5.74° at the righthand end. Each space on the **ST** scale represents 0.02°.

THE SINE OF A SMALL ANGLE. The sine of a small angle can be obtained by using the **ST** scale with the **D** scale. First, line up the righthand end of the **ST** scale with the righthand index of the **D** scale. Next, set the hairline of the runner to the angle on the **ST** scale. Then, read the sine of the angle on the **D** scale under the hairline. The **D** scale has a range from 0.01 to 0.1 for this purpose. A few examples will show how to do it.

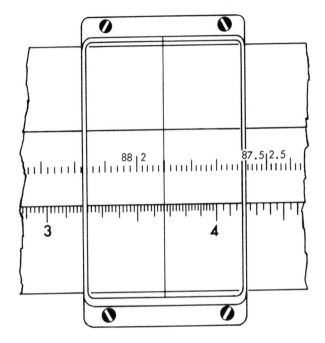

Fig. 9-3. Proper setting to find the sine of 2.1°.

ILLUSTRATIVE EXAMPLES

4. *Determine the sine of 2.1°.*

1) Line up the **ST** scale with the **D** scale.

2) Set the hairline of the runner to 2.1° on the **ST** scale.

3) Read the sine of 2.1° as 0.0366 on the **D** scale under the hairline. Fig. 9-3 shows the setting of the slide rule.

5. *What is the sine of 4.35°.*

1) Line up the **ST** scale with the **D** scale.

2) Set the hairline of the runner to 4.35° on the **ST** scale.

3) Read the sine of 4.35° as 0.0758 on the **D** scale under the hairline.

PRACTICE PROBLEMS

This is an easy operation but you should practice it. Check your answers with the correct answers in the back of the book. Just obtain the sine of each of these angles.

1. 0.62°	**2.** 1.15°
3. 3.5°	**4.** 2.16°
5. 5.1°	**6.** 0.93°
7. 4.17°	**8.** 1.81°
9. 2.95°	**10.** 3.23°

THE COSINE OF AN ANGLE. The cosine of an angle can also be obtained by using the **S** or **ST** scale with the **D** scale. The other numbers on the **S** and **ST** scales, the numbers just to the left of the divisions, are used for this purpose. They are read from right to left. They are printed in red on some slide rules. If the **ST** scale doesn't have this second set of numbers, each can be obtained by subtracting a number on the **ST** scale from 90°. The **S** scale has a range from 0° at the righthand end to 84.26° at the lefthand end. The **ST** scale has a range from 84.26° at the righthand end to 89.427° at the lefthand end.

The way to obtain the cosine of an angle is to line up the **S** and **ST** scales with the **D** scale. Then, set the hairline of the runner to the angle on the **S** or **ST** scale, and read the cosine on the **D** scale under the hairline. The **D** scale has a range from 0.01 to 0.1 for the **ST** scale and a range from 0.1 to 1 for the **S** scale. Now, follow these examples.

ILLUSTRATIVE EXAMPLES

6. *What is the cosine of 33°?*

1) Line up the **S** scale with the **D** scale.
2) Set the hairline of the runner to 33° on the **S** scale, using the cosine numbers and reading from right to left.
3) Read the cosine of 33° as 0.839 on the **D** scale under the hairline.

7. *Determine the cosine of 87.7°.*

1) Line up the **ST** scale with the **D** scale.

2) Set the hairline of the runner to 87.7° on the **ST** scale, being careful to read from right to left.

3) Read the cosine of 87.7° as 0.0401 on the **D** scale under the hairline.

PRACTICE PROBLEMS

The most important point here is to remember to read the **S** and **ST** scales from right to left. You can check your answers with the correct answers in the back of the book. Determine the cosine of each of these angles.

1. 67.5°	2. 20.3°
3. 41°	4. 17°
5. 85.5°	6. 88.2°
7. 39.6°	8. 55°
9. 83.7°	10. 86.4°

THE ARC SINE OF A NUMBER. The arc sine or inverse sine of a number is the angle for which the number is the sine. It is written in this way: sin⁻¹, 0.6 which means the angle for which the sine is 0.6. You can get the arc sine in this way. First, line up the **S** and **ST** scales with the **D** scale. Next, set the hairline of the runner to the number on the **D** scale. Then, read the angle on the **S** or **ST** scale under the hairline. If the number is between 0.1 and 1, read the angle on the **S** scale. If the number is between 0.01 and 0.1, read the angle on the **ST** scale.

Rule 5. (b) The Arc Sine. (Applies only to slide rules with both the S and ST scales.) *Set the hairline of the runner to the number on the D scale. Read the angle which is the arc sine of the number on the righthand markings of the ST or S scale under the hairline.*

ILLUSTRATIVE EXAMPLES

8. *What is sin⁻¹ 0.812?*

1) Line up the **S** and **D** scales.
2) Set the hairline of the runner to 0.812 on the **D** scale.
3) Read the angle as 54.3° on the **S** scale under the hairline.

9. *What is sin⁻¹ 0.0347?*

1) Line up the **ST** and **D** scales.
2) Set the hairline of the runner to 0.0347 on the **D** scale.
3) Read the angle as 1.99° on the **ST** scale under the hairline.

PRACTICE PROBLEMS

After you have determined the arc sine of each of these numbers, check your answers with the correct answers in the back of the book.

1. 0.145	**2.** 0.672
3. 0.091	**4.** 0.723
5. 0.295	**6.** 0.0433
7. 0.584	**8.** 0.0618
9. 0.0169	**10.** 0.367

PART B—SLIDE RULES WITH ONLY THE S SCALE.

Some slide rules have the **S** scale on the front of the stock, but some other slide rules have the **S** scale on the back of the slide. In each case, the range of the **S** scale is from 34′ to 90°, and the **S** scale is keyed to the **A** or **B** scale.

This kind of scale is marked in degrees and minutes.

THE S SCALE. There may be slight variations from one slide rule to another, but most are marked in this way.

The numbers 40 and 50 near the lefthand end of the **S** scale represent minutes. All other numbers represent degrees.

Between the lefthand end of the **S** scale and the number 3, each space represents 2′ of angle. Fig. 9-4 shows the location of the angle to 2° 25′ on the **S** scale.

Between the numbers 3 and 10, each space represents 5′ of angle. Fig. 9-5 shows the location of the angle 6° 47′ on the **S** scale.

Between the numbers 10 and 20, each space represents 10′ of angle.

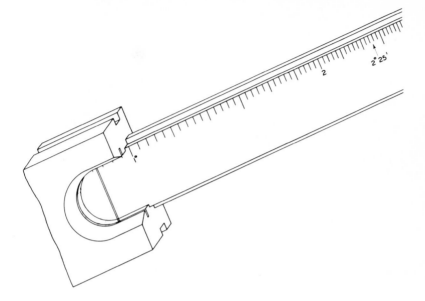

Fig. 9-4. Location of small angle 2°25' on S scale of Mannheim type slide rule, which has no ST scale.

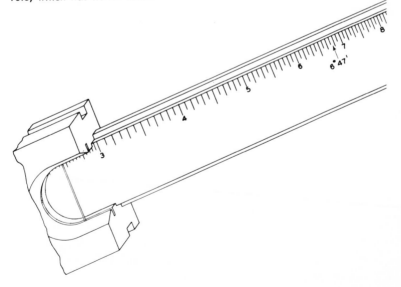

Fig. 9-5. Location of 6°47' on S scale of Mannheim type slide rule.

Between the numbers 20 and 40, each space represents 30' (0.5°) of angle.

Between the numbers 40 and 70, each space represents 1° of angle.

The five spaces immediately to the right of the number 70 each represent 2° of angle.

The next to the last mark on this **S** scale represents 80°.

The last mark represents 90°.

THE SINE OF AN ANGLE. The problem is to find the sine of an angle. The angle is expressed in degrees and minutes, or in degrees and decimal fractions of a degree. The sine is always a decimal fraction, such as 0.749 or 0.0285. The first step in finding the sine of an angle is to locate the angle on the **S** scale.

If the **S** scale is on the **stock,** you can just set the hairline of the runner to the angle and then read the sine of the angle on the **A** scale under the hairline.

If the **S** scale is on the back of the slide, you can turn the slide rule over and set the angle to the mark or edge of the plastic insert, or to the mark on the slide rule if there is no plastic insert. Then, read the sine of the angle on the **B** scale under the righthand index of the **A** scale.

The **A** and **B** scales are double scales and, for the purpose of finding the sine of an angle, the numbers on them should be considered as ranging from 0.01 at the lefthand index to 1.0 at the righthand index. The center index has the value 0.1 as the sine of the angle. Numbers in the lefthand half are between 0.01 and 0.1. Numbers in the righthand half are between 0.1 and 1.0. For example, the number 4 in the lefthand half of the **A** or **B** scale would be read as 0.04 as the sine of an angle; the number 4 in the righthand half would be read as 0.4.

Rule 5. (c) **The Sine. (Applies only to slide rules with the S scale but not the ST scale.)** *Set the hairline of the runner to the angle on the S scale. Read the sine of the angle on the A or B scale.*

ILLUSTRATIVE EXAMPLES

10. *Find the sine of 30°.*

1) Set the hairline of the runner to 30° on the **S** scale, or turn the slide rule over and set 30° against the mark.

2) Read the sine of 30° as 0.5, either on the **A** scale under the hairline or on the **B** scale under the righthand index of the **A** scale. You know that the answer is 0.5 and not 0.05 because it is read in the righthand half of the scale and must be between 0.1 and 1.0.

11. *Find the sine of 48° 30'.*

1) Set the hairline of the runner to 48° 30' on the **S** scale, or turn the slide rule over and set 48° 30' against the mark. Remember that 30' is half of 1°, so 48° 30' is halfway between 48° and 49°.

2) Read the sine of 48° 30' as 0.749, either on the **A** scale under the hairline or on the **B** scale under the righthand index of the **A** scale.

12. *Find the sine of 3° 25'.*

1) Set the hairline of the runner to 3° 25' on the **S** scale, or turn the slide rule over and set 3° 25' against the mark. Notice that each space between 3 and 4 on the **S** scale represents 5' of angle.

2) Read the sine of 3° 25' on the **A** scale under the hairline or on the **B** scale under the righthand index of the **A** scale. The sequence of numbers in the answer is 596. Since you read it in the lefthand half of the scale, it must be between 0.01 and 0.1. Therefore, it is 0.0596.

13. *Find the sine of 1° 38'.*

1) Set the hairline of the runner to 1° 38' on the **S** scale, or turn the slide rule over and set 1° 38' against the mark.

2) Read the sine of 1° 38' as 0.0285, either on the **A** scale under the hairline or on the **B** scale under the righthand index of the **A** scale.

Remember that there are 60' in 1°. Consequently, the distance between two consecutive degree marks on the **S** scale represents 60'.

PRACTICE PROBLEMS

After you have worked all the following problems, check your answers with the correct answers shown in the back of the book.

Find the sine of each of the following angles:

1. 67°	**3.** 10°30′	**6.** 4°28′	**9.** 2°45′
2. 53°10′	**4.** 60°	**7.** 26°32′	**10.** 73°
	5. 45°	**8.** 15°20′	

11. The vertical component of a force is equal to the product of the force and the sine of the angle which it makes with the horizontal. Find the vertical component of a force of 230 pounds at an angle of 40° with the horizontal.

12. A force at an angle of 22°30′ with the horizontal has a vertical component of 18 pounds. Find the force.

Verify each of the following equations:

13. $\sin 65° = 2 \sin 32°30′ \sin 57°30′$

14. $\sin 50° = 2 \sin 25° \sin 65°$

15. $\sin 55° + \sin 10° = 2 \sin 32°30′ \sin 67°30′$

16. $\sin^2 40° + \sin^2 50° = 1$

17. $\sin^2 30° = \frac{1}{2} \sin 30°$

18. $\dfrac{7.4}{\sin 25°} = \dfrac{12.36}{\sin 45°}$

Basis of the Process. The **B** scale can be thought of as a scale, ranging from *0.01* to *1,* in which the distance from the left index to the number represents the logarithm of the number. The sine scale, which is of the same length as the **B** scale, is laid off to correspond with the **B** scale so that the distance from the left end represents the logarithm of the sine of the angle. Thus the relation between the number on the **B** scale and the angle on the sine scale is,

*logarithm of number on **B** scale = logarithm of sine of angle on sine scale*

If the logarithms of two quantities are equal, the two quantities must be equal. Thus,

*number on **B** scale = sine of angle on sine scale*

THE COSINE OF AN ANGLE. There is no cosine scale on the slide rule but none is necessary. The cosine of an angle can be found by using the sine scale, since the cosine of an angle is equal to the sine of 90° minus the angle. Thus the cosine of 30° is equal to the sine of 90° — 30°, that is, the sine of 60°. The sine of 60° can be found in the usual way.

ILLUSTRATIVE EXAMPLES

14. *Find the cosine of 50°.*

1) The cosine of 50° is equal to the sine of *90° — 50°*, or the sine of *40°*.
2) The sine of *40°* is *0.643*. Hence the cosine of 50° is *0.643*. There are only 60′ in 1°. Remember this when you subtract an angle from 90°.

15. *Find the cosine of 63°20′.*

1) The cosine of *63°20′* is equal to the sine of *90° — 63°20′*, or the sine of *26°40′*.
2) The sine of *26°40′* is *0.449*. Hence, *0.449* is the cosine of *63°20′*.

16. *Find the cosine of 42°15′.*

1) The cosine of *42°15′* is equal to the sine of *90° — 42°15′*, which is the sine of *47°45′*.
2) The sine of *47°45′* is *0.740,* so the cosine of *42°15′* is *0.740.*

PRACTICE PROBLEMS

After you have worked all of the following problems, check your answers with the correct answers at the back of the book.

Find the cosine of each of the following angles:

1. 34°15′	**3.** 51°40′	**6.** 88°30′	**9.** 76°30′
2. 25°30′	**4.** 47°30′	**7.** 89°45′	**10.** 65°40′
	5. 20°	**8.** 59°10′	

THE SINE OF AN ANGLE BETWEEN 70° AND *90°*. The usual method of determining the sine of an angle is not very precise if the angle is between 70° and 90°, because the distance between 70° and 90° on the sine scale is so small. However, the sine of any such angle θ can be found by using the formula,

$$\sin \theta = \sqrt{1 - \sin^2 (90° - \theta)}$$

If the angle θ is larger than 70°, the sine of 90° — θ can be found easily from the slide rule. You already know how to square a number and how to find the square root. (If you do not, read the chapter on "Square and Square Root.") Thus you can work out the formula. With practice you will be able to do it without writing down any intermediate results.

ILLUSTRATIVE EXAMPLES

17. *Find the sine of 85°.*

1) *90° — 85° = 5°.* The sine of *5° is 0.0872.*
2) Square *0.0872.* The result is *0.0076.* This is sin² (90° — θ).
3) Next find 1 — sin² (90° — θ). This is *1 — 0.0076 = 0.9924.*
4) The square root of *0.9924* is *0.996.* Hence the sine of *85°* is *0.996.*

18. *Find the sine of 77°30′.*

1) *90° — 77°30′.* The sine of *12°30′* is *0.216.*
2) Square *0.216.* The result is *0.0467.*
3) *1 — 0.0467 = 0.9533.*
4) Find the square root of *0.9533.* This is *0.977,* so the sine of *77°30′* is *0.977.*

19. *Find the sine of 81°15′.*

1) *90° — 81°15′ = 8°45′.* The sine of *8°45′* is *0.152.*
2) Square *0.152.* The result is *0.0232.*
3) *1 — 0.0232 = 0.9768.*
4) Find the square root of *0.9768.* The result is *0.988,* so *0.988* is the sine of *81°15′.*

PRACTICE PROBLEMS

After you have worked all of the following problems, check your answers with the correct answers at the back of the book.

Find the sine of each of the following angles:

1. 82°30′	6. 73°15′
2. 71°45′	7. 79°20′
3. 76°10′	8. 78°30′
4. 81°50′	9. 80°
5. 83°40′	10. 75°22′

Basis of the Process. The basis of this process is the trigonometric identity,

$$\sin^2 \theta + \cos^2 \theta = 1$$

This is true for any angle θ. The term $\cos^2 \theta$ can be transposed, leaving,

$$\sin^2 \theta = 1 - \cos^2 \theta$$

Then substitute for $\cos \theta$,

$$\cos \theta = \sin (90° - \theta)$$

This gives,

$$\sin^2 \theta = 1 - \sin^2 (90° - \theta)$$

Next take the square root of each side. The result is,

$$\sin \theta = \sqrt{1 - \sin^2 (90° - \theta)}$$

THE ARC SINE OF A NUMBER. You will find many problems in which you calculate the sine of an angle by division or multiplication, and then want to know what the angle is. The sine of an angle is a number. The arc sine (sometimes called the inverse sine) of a number is the angle which has that number for its sine. The process of finding the angle when its sine is known is just the reverse of the process of finding the sine when the angle is known.

Depending on where the **S** scale is located on your slide rule, either you can set the hairline of the runner to the number on the **A** scale and read the angle on the **S** scale under the hairline, or you can bring the number on the **B** scale under the righthand index of the **A** scale and read the angle on the **S** scale on the back of the slide against the mark.

The following examples will make the process clear. Carry them out on your own slide rule. Remember that when working with the sine of an angle, the **A** and **B** scales are thought of as extending from 0.01 at the lefthand index to 1.0 at the righthand index. A number between 0.01 and 0.1 is located in the lefthand half of the scale, and a number between 0.1 and 1.0 is located in the righthand half.

Rule 5. (d) The Arc Sine. (Applies only to slide rules with the S scale but not the ST scale.) *Set the hairline of the runner to the number on the A or B scale. Read the angle on the S scale.*

ILLUSTRATIVE EXAMPLES

20. *Find arc sine 0.346,* that is, find the angle whose sine is 0.346.

1) Set the hairline of the runner to 0.346 in the righthand half of the **A** scale, or bring 0.346 in the righthand half of the **B** scale under the righthand index of the **A** scale.

2) Read the angle as 20° 15′ on the **S** scale under the hairline, or on the **S** scale on the back of the slide against the mark.

21. *Find arc sine 0.0346.*

1) Set the hairline of the runner to 0.0346 in the lefthand half of the **A** scale, or bring 0.0346 in the lefthand half of the **B** scale under the righthand index of the **A** scale.

2) Read the angle whose sine is 0.0346 on the **S** scale under the hairline, or on the back of the slide against the mark. This angle is 1° 59′.

PRACTICE PROBLEMS

After you have worked all of the following problems, check your answers with the correct answers in the back of the book.

Find the arc sine for each of the following numbers:

1. 0.748	3. 0.0569	6. 0.205	9. 0.350
2. 0.157	4. 0.667	7. 0.0835	10. 0.500
	5. 0.430	8. 0.905	

PART C–OPERATIONS COMMON TO BOTH KINDS OF S SCALES

There are some operations which can be explained in the same way, no matter which kind of **S** scale you have on your slide rule. Some of these operations are for angles greater than 90°. Others are for very small angles.

THE SINE OF AN ANGLE GREATER THAN 90°. The sine of an angle greater than 90° cannot be found directly from the slide rule. However, the sine of such an angle can always be expressed in terms of the sine of an angle between 0° and 90° and the sine of an angle between 0° and 90° can be found directly from the slide rule.

Angles between 90° and 180°. For any angle θ between 90° and 180°, the following equation is true,

$$\sin \theta = \sin (180° - \theta)$$

If θ is between 90° and 180°, then $(180° - \theta)$ must be between 0° and 90°. The sine of $(180° - \theta)$ can be found with the slide rule.

ILLUSTRATIVE EXAMPLES

22. *Find the sine of 145°.*

1) Sin *145°* = sin *(180° — 145°)* = *35°.*
2) The sine of *35°* is *0.570.* Hence, the sine of *145°* is 0.570.

23. *Find the sine of 166°40'.*

1) Sin *166°40'* = sin *(180° — 166°40')* = sin *13°20'.*
2) The sine of *13°20'* is *0.231,* so the sine of *166°40'* is *0.231.*

Angles between 180° and 270°. When an angle θ is between 180° and 270°, you can use the relation

$$\sin \theta = - \sin (\theta - 180°)$$

If θ is between 180° and 270°, then $(\theta - 180°)$ is between 0° and 90°. Hence you can find the sine of $(\theta - 180°)$ directly from the slide rule.

ILLUSTRATIVE EXAMPLES

24. *Find the sine of 220°.*

1) Sin *220°* = — sin *(220° — 180°)* = — sin *40°.*
2) The sine of *40°* is *0.643.* Thus the sine of *220°* is (— *0.643*).

25. *Find the sine of 243° 30'.*

1) sin *243°30'* = — sin *(243°30' — 180°)* = — sin *63°30'.*
2) The sine of *63°30'* is *0.895.* Hence, the sine of *243°30'* is (— *0.895*).

Angles between 270° and 360°. The equation that is to be used when the angle θ is between 270° and 360° is

$$\sin \theta = - \sin (360° - \theta)$$

When θ is between 270° and 360°, the angle $(360° - \theta)$ is between 0° and 90°.

ILLUSTRATIVE EXAMPLES

26. *Find the sine of 293°20′.*

1) Sin *293°20′* $= -$ sin *(360°* $-$ *293°20′)* $= -$ *sin 66°40′*.
2) The sine of *66°40′* is *0.918.* Therefore, the sine of *293°20′* is $(- 0.918)$.

27. *Find the sine of 337°45′.*

1) Sin *337°45′* $= -$ sin *(360°* $-$ *337°45′)* $= -$ sin *22°15′*.
2) The sine of *22°15′* is *0.379,* so the sine of *337°45′* is (-0.379).

PRACTICE PROBLEMS

After you have worked all of the following problems, check your answers with the correct answers at the back of the book.

Find the sine of each of the following angles:

1. 205°	**6.** 330°
2. 310°	**7.** 188°45′ (188.8°)
3. 170°	**8.** 171°15′ (171.3°)
4. 123°15′ (123.3°)	**9.** 321°20′ (321.3°)
5. 242°30′ (242.5°)	**10.** 212°50′ (212.8°)

THE COSINE OF AN ANGLE GREATER THAN 90°. The cosine of any large angle can be expressed in terms of the sine of an angle between 0° and 90°. Since you can find the sine of an angle between 0° and 90° with the slide rule, you can find the cosine of any large angle.

Angles between 90° and 180°. When the angle θ is between 90° and 180°, use the equation,

$$\cos \theta = - \sin (\theta - 90°)$$

If θ is between 90° and 180°, then $(\theta - 90°)$ is between 0° and 90°.

ILLUSTRATIVE EXAMPLES

28. *Find the cosine of 135°.*

1) Cos *135°* = − sin (*135°* − *90°*) = − sin *45°*.
2) The sine of *45°* is *0.707*. Hence, the cosine of *135°* is (− *0.707*).

29. *Find the cosine of 98°10′.*

1) Cos *98°10′* = − sin (*98°10′* − *90°*) = − sin *8°10′*.
2) The sine of *8°10′* is *0.142*. Therefore, the cosine of *98°10′* is (− *0.142*).

Angles between 180° and 270°. For any angle θ between 180° and 270°, the following equation is true,

$$\cos \theta = -\sin (270° - \theta)$$

When θ is between 180° and 270°, the angle (270° − θ) is between 0° and 90°.

ILLUSTRATIVE EXAMPLES

30. *Find the cosine of 243°30′.*

1) Cos *243°30′* = − sin (*270°* − *243°30′*) = − sin *26°30′*.
2) The sine of *26°30′* is *0.446,* so the cosine of *243°30′* is (− *0.446*).

31. *Find the cosine of 214°40′.*

1) Cos *214°40′* = − sin (*270°* − *214°40′*) = − sin *55°20′*.
2) The sine of *55°20′* is *0.821*. Hence, the cosine of *214°40′* is (− *0.821*).

Angles between 270° and 360°. If the angle θ is between 270° and 360°, you can use

$$\cos \theta = \sin (\theta - 270°)$$

The angle (θ − 270°) must be between 0° and 90° if θ is between 270° and 360°.

ILLUSTRATIVE EXAMPLES

32. *Find the cosine of 288°45′.*

1) Cos *288°45′* = sin (*288°45′* − *270°*) = sin *18°45′*.
2) The sine of *18°45′* is *0.321,* so the cosine of *288°45′* is *0.321*.

33. *Find the cosine of* $312°10'$.

1) Cos $312°10' = $ sin $(312°10' - 270°) = $ sin $42°10'$.
2) The sine of $42°10'$ is 0.671. Hence, the cosine of $312°10'$ is 0.671.

PRACTICE PROBLEMS

After you have worked all of the following problems, check your answers with the correct answers at the back of the book.

Find the cosine of each of the following angles:

1. $150°$
2. $117°30'$ $(117.5°)$
3. $281°15'$ $(281.3°)$
4. $330°$
5. $260°10'$ $(260.2°)$

6. $135°$
7. $222°30'$ $(222.5°)$
8. $95°40'$ $(95.7°)$
9. $315°$
10. $157°30'$ $(157.5.°)$

THE SINE OF A VERY SMALL ANGLE. The smallest angle on the sine scale is $0°34'$. Hence the sine of an angle smaller than this cannot be found in the usual way. Such an angle would be expressed in minutes and seconds as, for instance, $20'33''$.* The first step in finding the sine is to convert the number of seconds to a decimal fraction of a minute. This is done by dividing by 60 since there are $60''$ in $1'$. For example, 33 divided by 60 is 0.55, so $20'33''$ is $20.55'$. Next the number of minutes, for instance, 20.55, is divided by 3440. The result is the sine of the angle as a decimal fraction. The sine of the angle $20'33''$ is 0.00598.

ILLUSTRATIVE EXAMPLES

34. *Find the sine of* $15'45''$.

1) Convert $45''$ to a decimal fraction of $1'$ by dividing 45 by 60. (Do this by setting the hairline of the runner to 45 on the **D** scale. Next bring 60 on the **C** scale under the hairline. Read the answer on the **D** scale under the right index of the **C** scale.) The result is 0.75.
2) Thus $15'45''$ is $15.75'$.
3) Divide 15.75 by 3440. (The first step in this division is to set the hairline of the runner to 15.75 on the **D** scale. Next slide

---

*The double mark " is read as seconds.

3440 on the **C** scale under the hairline. Read the digits in the result as *458* on the **D** scale under the right index of the **C** scale. The digit count† for *15.75* is two, and four is the digit count for *3440*. In accordance with the rules given in the chapter on Division, in this case subtract four from two. The result is minus two and this is the digit count for the answer. This means that there must be two zeros immediately following the decimal point.) The result is *0.00458*. Thus, the sine of *15′45″* is *0.00458*.

35. *Find the sine of 0′23″*.

1) Convert *23″* to a decimal fraction of *1′* by dividing *23* by *60*. The result is *0.383*.
2) Thus *0′23″* is *0.383′*.
3) Divide *0.383* by *3440*.
4) The result is *0.0001112* and this is the sine of *0′23″*.

36. *Find the sine of 6′0″*.

1) This is *6.0′*.
2) Divide *6* by *3440*.
3) The result is *0.001745*. This is the sine of *6′0″*.

PRACTICE PROBLEMS

After you have worked all of the following problems, check your answers with the correct answers at the back of the book.

Find the sine of each of the following angles:

1. 32′20″	3. 1′12″	6. 14′05″	9. 0′37″
2. 25′30″	4. 11′0″	7. 8′15″	10. 21′17″
	5. 19′52″	8. 6′27″	

11. Find the vertical component of a force of 2100 pounds at an angle of 16′30″ with the horizontal.

12. A train travels for 6.5 miles up a grade which makes an angle of 45′ with the horizontal. What is the change in altitude of the train? (*Hint:* Multiply 6.5 miles by the sine of 45′.)

13. How far must an automobile travel on a 30′ grade to gain 100 feet in altitude?

14. The hypotenuse of a certain right triangle is 28.3 inches in length and makes an angle of 25' with the base. Find the altitude of the triangle. (*Hint:* Multiply 28.3 by the sine of 25'.)

Basis of the Process. The sine of a very small angle is very nearly equal to the angle expressed in radians.* The difference between the sine and the value of the angle in radians can be neglected. Thus the problem is to express the angle in radians. One radian is 57.3 degrees. If the angle, expressed in minutes, is divided by 60, the result is the angle expressed in degrees. Then if the angle in degrees is divided by 57.3, the result is the angle in radians, and this value can be used as the sine of the angle. The process is,

$$\frac{\text{angle in minutes}}{60 \times 57.3} = \text{angle in radians} = \text{sine of angle}$$

or,

$$\frac{\text{angle in minutes}}{3440} = \text{sine of angle}$$

This expression can be used when the angle is less than about 6°. It is only necessary to use it when the angle is less than 0°34'.

THE ARC SINE OF A NUMBER LESS THAN 0.01. The arc sine of a number less than 0.01 cannot be found in the usual way, since the **B** or **D** scales are considered to extend from 0.01 to 1 in working with the sine or arc sine. However, for any number less than 0.01, the arc sine, expressed in minutes, is equal to 3440 times the number. Thus arc sine *0.006* is *17.2'*. Here the angle contains a decimal fraction. This decimal fraction can be converted to seconds of angle by multiplying by 60 since there are 60" in 1'. The decimal fraction *0.2* is then, *0.2 × 60 = 12"*, so the angle is *17'12"*.

ILLUSTRATIVE EXAMPLES

37. *Find arc sine 0.00625.*

1) Multiply *3440* by *0.00625*. The result is *21.5*. Hence, the angle is *21.5'*.

2) Multiply the decimal fraction, *0.5,* by *60*. The result is *30,* and this is the number of seconds. Hence arc sine *0.00625* is *21'30"*.

---

*The radian is a unit by means of which an angle may be expressed or measured. It can be shown by means of calculus that the sine of a very small angle is approximately equal to the angle in radians.

38. *Find arc sine 0.0001.*

1) Multiply *3440* by *0.0001*. The result is *0.344,* so the angle is *0.344'.*

2) Convert this decimal fraction to seconds of angle by multiplying by *60*. The result is *20.7*. Therefore, arc sine *0.0001* is *20.7".* To the nearest second, this is *21".*

PRACTICE PROBLEMS

After you have worked all of the problems, check your answers with the correct answers in the back of the book.

Find the arc sine of each of the following numbers. Express the result in minutes and seconds:

1. 0.0098	**3.** 0.000725	**6.** 0.000875	**9.** 0.00684
2. 0.00331	**4.** 0.001932	**7.** 0.00386	**10.** 0.001
	5. 0.00541	**8.** 0.001203	

THE ARC COSINE OF A NUMBER. The arc cosine of a number is the angle which has that number for its cosine. You cannot find the arc cosine directly. However, you can find the arc sine, that is, the angle which has the number for its sine. Then you use the fact that the cosine of an angle is the sine of 90° minus the angle. Or, vice versa, the cosine of 90° minus the angle is equal to the sine of the angle. If this statement is made in terms of the arc cosine and arc sine, it is: The arc cosine of a number is 90° minus the arc sine of the number. You know how to find the arc sine. After you have it as an angle, subtract it from 90°. The result is the arc cosine.

ILLUSTRATIVE EXAMPLES

39. *Find arc cosine 0.55.*

1) First find the arc sine of *0.55*. This is *33°20'.*
2) The arc cosine of *0.55* is *90° — 33°20',* or *56°40'.*

40. *Find arc cosine 0.093.*

1) Find the arc sine of *0.093*. This is *5°20'.*
2) The arc cosine of *0.093* is *90° — 5°20',* or *84°40'.*

PRACTICE PROBLEMS

After you have worked all of the following problems, check your
answers with the correct answers shown in the back of the book.

Find the arc cosine of each of the following numbers:

1. 0.852	**3.** 0.278	**6.** 0.712	**9.** 0.932
2. 0.304	**4.** 0.187	**7.** 0.667	**10.** 0.417
	5. 0.500	**8.** 0.100	

THE ARC SINE OF A NUMBER BETWEEN 0.95 AND 1.

The usual method of finding the arc sine of a number lacks precision when the number is between 0.95 and 1. There is, however,
a formula which will give good results. If the number be designated
by *x,* and the arc sine of the number by θ, then,

$$\theta = 90° - \text{arc sine } \sqrt{1 - x^2}$$

The problem is to find the angle θ which has *x* for its sine. Start
by calculating $\sqrt{1 - x^2}$. Then find arc sine $\sqrt{1 - x^2}$ in the
usual way. Last, subtract arc sine $\sqrt{1 - x^2}$ from *90°*. The result is
θ, which is arc sine *x*. Try it in these examples and problems. The
method is very useful and is worth learning. With practice, you can
learn to work without writing down any intermediate results.

ILLUSTRATIVE EXAMPLES

41. *Find the arc sine of 0.98.*

1) The value of *x* is *0.98*. Square *0.98*. This is *0.96*.
2) Subtract *0.96* from *1*. The result is *0.04*.
3) Find the square root of *0.04*. This is *0.2*.
4) The angle (*90°* — θ) is arc sine *0.2*. This is *11°32'*.
5) The angle θ is *90°* — *11°32'*, or *78°28'*. This is arc sine of *0.98*.
   Try to get it as close in the usual way.

42. *Find the arc sine of 0.957.*

1) The value of *x* is *0.957*. Square it. You obtain *0.916*.
2) Subtract *0.916* from *1*. The result is *0.084*.
3) The square root of *0.084* is *0.290*.
4) The angle (*90°* — θ) is arc sine *0.290* and is *16°50'*.
5) The angle θ is *90°* — *16°50'*, or *73°10'*. This is arc sine of *0.957*.

PRACTICE PROBLEMS

After you have worked all of the following problems, check your answers with the correct answers shown in the back of the book.

Find the arc sine of each of the following numbers:

1. 0.961	**3.** 0.984	**6.** 0.968	**9.** 0.995
2. 0.977	**4.** 0.990	**7.** 0.970	**10.** 0.965
	5. 0.950	**8.** 0.972	

Basis of the Process. The process rests on the trigonometric identity.

$$\sin^2 \theta + \cos^2 \theta = 1$$

which is true for any angle θ. You know *sin* θ, which we will call x and you want to find θ. Replacing *sin* θ by x, the equation becomes,

$$x^2 + \cos^2 \theta = 1$$

When the term x^2 is transposed to the right side of the equation, there results,

$$\cos^2 \theta = 1 - x^2$$

Next take the square root of each side. This leaves,

$$\cos \theta = \sqrt{1 - x^2}$$

But,

$$\cos \theta = \sin (90° - \theta)$$

When this is substituted, the equation becomes,

$$\sin (90° - \theta) = \sqrt{1 - x^2}$$

This can be rewritten as,

$$90° - \theta = \text{arc sine } \sqrt{1 - x^2}$$

from the definitions of the sine and arc sine. A last rewriting gives

$$\theta = 90° - \text{arc sine } \sqrt{1 - x^2}$$

which is the desired result.

RECIPROCAL FUNCTIONS

Trigonometric functions found by use of the **S** and **ST** scales are mainly the sine and cosine, because these are the ones most often used in the solution of technical problems. However, it is sometimes useful to find their reciprocal function, the cosecant and secant. This is very easy to do because of the fact that

$$\text{cosecant} = \frac{1}{\text{sine}}, \text{ and secant} = \frac{1}{\text{cosine}}$$

The left index of the **CI** scale must be set in alignment with the left index of the **D** scale. Then, when the hairline of the runner is set to the sine of an angle on the **D** scale, the cosecant is automatically set under the hairline on the **CI** scale.

Similarly, cosines set on the **D** scale can be read as secants under the hairline on the **CI** scale.

ILLUSTRATIVE EXAMPLES

43. *The sine of a 32° angle is found to be 0.530 on the slide rule. What is the cosecant of this angle?* Steps to be followed are these:

1) With **CI** and **D** scales in alignment, set the sine, 0.530, by moving the runner until the hairline is over this number on the **D** scale. (In finding the sine the first time, the hairline will be in this position.)
3) Leave the runner in this position and read the cosecant as *1.887* under the hairline on the **CI** scale.

44. *The cosine of a 14° angle is found to be 0.970 on the slide rule. What is the secant of this angle?* The procedure is identical to that followed in Example 43:

1) With the **CI** and **D** scales in alignment, set the cosine, 0.970, by moving the runner until the hairline is over this number on the **D** scale (unless the runner is already in this position).
2) Leave the runner in this position and read the secant as *1.031* under the hairline on the **CI** scale.

REVIEW PROBLEMS

Answers to Review Problems are not given in the back of the book. Readers who are working alone may check their answers if desired by looking up the sine or cosine in a set of tables of trigonometric functions.

By this time you know how to find the sine or cosine of any angle. Also you know how to find the arc sine and arc cosine. Practice on these problems and questions. You can learn a process very quickly, but unless you use it you will forget it quickly.

1. Find the cosine of arc sine 0.600.

2. Find the sine of arc cosine 0.45.

3. The base of a right triangle is equal to the hypotenuse times the cosine of the angle between the hypotenuse and the base. Find the base of a right triangle of which the hypotenuse is 11.27 inches at an angle of 35° with the base.

4. Find the altitude of the triangle described in problem 3.

5. What is the angle between the base and hypotenuse of a right triangle of which the base is 126 feet and the hypotenuse is 234 feet?

6. Find the angle between the base and hypotenuse of a right triangle of which the altitude is 9.3 inches and the hypotenuse is 31.7 inches.

7. The altitude of a certain right triangle is 2.13 inches and the angle between the base and hypotenuse is 12°30′. Find the hypotenuse.

8. Which scales are used to find the sine of 20°?

9. Find the sine of arc cosine 0.75.

10. What is the vertical projection of a length of 1250 feet at an angle of 7°30′ with the horizontal?

Verify each of the following equations:

11. Sin 40° = 2 sin 20° cos 20°

12. Sin 55° = 2 sin 27°30′ cos 27°30′

13. Sin 15° + sin 35° = 2 sin 25° cos 10°

14. Sin 60° — sin 20° = 2 cos 40° sin 20°

15. Sin 45° = sin 10° cos 35° + cos 10° sin 35°

16. Sin² 67°30′ + cos² 67°30′ = 1

17. Cos 50° = cos 65° cos 15° + sin 65° sin 15°

18. 2 sin 42°30′ cos 22°30′ = sin 65° + sin 20°

19. Cos 48°20′ + cos 20° = 2 cos 34°10′ cos 14°10′

20. Cos 35° = 1 — 2 sin² 17°30′

Find the sine of each of the following angles:

21. 20′30″	23. 0°24′	26. 30′	29. 5′22″
22. 1°46′	24. 83°10′	27. 86°	30. 42°20′
	25. 79°30′	28. 89°	

Find the arc sine of each of the following numbers:

31. 0.00342	**33.** 0.487	**35.** 0.633
32. 0.971	**34.** 0.185	

Find the cosine of each of the following angles:

36. 17°10′	**38.** 64°45′	**40.** 54°40′
37. 85°22′	**39.** 40°40′	

CHAPTER 10

THE TANGENT OF AN ANGLE

The tangent of an angle appears in many problems you want to solve with the slide rule. You will find it very convenient to be able to determine the tangent of an angle from the slide rule, and not be forced to consult a set of tables. The operation can be performed rapidly and the value you obtain for the tangent is precise enough for most practical calculations.

All slide rules in common use today have **T** (tangent) scales, but there are two distinct kinds of **T** scales. Besides this, some slide rules also have **ST** (sine-tangent) scales.

If your slide rule has both **T** and **ST** scales, you should read **Part A** of this chapter to learn how to use these scales, and then read **Part C** to learn how to work with large angles.

If your slide rule has a **T** scale but not an **ST** scale, you should read **Part B** of this chapter to learn how to use this **T** scale, and then read **Part C** to learn how to work with large angles.

PART A–SLIDE RULES WHICH HAVE BOTH T AND ST SCALES

Most modern slide rules, especially the large and expensive ones, have both **T** and **ST** scales. These scales may be on the front of the stock or on the back of the slide. In either case, there is a **D** scale on the same face of the slide rule, and these scales are keyed to the **D** scale.

THE T SCALE. The **T** scale is marked in degrees and decimal fractions of a degree. It has a range from 5.7° at the lefthand end to 45° at the righthand end.

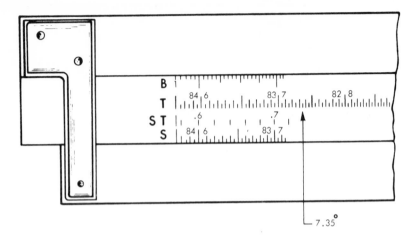

Fig. 10-1. Locating angle of 7.35° with the righthand markings of the T scale of decimal-trig. slide rule.

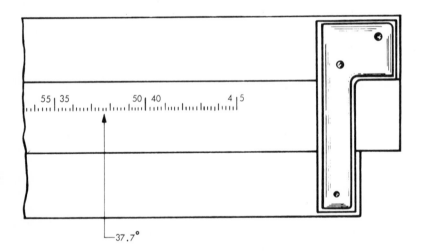

Fig. 10-2. Locating angle of 37.7° with the righthand markings of the T scale of decimal-trig. slide rule.

Some slide rules have two sets of numbers on the **T** scale. One set is just to the left of the divisions (these may be in red) and the other is just to the right. The righthand numbers are the ones we will use first. The others will be explained later.

Between 5.7° and 30° (20° on some slide rules), each space represents 0.1°. Fig. 10-1 shows the location of the angle 7.35° on the **T** scale.

Between 30° (20° on some slide rules) and 45°, each space represents 0.2°. Fig. 10-2 shows the location of 37.7° on the **T** scale.

THE TANGENT OF AN ANGLE. The tangent of an angle between 5.7° and 45° can be determined in this way. First, line up 45° on the **T** scale with the righthand index of the **D** scale.* Then, set the hairline of the runner to the angle on the **T** scale, and read the tangent of the angle on the **D** scale under the hairline. For this purpose, the **D** scale has a range from 0.1 at the lefthand index to 1 at the righthand index. Other ranges will be explained.

Rule 6. (a) The Tangent. (Applies only to slide rules with both T and ST scales.) For angles between **0.574° and 45°**, *set the hairline of the runner to the angle on the righthand markings of the ST or T scale and read the tangent of the angle on the D scale.* For angles between **45° and 84.26°**, *set the hairline of the runner to the angle on the lefthand markings of the T scale and read the tangent of the angle on the CI scale aligned with the D scale.* For angles between **84.26° and 89.27°**, *set the hairline of the runner to the angle on the lefthand markings of the ST scale and read the tangent of the angle on the CI scale aligned with the D scale.*

ILLUSTRATIVE EXAMPLES

1. *What is the tangent of 18.4°?*

1) Line up the **T** scale with the **D** scale.
2) Set the hairline of the runner to 18.4° on the **T** scale.

---

*If your slide rule has the **T** scale on the stock, it is already lined up with the **D** scale and you can ignore this direction. However, it will be repeated frequently for the benefit of people whose slide rules have the **T** scale on the slide.

3) Read the tangent as 0.332 on the **D** scale under the hairline.

    2. *Determine the tangent of 40.7°.*

1) Line up the **T** scale with the **D** scale.
2) Set the hairline of the runner to 40.7° on the **T** scale.
3) Read the tangent as 0.860 on the **D** scale under the hairline.

PRACTICE PROBLEMS

    This procedure will seem easy after you do these problems. Then, check your answers with the correct answers in the back of the book. What is the tangent of each of these angles?

1. 27.5°	**6.** 31.6°
2. 34.2°	**7.** 9.2°
3. 7.35°	**8.** 22.2°
4. 11.57°	**9.** 14.8°
5. 43.3°	**10.** 40°

    Basis of the Proces. The **D** scale is a logarithmic scale in that the distance from the lefthand index to the location of a particular number represents the logarithm of the number. The tangent scale is laid out to correspond to the **D** scale so that the distance from its lefthand end to a particular angle represents the logarithm of the tangent of the angle. Thus when the runner is set to find the tangent of an angle, the following relation is true,

    logarithm of number on **D** *scale = logarithm of tangent of angle.*

If the logarithms of two quantities are equal, the two quantities must be equal, and so,

        number on **D** *scale = tangent of angle.*

    THE TANGENT OF A SMALL ANGLE. If an angle is less than 5.74°, the **ST** scale can be used with the **D** scale to obtain the tangent. The **ST** scale has a range from 0.57° at the lefthand end to 5.74° at the righthand end. This is the way to do it. First, line up the righthand end of the **ST** scale with the righthand index of the **D** scale. Then, set the hairline of the runner to the angle on the **ST** scale. Finally, read the tangent of the angle on the **D** scale under the hairline. The **D** scale has a range from 0.01 to 0.1 for this purpose. A couple of examples will show you how.

ILLUSTRATIVE EXAMPLES

3. *Determine the tangent of 3.4°.*

1) Line up the **ST** and **D** scales.
2) Set the hairline of the runner to 3.4° on the **ST** scale.
3) Read the tangent of 3.4° as 0.0594 on the **D** scale under the hairline. Fig. 10-3 shows this setting on the slide rule.

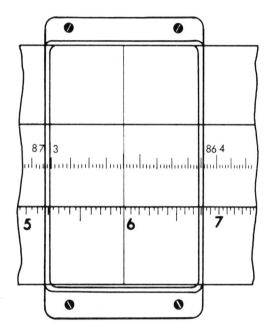

Fig. 10-3. Setting to find tangent of 3.4°.

4. *What is the tangent of 1.15°?*

1) Line up the **ST** and **D** scales.
2) Set the hairline of the runner to 1.15° on the **ST** scale.
3) Read the tangent as 0.0203 on the **D** scale under the hairline.

PRACTICE PROBLEMS

Determine the tangent of each of these angles and then check your answers with the correct answers in the back of the book.

1. 5.6°	6. 2.85°
2. 0.75°	7. 0.98°
3. 2.1°	8. 1.6°
4. 4.73°	9. 4.11°
5. 3.93°	10. 5.23°

THE TANGENT OF A VERY SMALL ANGLE. If an angle is less than 0.57°, it is too small for you to find the tangent by using the **T** and **ST** scales. However, you can convert the angle from degrees to radians, by dividing by 57.3, and use the value in radians as a very good approximation for the tangent. Let's try it.

ILLUSTRATIVE EXAMPLES

5. *Find the tangent of 0.45°.*

1) Divide 0.45 by 57.3. The result is 0.00786. This is the tangent of 0.45°.

6. *Find the tangent of 0.33°.*

1) Divide 0.33° by 57.3. The result is 0.00577. The tangent of 0.33° is 0.00577.

PRACTICE PROBLEMS

After you have worked all of these problems, check your answers with the correct answers in the back of the book. Just find the tangent of each of these angles.

1. 0.5°	6. 0.23°
2. 0.17°	7. 0.425°
3. 0.37°	8. 0.51°
4. 0.080°	9. 0.115°
5. 0.480°	10. 0.27°

THE TANGENT OF AN ANGLE BETWEEN 45° AND 84.26°. The tangent of an angle between 45° and 84.26° has a value between 1 and 10. The tangent can be obtained from the slide rule by using the **T** scale with the **CI** (reciprocal) scale. The **T** scale is read from right to left for this purpose, using the set of numbers (often in red) on the lefthand side of each division mark. The **CI** scale is read from right to left, with a range from 1 to 10 for this purpose. Here is the way to do it. First, line up the **T** scale with the **D** scale. Then, set the hairline of the runner to the angle on the **T** scale. Finally, read the tangent to the **CI** scale under the hairline. Many slide rules have to be turned over to read the **CI** scale. Let's try this.

ILLUSTRATIVE EXAMPLES

7. *What is the tangent of 65°?*

1) Line up the **T** scale with the **D** scale.
2) Set the hairline of the runner to 65° on the **T** scale. The mark for 65° has 65° on the lefthand side and 25° on the righthand side.
3) Turn the slide rule over, if necessary, and read the tangent as 2.14 on the **CI** scale under the hairline. (See Fig. 10-4)

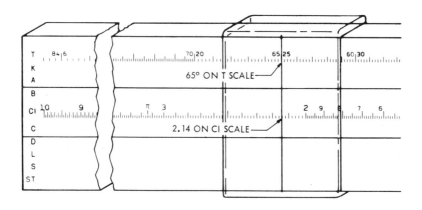

Fig. 10-4. Setting for tangent of 65°.

8. *Determine the tangent of 77.3°.*

1) Line up the **T** scale with the **D** scale.
2) Set the hairline of the runner to 77.3° on the **T** scale.
3) Turn the slide rule over, if necessary, and read the answer as 4.44 on the **CI** scale under the hairline.

Basis of the Process. When you use the lefthand set of numbers to locate an angle (call it θ) on the **T** scale, you are really setting the hairline of the runner to $90° - \theta$ on the **T** scale. Further, when you read the tangent on the **CI** scale under the hairline, you are really reading the reciprocal of the tangent of the angle θ. Thus, you are using the very well known trigonometric identity.

$$\tan \theta = \frac{\tan (90° - \theta)}{1}.$$

PRACTICE PROBLEMS

Now determine the tangent of each of these angles, remembering to read the **T** and **CI** scales from right to left. Then, check your answers with the correct answers in the back of the book.

1. 51°
2. 84°
3. 73.5°
4. 47.2°
5. 69.4°

6. 48.8°
7. 57.5°
8. 82.3°
9. 62.7°
10. 75.4°

THE TANGENT OF AN ANGLE BETWEEN 84.26° AND 89.27°. The tangent of an angle between 84.26° and 89.27° has a value between 10 and 100. You can use the **ST** scale with the **CI** scale to obtain it. Use the lefthand set of numbers on the **ST** scale and read from right to left. Do the problem in this way. First, line up the **ST** scale with the **D** scale. Then, set the hairline of the runner to the angle on the **ST** scale. Finally, turn the slide rule over, if necessary, and read the tangent on the **CI** scale under the hairline, remembering that the range of the **CI** scale is from 10 to 100 for this purpose. We'll show you.

ILLUSTRATIVE EXAMPLES

9. *What is the tangent of 87°?*
1) Line up the **ST** scale with the **D** scale.
2) Set the hairline of the runner to 87° on the **ST** scale.
3) Turn the slide rule over, if necessary, and read the tangent of 87° as 19.1 on the **CI** scale under the hairline. (See Fig. 10-5)

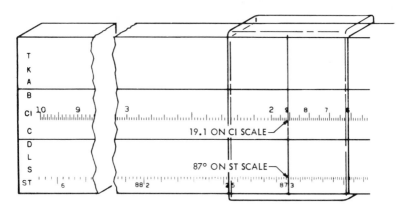

Fig. 10-5. Setting for tangent of 87°.

10. *Determine the tangent of 89.25°.*

1) Line up the **ST** scale with the **D** scale.
2) Set the hairline of the runner to 89.25° on the **ST** scale.
3) Turn the slide rule over, if necessary, and read the answer as 76.4 in the **CI** scale under the hairline.

PRACTICE PROBLEMS

After you have determined the tangent of each of these angles, check your answers with the correct answers in the back of the book.

1. 85°		**6.** 89.4°	
2. 86.1°		**7.** 85.8°	
3. 88.7°		**8.** 88.2	
4. 87.4°		**9.** 84.9°	
5. 84.5°		**10.** 86.6°	

THE TANGENT OF AN ANGLE BETWEEN 89.27° AND 90°. When the angle is between 89.27° and 90°, you cannot use the **T** or **ST** scales to find the tangent, but there is another way to do it. You first subtract the angle from 90°. Then you divide 57.3 by this result to get the tangent. Try it now by following these examples.

ILLUSTRATIVE EXAMPLES

11. *Find the tangent of 89.5°.*
1) Subtract 89.5° from 90° The result is 0.5°.
2) Divide 57.3 by 0.5, and get 114.6 as the tangent of 89.5°.

12. *Find the tangent of 89.75°.*

1) Subtract 89.75° from 90°. The result is 0.25°.
2) Divide 57.3 by 0.25, to get 229 as the tangent of 89.75°.

PRACTICE PROBLEMS

After you have done these problems, check your answers with the correct answers in the back of the book. Find the tangent of each of these angles.

1. 89.2°	6. 89.9°
2. 89.33°	7. 89.8°
3. 89.56°	8. 89.68°
4. 89.45°	9. 89.29°
5. 89.72°	10. 89.78°

THE ARC TANGENT OF A NUMBER. The arc tangent, or inverse tangent, of a number is the angle for which the number is the tangent. It is written, for example, as tan⁻¹ 0.8, which means the angle for which the tangent is 0.8.

This is the way to determine the arc tangent when the number is less than 1. First, line up the **T** and **ST** scales with the **D** scale. Then, set the hairline of the runner to the number on the **D** scale. Finally, read the angle on the **T** scale if the number is between 0.1 and 1, and on the **ST** scale if the number is between 0.01 and 0.1. Follow these examples.

Rule 6. (b) The Arc Tangent. (Applies only to slide rules with both T and ST scales.) If the number is less than 1, *set the hairline of the runner to the number on the **D** scale and read the arc tangent of the number on the righthand markings of the **ST** or **T** scale.* **If the number is greater than 1,** *set the hairline of the runner to the number on the **CI** scale and read the arc tangent of the number on the lefthand markings of the **T** or **ST** scale.*

ILLUSTRATIVE EXAMPLES

13. *Determine* $\tan^{-1} 0.63$.

1) Line up the **T** scale with the **D** scale.
2) Set the hairline of the runner to 0.63 on the **D** scale.
3) Read $\tan^{-1} 0.63$ as 32.2° on the **T** scale under the hairline.

14. *What is* $\tan^{-1} 0.0257$?

1) Line up the **ST** scale with the **D** scale.
2) Set the hairline of the runner to 0.0257 on the **D** scale.
3) Read $\tan^{-1} 0.0257$ as 1.47° on the **ST** scale under the hairline.

PRACTICE PROBLEMS

Doing these problems will help you to remember this procedure. After you have determined the arc tangent of each of these numbers, check your answers with the correct answers in the back of the book.

1.	0.117	6.	0.428
2.	0.924	7.	0.216
3.	0.072	8.	0.0185
4.	0.531	9.	0.067
5.	0.038	10.	0.395

THE ARC TANGENT OF A NUMBER GREATER THAN 1.

When a number is greater than 1, its arc tangent is between 45° and 90°. Then, you can use the **CI** (reciprocal) scale with the **T** and **ST** scales, being careful to use the lefthand set of numbers on the **T** and **ST** scales, and to read the **T, ST,** and **CI** scales from right to left.

This is the way to do it. First, line up the **T** and **ST** scales with the **D** scale. Next, turn the slide rule over, if necessary, and set the hairline of the runner to the number on the **CI** scale. Then, turn the slide rule back over, if necessary, and read the angle on the **T** scale if the number is between 1 and 10, or on the **ST** scale if the number is between 10 and 100. A couple of examples will show you how.

ILLUSTRATIVE EXAMPLES

15. *What is tan⁻¹ 3.65?*

1) Line up the **T** scale with the **D** scale.
2) Turn the slide rule over, if necessary, and set the hairline of the runner to 3.65 on the **CI** scale.
3) Turn the slide rule back over, if necessary, and read the answer as 74.7° on the **T** scale.

16. *Determine tan⁻¹ 27.*

1) Line up the **ST** scale with the **D** scale.
2) Turn the slide rule over, if necessary, and set the hairline of the runner to 27 on the **CI** scale.
3) Turn the slide rule back over, if necessary, and read tan⁻¹ 27 as 87.88° on the **ST** scale under the hairline.

PRACTICE PROBLEMS

Determine the arc tangent of each of these numbers and be sure to read the scales from right to left. Then, check your answers with the correct answers in the back of the book.

1. 1.35		**6.**	11.60
2. 40		**7.**	15
3. 6.21		**8.**	7.4
4. 2.27		**9.**	8.21
5. 4.23		**10.**	23

THE ARC TANGENT OF A NUMBER LESS THAN 0.01. If a number is less than 0.01, the arc tangent cannot be obtained from the **T** or **ST** scales, but the number can be multiplied by 57.3 to get the angle in degrees.

ILLUSTRATIVE EXAMPLES

17. *Find arc tangent 0.0085.*

1) Multiply 0.0085 by 57.3 to get the angle in degrees. It is 0.487°.

18. *Find arc tangent 0.0022.*

1) Multiply 0.0022 by 57.3 to get 0.126° as the answer.

PRACTICE PROBLEMS

After you have worked these practice problems, check your answers with the correct answers in the back of the book. Just find the arc tangent of each of these numbers.

1. 0.00933	**6.** 0.0006
2. 0.0002	**7.** 0.0062
3. 0.0075	**8.** 0.00435
4. 0.0054	**9.** 0.00733
5. 0.0017	**10.** 0.0004

THE ARC TANGENT OF A NUMBER GREATER THAN 100. If a number is greater than 100, its arc tangent cannot be obtained by using the **T** and **ST** scales, but there is a way to do it. First, you divide 57.3 by the number. This gives you an angle, and you subtract this angle from 90° to get the final answer. Follow these examples to see how it goes.

ILLUSTRATIVE EXAMPLES

19. *Find arc tangent 150.*

1) Divide 57.3 by 150 to get 0.382.
2) Subtract 0.382° from 90° to get 89.618° as the answer.

20. *Find arc tangent 1000.*

1) Divide 57.3 by 1000 to get 0.0573.
2) Subtract 0.0573° from 90° to get 89.9427° as the answer.

PRACTICE PROBLEMS

Work all of these problems and then check your answers with the correct answers in the back of the book. Find the arc tangent of each of these numbers.

1. 125	6. 227
2. 256	7. 500
3. 343	8. 188
4. 105	9. 274
5. 195	10. 117

PART B—SLIDE RULES WITH ONLY THE T SCALE

Some of the less expensive slide rules have a **T** scale but not an **ST** scale. Some of the older slide rules are this way too.

The **T** scales may be on the front of the stock, in which case it is keyed to the **D** scale. Or, it may be on the back of the slide and be keyed to the **C** scale. Whichever arrangement you have on your slide rule, you can learn how to use it in this chapter .

THE T SCALE. This **T** scale is usually marked in degrees and minutes. (There are 60 minutes in one degree.) The range of the scale is from 5°43′ at the lefthand end to 45° at the righthand end.

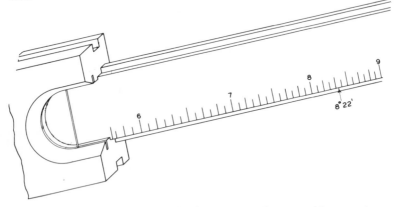

Fig. 10-6. Location of the angle 8°22′ on the T scale of an older Mannheim type slide rule with no ST scale.

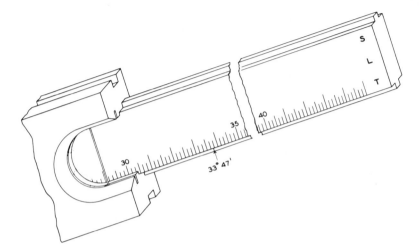

Fig. 10-7. Location of the angle 33°47′ on the T scale, which is on the back of the slide.

Between the lefthand end of the **T** scale and 20°, each space represents 5′ of angle. Fig. 10-6 shows the location of the angle 8°22′ on the **T** scale.

Between 20° and 45° on the **T** scale, each space represents 10′ of angle. Fig. 10-7 shows the location of the angle 33°47′ on the **T** scale.

THE TANGENT OF AN ANGLE. The problem is to find the tangent of an angle. The angle is expressed in degrees and minutes, and the tangent is a number. Now read carefully, because we are going to explain two special cases at the same time.

If your slide rule has the **T** scale on the front of the stock, you can just set the hairline of the runner to the angle on the **T** scale, and then read the tangent of the angle on the **D** scale under the hairline.

If your slide rule has the **T** scale on the back of the slide, you can turn the slide rule over and set the angle on the **T** scale against the mark on the plastic insert. (If there is no mark on the plastic insert, use the righthand edge of the insert. On those slide rules which do not have a plastic insert, you will find a mark on the stock. Use this.) Then, turn the slide rule back over and read the tangent of the angle on the **C** scale over the righthand index of the **D** scale.

Rule 6 (c). The Tangent. (Applies only to slide rules with the T scale but no ST scale.) *Set the angle (from 5°43′ to 45°) on the **T** scale and read the tangent of the angle on the **C** or **D** scale. The tangent of an angle between 45° and 84°17′ is also found by using the **T** scale. In the case of these larger angles, first subtract the angle from 90°, then set the result on the **T** scale. Read the tangent on the **CI** scale lined up with the **D** scale on slide rules with the **T** scale on the front of the stock; on slide rules having the **T** scale on the back of the slide, read the tangent on the **D** scale under the lefthand index of the **C** scale.*

For the purpose of finding the tangent, the **C** and **D** scales may be thought of as extending from 0.1 at the lefthand index to 1.0 at the righthand index.

Here is a word of caution. Remember that there are 60′ in 1°. Keep this in mind when you read the tangent scale.

ILLUSTRATIVE EXAMPLES

21. *Find the tangent of 30°.*

1) Either set the hairline of the runner to 30° on the **T** scale or turn the slide rule over and set 30° on the **T** scale against the mark.

2) Read the tangent of 30° as 0.577 on the **D** scale under the hairline, or on the **C** scale over the righthand index of the **D** scale.

22. *Find the tangent of 11°25′.*

1) Either set the hairline of the runner to 11°25′ on the **T** scale, or turn the slide rule over and set 11°25′ against the mark.

2) Read the tangent of 11°25′ as 0.202 on the **D** scale under the hairline, or on the **C** scale over the righthand index of the **D** scale.

PRACTICE PROBLEMS

After you have worked all of the following problems, check your answers with the correct answers shown in the back of the book.

Find the tangent of each of the following angles:

1. 33°45'   5. 5°55'
2. 26°30'   7. 20°15'
3. 17°25'   8. 12°48'
4. 42°30'   9. 37°30'
5. 8°37'   10. 18°45'

11. The altitude of a right triangle is equal to the base times the tangent of the angle between the base and the hypotenuse. Find the altitude of a right triangle which has a base of 137.5 feet and in which the angle between the base and hypotenuse is 22°45'.

12. Find the base of a right triangle of which the altitude is 4.85 inches and the angle between the base and hypotenuse is 41°20'.

Verify each of the following equations:

13. $\text{Tan } 55° = \dfrac{\tan 30° + \tan 25°}{1 - \tan 30° \tan 25°}$

14. $\text{Tan } 45° = \dfrac{2 \tan 22°30'}{1 - \tan^2 22°30'}$

15. $\text{Tan } 15° = \dfrac{\tan 35° - \tan 20°}{1 + \tan 35° \tan 20°}$

Basis of the Process. The **C** and **D** scales are logarithmic scales in that the distance from the lefthand index to the location of a particular number represents the logarithm of the number. The tangent scale is laid out to correspond with the **C** and **D** scales so that the distance from its lefthand end to a particular angle represents the logarithm of the tangent of the angle. Thus, when the slide rule is set to find the tangent of an angle, the following relation is true,

logarithm of number on **C** *or* **D** *scale =*
logarithm of tangent of angle.

If the logarithms of two quantities are equal, the two quantities must be equal, and so,

number on **C** *or* **D** *scale = tangent of angle.*

THE TANGENT OF A VERY SMALL ANGLE. The tangent of an angle less than *5°43'* cannot be obtained in the usual way because the angle cannot be set on the tangent scale. However, a special method is available for such angles.

When the Angle Is between 1° and 5°43'. If the angle is between 1° and 5°43', the first step is to convert it to a number of degrees plus a decimal fraction. Thus *2°30'* is *2.5°*, since *30'* is one-half of 1°. The general procedure here is to divide the number of minutes by 60 and attach it to the number of degrees as a decimal fraction. Thus, for the angle, *1°50'*, the number *50* is divided by *60*. The result is *0.833* and this is attached to *1°* giving *1.833°* for the angle. When the angle is obtained in this form, it is divided by *57.3*. The result is a close approximation of the tangent of the angle, so close that it suffices for practically all calculations.

ILLUSTRATIVE EXAMPLES

23. *Find the tangent of 3°34'.*

1) Convert *34'* to a decimal fraction of 1° by dividing by 60. The result is *0.567°*.
2) The angle *3°34'* is *3.567°*.
3) Divide *3.567* by *57.3*. The result is *0.0623* and this is the tangent of *3°34'*.

24. *Find the tangent of 1°17'.*

1) Convert *17'* to a decimal fraction of 1° by dividing by 60. The result is *0.283°*.
2) The angle *1°17'* is *1.283°*.
3) Divide *1.283* by *57.3*. The result is *0.0224*. The *tangent of 1°17'* is *0.0224*.

A guide in locating the decimal point is that the tangent of *1°* is *0.0175* and the tangent of *5°43'* is *0.1*. Thus if the angle is between *1°* and *5°43'*, the tangent of the angle is between *0.0175* and *0.1*.

PRACTICE PROBLEMS

After you have worked all of the following problems, check your answers with the correct answers shown in the back of the book.

Find the tangent of each of the following angles:

1. 5°30'	3. 3°22'	6. 2°25'	9. 3°56'
2. 1°51'	4. 4°	7. 1°15'	10. 2°11'
	5. 4°41'	8. 5°05'	

11. An automobile travels on a 2°45′ grade. The horizontal projection of the distance traveled is 2830 feet. What is the change in altitude?

12. Find the base of a right triangle of which the altitude is 0.375 inches and the angle between the base and hypotenuse is 1°17′.

When the Angle Is Less Than 1°. An angle less than 1° would ordinarily be expressed in minutes and seconds, as *32′20″*. The first step in the process is to convert the number of seconds to a decimal fraction of 1′ by dividing by 60. Then attach this decimal fraction to the number of minutes. For example, *20* divided by *60* is *0.333*, so *32′20″* is *32.333′*. When you have the angle expressed in this form, divide it by *3440*. The result may be used as the tangent of the angle. A guide to the location of the decimal point is the fact that the tangent of *1°* is *0.01746*. The tangent of an angle less than *1°* is less than *0.01746*.

ILLUSTRATIVE EXAMPLES

25. *Find the tangent of 25′32″.*

1) Divide *32* by *60*. The result is *0.533*.
2) The angle *25′32″* is *25.533′*.
3) Divide *25.533* by *3440*. The result is *0.00742*. Hence the tangent of *25′32″* is *0.00742*.

26. *Find the tangent of 0′53″.*

1) Divide *53* by *60*. The result is *0.883*.
2) The angle *0′53″* is *0.883′*.
3) Divide *0.883* by *3440*. The result is *0.000257*, so the tangent of *0′53″* is *0.000257*.

PRACTICE PROBLEMS

After you have worked all of the following problems, check your answers with the correct answers shown in the back of the book.

Find the tangent of each of the following angles:

1. 15′20″	**3.** 8′12″	**6.** 0′18″	**9.** 17′23″
2. 55′45″	**4.** 23′15″	**7.** 12′25.5″	**10.** 59′30″
	5. 45′	**8.** 38′30″	

Basis of the Process. The tangent of a very small angle is approximately equal to the angle in radians. One radian is 57.3°, so if the angle in degrees is divided by 57.3, the result is the angle in radians. This may be used as the tangent.

If the angle is expressed in minutes it must be divided by 60 in order to obtain it in degrees. Then it can be divided by 57.3 to obtain the tangent. The entire process is equivalent to dividing by 60 × 57.3, or 3440.

THE TANGENT OF AN ANGLE BETWEEN 45° AND 84°17′. The tangent of an angle between 45° and 84°17′ is greater than 1 and less than 10. It is found by subtracting the angle from 90° and setting the result on the **T** scale. Then, if the **T** scale is on the front of the stock, you can line the **CI** scale up with the **D** scale, and read the tangent on the **CI** scale. If the **T** scale is on the back of the slide, you can read the tangent on the **D** scale under the lefthand index of the **C** scale.

If you use the **CI** scale, remember to read from right to left, and that the range is from 1 to 10. If you use the **D** scale, remember that the range is from 1 to 10.

ILLUSTRATIVE EXAMPLES

27. *Find the tangent of 65°.*

1) Subtract 65° from 90°. The result is 25°.
2) Set the hairline of the runner to 25° on the **T** scale, or turn the slide rule over and set 25° on the **T** scale against the mark.

3) Read the tangent of 65° as 2.15 on the **CI** scale under the hairline, or on the **D** scale under the lefthand index of the **C** scale.

28. *Find the tangent of 82°30′.*

1) Subtract 82°30′ from 90°. The result is 7°30′.
2) Set the hairline of the runner to 7°30′ on the **T** scale, or turn the slide rule over and set 7°30′ on the **T** scale against the mark.
3) Read the tangent of 82°30′ as 7.60 on the **CI** scale under the hairline, or on the **D** scale under the lefthand index of the **C** scale.

PRACTICE PROBLEMS

After you have worked all of the following problems, check your answers with the correct answers in the back of the book.

Find the tangent of each of the following angles:

1. 46°30′	**3.** 83°46′	**6.** 77°45′	**9.** 80°37′
2. 72°15′	**4.** 50°	**7.** 63°28′	**10.** 84°17′
	5. 59°25′	**8.** 45°	

Basis of the Process. In order to find the tangent of an angle θ, you set $(90° - \theta)$ on the tangent scale. You have, then, the tangent of $(90° - \theta)$, which we will call x, on the **C** scale over the right index of the **D** scale. The number, call it y; on the **D** scale under the left index of the **C** scale is the result of dividing one by x. That is, y is the reciprocal of x. As an equation,

$$y = \frac{1}{x}$$

If you substitute, $y = \tan \theta$, and $x = \tan (90° - \theta)$, the equation becomes,

$$\tan \theta = \frac{1}{\tan (90° - \theta)}$$

This last formula can be verified in any book on trigonometry.

THE TANGENT OF AN ANGLE BETWEEN 84°17′ AND 90°. When the angle is greater than 84°17′, different measures must be used. First subtract the angle from 90°. This will usually give a result in degrees and minutes. The number of minutes should be converted to a decimal fraction of a degree by dividing by 60. Then this decimal fraction is attached to the number of degrees. When 57.3 is divided by this number of degrees, the result is the tangent of the original angle.

ILLUSTRATIVE EXAMPLES

29. *Find the tangent of 86°30′.*

1) Subtract *86°30′* from *90°*. The result is *3°30′*.
2) Convert *30′* to a decimal fraction of a degree by dividing by *60*. This gives *0.5*, so *3°30′* is equal to *3.5°*.
3) Divide *57.3* by *3.5*. The result is *16.36*, so *16.36* is the tangent of *86°30′*.

30. *Find the tangent of 88°48′.*

1) Subtract *88°48′* from *90°*. This gives *1°12′*.
2) Convert *12′* to a decimal fraction of a degree. Do this by dividing *12* by *60*. The result is *0.2*, so *1°12′* is *1.2°*.

3) Divide *57.3* by *1.2*. This gives *47.7* which is the tangent of *88°48'*.

PRACTICE PROBLEMS

After you have worked all of the following problems, check your answers with the correct answers in the back of the book.

Find the tangent of each of the following angles:

1. 85°	**3.** 89°15'	**6.** 87°22'	**9.** 86°55'
2. 85°57'	**4.** 84°45'	**7.** 88°34'	**10.** 87°12'
	5. 86°15'	**8.** 89°10'	

Basis of the Process. The basis of this process is the equation

$$\tan \theta = \frac{1}{\tan (90° - \theta)}$$

The problem is to find tan θ. If the angle θ is greater than 84°17', (90° − θ) is less than 5°43', so tan (90° − θ) is less than 0.1. Hence,

$$\tan (90° - \theta) = \frac{90° - \theta}{57.3}$$

This was explained under Basis of Process for finding the tangent of an angle less than 1°. Inverting each side of the equation,

$$\frac{1}{\tan (90° - \theta)} = \frac{57.3}{90° - \theta}$$

Therefore,

$$\tan \theta = \frac{57.3}{90° - \theta}$$

THE ARC TANGENT OF A NUMBER BETWEEN 0.1 AND 1. The arc tangent of a number is the angle which has the number for its tangent. The arc tangent is expressed in degrees and minutes, or in degrees and decimal fractions of a degree.

If your slide rule has the **T** scale on the front of the stock, you can just set the hairline of the runner to the number on the **D** scale, and read the angle on the **T** scale under the hairline.

If your slide rule has the **T** scale on the back of the slide, you can bring the number on the **C** scale over the righthand index of the **D** scale and read the angle on the **T** scale against the mark.

ILLUSTRATIVE EXAMPLES

31. *Find arc tangent 0.645.*

1) Set the hairline of the runner to 0.645 on the **D** scale, or bring 0.645 on the **C** scale over the righthand index of the **D** scale.
2) Read the angle as 32°52′ on the **T** scale under the hairline, or on the **T** scale against the mark.

32. *Find arc tangent 0.203.*

1) Set the hairline of the runner to 0.203 on the **D** scale, or bring 0.203 on the **C** scale over the righthand index of the **D** scale.
2) Read the angle as 11°30′ on the **T** scale under the hairline, or on the **T** scale against the mark.

PRACTICE PROBLEMS

After you have worked all of the following problems, check your answers with the correct answers shown in the back of the book.

Find the arc tangent of each of the following numbers:

1. 0.118	**3.** 0.866	**6.** 0.693	**9.** 0.198
2. 0.953	**4.** 0.333	**7.** 0.101	**10.** 0.300
	5. 0.707	**8.** 0.467	

THE ARC TANGENT OF A NUMBER BETWEEN 1 AND 10.

The arc tangent of a number between 1 and 10 is an angle between 45° and 84°17′. This is the way to find it.

If your slide rule has the **T** scale on the front of the stock, set the hairline of the runner to the number on the **CI** scale, being careful to read the **CI** scale from right to left. Then read the angle on the **T** scale under the hairline, and subtract this angle from 90° to get the right answer.

If your slide rule has the **T** scale on the back of the slide, set the lefthand index of the **C** scale over the number on the **D** scale.

Then read the angle on the **T** scale against the mark, and subtract this angle from 90° to get the final result.

ILLUSTRATIVE EXAMPLES

33. *Find arc tangent 2.5.*

1) Set the hairline of the runner to 2.5 on the **CI** scale, or set the lefthand index of the **C** scale over 2.5 on the **D** scale.
2) Read the angle of 21°50′ on the **T** scale under the hairline, or on the **T** scale against the mark.
3) Subtract 21°50′ from 90 to get 68°10′. The answer is 68°10′.

34. *Find arc tangent 1.234.*

1) Set the hairline of the runner to 1.234 on the **CI** scale, or set the lefthand index of the **C** scale over 1.234 on the **D** scale.
2) Read the angle of 39° on the **T** scale under the hairline, or on the **T** scale against the mark.
3) Subtract 39° from 90° to get 51°. The answer is 51°.

35. *Find arc tangent 8.48.*

1) Set the hairline of the runner to 8.48 on the **CI** scale, or set the lefthand index of the **C** scale over 8.48 on the **D** scale.
2) Read the angle of 6°44′ on the **T** scale under the hairline, or on the **T** scale against the mark.
3) Subtract 6°44′ from 90° to get 83°16′. The answer is 83°16′.

PRACTICE PROBLEMS

After you have worked all of the following problems, check your answers with the correct answers shown in the back of the book.

Find the arc tangent of each of the following numbers:

1. 1.012	**3.** 3.46	**6.** 6.67	**9.** 3.07
2. 1.500	**4.** 5.77	**7.** 1.853	**10.** 1.350
	5. 4.02	**8.** 2.13	

For review and reference, methods for finding arc tangents of numbers between 0.1 and 10 by means of the **T** scale are summarized in Rule 6(d). Arc tangents below and above this range cannot be found directly by using the **T** scale.

Rule 6 (d). The Arc Tangent. (Applies only to slide rules with the T scale but no ST scale.) *Set the number (between 0.1 and 1.0) in one of two ways. If your slide rule has the* ***T*** *scale on the front of the stock, set the number on the* ***D*** *scale and read the angle on the* ***T*** *scale. If your slide rule has the* ***T*** *scale on the back of the slide, bring the number on the* ***C*** *scale over the righthand index of the* ***D*** *scale and read the angle on the* ***T*** *scale against the mark.*

Numbers between 1 and 10 require a different procedure because the corresponding angles are between 45° and 84°17'. If your slide rule has the ***T*** *scale on the front of the stock, set the hairline of the runner to the number on the* ***CI*** *scale, then read the angle on the* ***T*** *scale under the hairline. Then subtract this angle from 90°.*

If your slide rule has the ***T*** *scale on the back of the slide, set the lefthand index of the* ***C*** *scale over the number of the* ***D*** *scale. Then read the angle on the* ***T*** *scale against the mark, and subtract this angle from 90° to get the final result.*

THE ARC TANGENT OF A NUMBER LESS THAN 0.1.

If the tangent of an angle is less than 0.1, the angle can be found by multiplying the number by 57.3. The result gives the angle in degrees, and usually this will be an integral number of degrees plus a decimal fraction of a degree. This decimal fraction can be converted to minutes by multiplying by 60, since there are 60' in 1°

ILLUSTRATIVE EXAMPLES

36. *Find arc tangent 0.0782.*

1) Multiply *0.0782* by *57.3.* The result is *4.48,* so the arc tangent of *0.0782* is *4.48°.*
2) Convert *0.48°* to minutes by multiplying by *60.* The answer is *28.8,* and *0.48°* is *28.8',* or, to the nearest minute, *29'.*
3) Arc tangent *0.0782* is *4°29'.*

When the angle is greater than 1°, it is usually sufficient to obtain the result to the nearest minute.

37. *Find arc tangent 0.0376.*

1) Multiply *0.0376* by *57.3.* This gives *2.16.* Hence, the angle is *2.16°.*
2) Convert *0.16°* to minutes by multiplying by *60.* The result is *9.6,* so *0.16°* is equal to *9.6'.* To the nearest minute, this is *10'.*
3) Arc tangent *0.0376* is *2°10'.*

If the angle is less than 1°, you may want to express it in minutes and seconds. When the number is multiplied by 3440, the result is the angle in minutes. Any decimal fraction attached to it can be converted to seconds by multiplying by 60, since there are 60″ in 1′. If the tangent is less than 0.01746, the angle must be less than 1°.

ILLUSTRATIVE EXAMPLES

38. *Find arc tangent 0.0137.*

1) Multiply *0.0137* by *3440.* The result is *47.2,* so the arc tangent *0.0137* is *47.2'.*
2) Convert *0.2'* to seconds. Do this by multiplying *0.2* by *60.* The result is *12,* so *0.2'* is equal to *12″.*
3) Arc tangent *0.0137* is *47'12″.*

39. *Find arc tangent 0.000862.*

1) Multiply *0.000862* by *3440.* This gives *2.97.* Hence, arc tangent *0.000862* is *2.97'.*
2) Convert *0.97'* to seconds by multiplying *0.97* by *60.* The result is *58.2,* so *0.97'* is equal to *58.2″.* To the nearest second this is *58″.*
3) Arc tangent of *0.000862* is *2'58″.*

PRACTICE PROBLEMS

After you have worked all of the following problems, check your answers with the correct answers shown in the back of the book.

Find the arc tangent of each of the following numbers:

1. 0.088	3. 0.097	6. 0.00105	9. 0.0073
2. 0.00281	4. 0.048	7. 0.00193	10. 0.025
	5. 0.01103	8. 0.066	

THE ARC TANGENT OF A NUMBER GREATER THAN

10. If the tangent of an angle is greater than 10, the angle must be between 84°17′ and 90°. The first step in finding the angle is to divide 57.3 by the number. Regard this as an angle in degrees and subtract it from 90°. The result is the angle which has the original number for its tangent. The angle obtained by dividing 57.3 by the number will usually contain a decimal fraction. It is best to convert this into minutes by multiplying by 60.

ILLUSTRATIVE EXAMPLES

40. *Find arc tangent 23.1.*

1) Divide *57.3* by *23.1*. The result is *2.48,* that is *2.48°*.
2) Convert *0.48°* to minutes by multiplying by *60*. The result is *28.8,* so *0.48°* is equal to *28.8′*. To the nearest minute, this is *29′*. Hence *2.48°* is *2°29′*.
3) Subtract *2°29′* from *90°*. This gives *87°31′* which is arc tangent *23.1.*

41. *Find arc tangent 37.5.*

1) Divide *57.3* by *37.5*. The result is *1.529,* which is *1.529°*.
2) Convert *0.529°* to minutes. Do this by multiplying by *60*. The result is *31.8,* or *31.8′*. To the nearest minute, this is *32′*, so *1.529°* is equal to *1°32′*.
3) Subtract *1°32′* from *90°*. This gives *88°28′* which is arc tangent *37.5.*

PRACTICE PROBLEMS

After you have worked all of the following problems, check your answers with the correct answers shown in the back of the book.

Find the arc tangent of each of the following numbers:

1. 10.75	**3.** 17.32	**6.** 11.08	**9.** 57.3
2. 42.3	**4.** 20.1	**7.** 31.4	**10.** 75
	5. 29.7	**8.** 21.9	

Find the tangent of each of the following angles:

11. 17°30′	**13.** 5°52′	**16.** 28°30′	**19.** 31°
12. 65°40′	**14.** 43°25′	**17.** 2°45′	**20.** 86°10′
	15. 77°10′	**18.** 81°17′	

Find the arc tangent of each of the following numbers:

21. 0.362   **23.** 0.085   **26.** 21.5   **29.** 0.854
22. 3.62   **24.** 0.747   **27.** 0.167   **30.** 0.0552
                  25. 1.525   **28.** 2.72

Verify each of the following equations:

31. $\text{Tan } 40° = \dfrac{\tan 25° + \tan 15°}{1 - \tan 25° \tan 15°}$

32. $\text{Tan } 75° = \dfrac{\tan 55° + \tan 20°}{1 - \tan 55° \tan 20°}$

33. $\text{Tan } 22°30' = \dfrac{\tan 45° - \tan 22°30'}{1 + \tan 45° \tan 22°30'}$

34. $\text{Tan } 20° = \dfrac{\tan 18° + \tan 2°}{1 - \tan 18° \tan 2°}$

35. $\text{Tan } 5°55' = \dfrac{\tan 37°55' - \tan 32°}{1 + \tan 37°55' \tan 32°}$

36. $\text{Tan } 5°55' = \dfrac{\tan 83°55' - \tan 78°}{1 + \tan 83°55' \tan 78°}$

PART C—THE TANGENT OF AN ANGLE GREATER THAN 90°

The process of finding the tangent of an angle greater than 90° can be explained in the same way, no matter what kind of slide rule you have, because it is all based on finding the tangent of an angle less than 90°, and you already know how to do this.

The tangent of an angle greater than 90° can always be expressed in terms of the tangent of an angle less than 90°. Then the tangent of the angle less than 90° can be found directly from the slide rule.

Angles between 90° and 180°. For any angle θ which is between 90° and 180°, the following equation is true:

$$\tan \theta = - \tan (180° - \theta)$$

After subtracting θ from 180°, the tangent of $(180° - \theta)$ is found by the methods discussed earlier.

ILLUSTRATIVE EXAMPLES

42. *Find the tangent of 157°30′.*

1) Tan *157°30′* $= -$ tan *(180° − 157°30′)* $= -$ tan *22°30′*.
2) The tangent of *22°30′* is *0.413*. Hence, the tangent of *157°30′* is $-$ *0.413*.

43. *Find the tangent of 103°.*

1) Tan *103°* $= -$ tan *(180° − 103°)* $= -$ tan *77°*.
2) The tangent of *77°* is *4.33*, so the tangent of *103°* is $-$ *4.33*.

Angles between 180° and 270°. When the angle θ is between 180° and 270°, the tangent is found by using the equation,

$$\tan \theta = \tan (\theta - 180°)$$

ILLUSTRATIVE EXAMPLES

44. *Find the tangent of 235°30′.*

1) Tan *235°30′* $=$ tan *(235°30′ − 180°)* $=$ tan *55°30′*.
2) The tangent of *55°30′* is *1.456*. Therefore, the tangent of *235°30′* is *1.456*.

45. *Find the tangent of 187°45′.*

1) Tan *187°45′* $=$ tan *(187°45′ − 180°)* $=$ tan *7°45′*.
2) The tangent of *7°45′* is *0.136*, so the tangent of *187°45′* is *0.136*.

Angles between 270° and 360°. If the angle θ is between 270° and 360°, the proper equation to use is,

$$\tan \theta = - \tan (360° - \theta)$$

ILLUSTRATIVE EXAMPLES

46. *Find the tangent of 298°20′.*

1) Tan298°20′ = − tan (360° − 298°20′) = − tan *61°40′.*
2) The tangent of *61°40′* is *1.857,* so the tangent of *298°20′* is − *1.857.*

47. *Find the tangent of 323°30′.*

1) Tan *323°30′* = − tan (360° − *323°30′*) = − tan *36°30′.*
2) The tangent of *36°30′* is *0.739.* Hence, the tangent of *323°30′* is − *0.739.*

PRACTICE PROBLEMS

After you have worked all of the following problems, check your answers with the correct answers shown in the back of the book.

Find the tangent of each of the following angles:

1. 227°20′   3. 171°35′   6. 145°   9. 207°30′
2. 132°15′   4. 346°10′   7. 225°   10. 315°
              5. 301°30′   8. 99°50′

THE RECIPROCAL FUNCTION

The trigonometric function found by use of the **T** and **ST** scales is mainly the tangent, because this is the one most often used in the solution of technical problems. However, it is sometimes useful to find its reciprocal, the cotangent. One easy way to do this utilizes the fact that

$$\text{cotangent} = \frac{1}{\text{tangent}}$$

The left index of the **CI** scale must be set in alignment with the left index of the **D** scale. Then, when the hairline of the runner is set to the tangent of an angle on the **D** scale, the cotangent is automatically set under the hairline on the **CI** scale.

ILLUSTRATIVE EXAMPLE

48. *The tangent of a 35° angle is found to be 0.700 on the slide rule. What is the cotangent of this angle?* Steps to be followed are these:

1) With the **CI** and **D** scales in alignment, set the tangent, *0.700*, by moving the runner until the hairline is over this number on the **D** scale. (In finding the tangent the first time on the decimal trig type of slide rule, the hairline will be in this position.)
2) Leave the runner in this position and read the cotangent, *1.428* under the hairline on the *CI* scale.

REVIEW PROBLEMS

Answers to Review Problems are not given in the back of the book. Readers who are working alone may check their answers by looking up the tangent or arc tangent in a set of tables.

Here is another opportunity to learn by practice.

1. The base of a certain right triangle is 52.3 feet in length and the angle between the base and hypotenuse is 12°10′. Find the altitude.

2. A right triangle has an altitude of 7.93 inches and base of 6.17 inches. What is the angle between the base and the hypotenuse?

3. Find the tangent of arc sine 0.62.

4. Which scales are used in finding the tangent of an angle?

5. The sun's rays, at an angle of 33° with the horizontal, cast the shadow of a building to a distance of 285 feet from the base of the building. How high is the building?

Find the tangent of each of the following angles:

6. 19°50′	**8.** 40°30′	**11.** 4°25′	**14.** 73°10′
7. 83°47′	**9.** 57°45′	**12.** 1°17′	**15.** 27°15′
	10. 6°32′	**13.** 88°30′	

Find the arc tangent for each of the following numbers:

16. 8.55	**18.** 0.1008	**21.** 0.075	**24.** 0.00345
17. 0.433	**19.** 1.940	**22.** 0.017	**25.** 0.948
	20. 0.693	**23.** 2.37	

Verify each of the following equations:

26. $\operatorname{Tan} 25° = \dfrac{\sin 50°}{1 + \cos 50°}$

27. $\operatorname{Tan} 30° = \dfrac{\tan 20° + \tan 10°}{1 - \tan 20° \tan 10°}$

28. $\operatorname{Tan} 34° = \dfrac{2 \tan 17°}{1 - \tan^2 17°}$

29. $\operatorname{Tan} 16° = \dfrac{\tan 74° - \tan 58°}{1 + \tan 74° \tan 58°}$

30. $1 + \tan^2 75° = \dfrac{1}{\cos^2 75°}$

CHAPTER 11

THE LOGARITHM OF A NUMBER WITH THE L SCALE

Many engineering formulae, for instance the formula for belt friction, contain the logarithm of a number. Also many calculations, such as raising a number to a fractional power, require the use of logarithms. For these reasons, it is desirable to be able to find the logarithm of a number from the slide rule, and also to be able to reverse this process; that is, to find the number which has a certain logarithm.

In speaking of a logarithm it is necessary to state the base of the logarithm; that is, the logarithm of a number to the base 10, or the base a, or the base b. The logarithm of a number to a certain base is the power to which the base must be raised to equal the number. Thus the logarithm of 1000 to the base 10 is three, since 10 must be raised to the power three to equal 1000. Any positive number except 1 can be used as a base for logarithms, but only two are used widely. In the common logarithm of a number, the base 10 is used. This is very convenient for calculation, as will be seen later. For the natural logarithm of a number, the base is a number called e. The value of e is 2.7183————. The greatest advantage of the base e is in work involving higher mathematics, calculus and beyond. You may not be interested in calculus, but you probably are interested in formulae which other people have derived by the use of calculus. Many of these formulae contain natural logarithms so you may have occasion to use them.

Both kinds of logarithms, common and natural, will be discussed in this chapter.

First, we'll explain the log scale, and then we'll show you how to find the logarithm of a number.

The log scale is the simplest scale on the slide rule. It usually has the letter **L** at the lefthand end.

Most slide rules have the log scale on the front or back of the stock. Whether the log scale is on the front or back of the stock, there is a **D** scale on the same face, and the log scale is keyed to this **D** scale.

Some slide rules, mostly the older ones, have the log scale on the back of the slide. In this case, the log scale is keyed to the **C** scale.

Now, we are going to explain how to use both of these types of slide rule at the same time, so read carefully.

THE LOG SCALE. The **L** (log) scale is divided in the same way throughout its length. Each space represents 2 in the third digit of the number. Fig. 11-1 shows the locations of the numbers 078, 105, and 167 on the **L** scale.

The **L** scale is used to find the mantissa of the logarithm of a number to the base 10, or to find the digits of a number when the mantissa of the logarithm of the number is known.

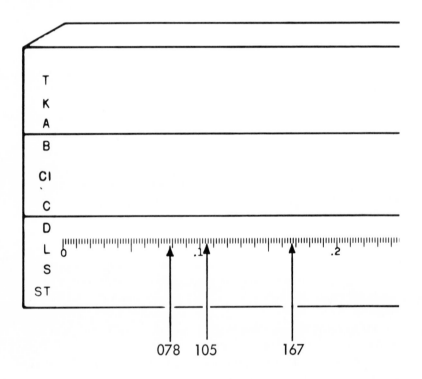

Fig. 11-1. Locations of numbers 078, 105, and 167 on L scale, which on this particular slide rule is on the lower stock immediately below the D scale.

THE LOGARITHM OF A NUMBER TO THE BASE 10.

The logarithm (often abbreviated as *log*) of a number to the base 10 has two parts. For example, the log of 388 is 2.589. The number to the left of the decimal point of the log is the *characteristic* of the log, and it is one less than the number of digits to the left of the decimal point of the number. Since there are three digits to the left of the decimal point in the number 388, the characteristic of the log of 388 is 2.

The *mantissa* of the log of the number is the part to the right of the decimal point. The mantissa can be read from the slide rule. The mantissa depends only on the sequence of numbers in the number and not on the location of the decimal point. Thus, the mantissa is 589 for all of the numbers 3.88, 38.8, 388, 3880, etc.

The mathematical definition of the log of a number to the base 10 is that it is the power to which 10 must be raised to equal the number.

The way to obtain the log of a number to the base 10 is:
1) Write the characteristic, which is one less than the number of digits to the left of the decimal point of the number.
2) If your slide rule has the **L** scale on the stock, set the hairline of the runner to the number on the **D** scale. If your slide rule has the **L** scale on the back of the slide, bring the number on the **C** scale over the righthand index of the **D** scale.
3) If your slide rule has the **L** scale on the stock, read the mantissa of the log of the number on the **L** scale under the hairline. If your slide rule has the **L** scale on the back of the slide, read the mantissa of the log on the **L** scale against the mark.*
4) Put the characteristic and mantissa together to get the log.

If the number is less than 1, and there are some zeros immediately after the decimal point, each zero counts as a negative digit to the left of the decimal point for the purpose of determining the characteristic of the log of the number. The following table may be helpful to you at this point:

---

*The mark may be a line on a plastic insert. If there is no line, the edge of the insert is to be used. If there isn't even a plastic insert, there will be a mark on the stock of the slide rule.

TABLE 11-1. CHARACTERISTICS					
Numbers Between			CALCULATION OF CHARACTERISTIC		
			No. of Digits	Less 1	Characteristic
100,000	and	1,000,000	6	$-1 =$	5
10,000	and	100,000	5	$-1 =$	4
1,000	and	10,000	4	$-1 =$	3
100	and	1,000	3	$-1 =$	2
10	and	100	2	$-1 =$	1
1	and	10	1	$-1 =$	0
0.1	and	1	0	$-1 =$	-1†
0.01	and	0.1	-1	$-1 =$	-2
0.001	and	0.01	-2	$-1 =$	-3
0.0001	and	0.001	-3	$-1 =$	-4
0.00001	and	0.0001	-4	$-1 =$	-5

When you have determined a negative characteristics by this method, there is a special way in which you must write it. Suppose the number is 0.00388. We already know that the mantissa is 589. There are two zeros immediately after the decimal point in 0.00388, so we say there are two negative digits to the left of the decimal point. The characteristic is one less than minus two, so it is minus three. Now, you add 10 and subtract 10 from the characteristic. The result of adding 10 is put before the decimal point in the log. In this case, $-3 + 10 = 7$. The 10 which was subtracted is written at the end of the log, so we write the log of 0.00388 as $7.589 - 10$. Now let's see some examples.

ILLUSTRATIVE EXAMPLES

1. *What is the log of 4750 to the base 10?*
1) There are four digits to the left of the decimal point in *4750,* so the characteristic is *3.*
2) Set the hairline of the runner to *4750* on the **D** scale, or bring *4750* on the **C** scale over the righthand index of the **D** scale.
3) Read the mantissa as 677 on the **L** scale under the hairline, or on the **L** scale against the mark.
4) The log of *4750* to the base 10 is *3.677.*

---

† $-$ is read as *minus 1,* a negative number.

2. *Determine the log of 0.137 to the base 10.*

1) There are no digits to the left of the decimal point of *0.137,* so the characteristic is one less than zero. This is *—1.* We add *10* to *—1* to get *9.*
2) Set the hairline of the runner to *137* on the **D** scale, or bring *137* on the **C** scale over the righthand index of the **D** scale.
3) Read the mantissa as *137* on the **L** scale under the hairline, or on the **L** scale against the mark.
4) The log of *0.137* to the base *10* is *9.137 — 10.*

3. *Obtain the log of 0.00842 to the base 10.*

1) There are two zeros immediately after the decimal point, so they count as *—2* digits to the left of the decimal point. The characteristic is one less than *—2,* and this is *— 3.* We add *10* to *—3* to get *7.*
2) Set the hairline of the runner to *842* on the **D** scale, or bring *842* on the **C** scale over the righthand index of the **D** scale.
3) Read the mantissa as 925 on the **L** scale under the hairline, or on the **L** scale against the mark.
4) The log of *0.00842* to the base *10* is *7.925 — 10.*

PRACTICE PROBLEMS

Now, use your slide rule to get the log of each of these numbers to the base 10, and then check your answers with the correct answers in the back of the book.

1. 7.6	**6.** 0.256
2. 228	**7.** 22000
3. 1440	**8.** 516
4. 1.27	**9.** 0.00182
5. 0.0615	**10.** 45.4

Basis of the Process. You should remember from the discussions of the previous chapters that the **C** and **D** scales are laid out so that the distance from the lefthand index to the location of a particular number represents the mantissa of the log of the number to the base 10. The log scale, as can be seen by looking at it, is laid out so that the distance from its lefthand end to the location of a particular number represents the magnitude of the number. Thus when these scales are properly aligned, the following relation is true.

> *mantissa of log of number to base 10, on **C** or **D** scale =*
> *number on **L** scale.*

This equation shows the process to be valid.

THE ANTILOG OF A LOGARITHM TO THE BASE 10.

The antilog of a number is a second number for which the given number is the log. A typical problem might be stated as, "What is the antilog of 1.780?" Another way of stating the same problem is, "If 1.780 is the log of a number, what is the number?"

So the problem is to find a number when the log of the number is known. Here, it is important to remember that the number to the left of the decimal point in the log is the characteristic and only serves to locate the decimal point in the number. The number to the right of the decimal point in the log is the mantissa, and it is the mantissa which determines the sequence of numbers in the answer.

This is the procedure in finding the antilog.

1) Set the hairline of the runner to the mantissa of the log on the **L** scale, or set the mantissa on the **L** scale against the mark.
2) Read the sequence of numbers in the antilog on the **D** scale under the hairline, or on the **C** scale over the righthand index of the **D** scale.
3) Position the decimal point in the answer so that the number of digits to the left of the decimal point is one more than the characteristic.

Be careful when the log has -10 at the end, for example $8.454 - 10$. Since $8 - 10 = -2$, this means that the characteristic is really -2, and from Table 1 there must be one zero immediately after the decimal point.

ILLUSTRATIVE EXAMPLES

4. *If the log of a given number to the base 10 is 1.780, what is the number?*

1) The mantissa is *780*. Set the hairline of the runner to *780* on the **L** scale, or set *780* on the **L** scale against the mark.
2) Read the digits of the number as *603* on the **D** scale under the hairline, or on the **C** scale over the righthand index of the **D** scale.

3) The characteristic of the log is one, and one more than one is two, so there are two digits to the left of the decimal point. The answer is 60.3.

    5. *What is the antilog of 9.223 — 10?*

1) The mantissa is *223*. Set the hairline of the runner to *223* on the **L** scale, or set *223* on the **L** scale against the mark.

2) Read the digits of the number as *167* on the **D** scale under the hairline, or on the **C** scale over the righthand index of the **D** scale.

3) The characteristic of the log is *9 — 10 = —1*, and one more than *—1* is zero, so there are no digits to the left of the decimal point in the answer and it is 0.167.

    6. *What is the antilog of 6.844 — 10?*

1) The mantissa is *844*. Set the hairline of the runner to *844* on the **L** scale, or set *844* on the **L** scale against the mark.

2) Read the digits of the answer as *697* on the **D** scale under the hairline, or on the **C** scale over the righthand index of the **D** scale.

3) The characteristic *is 6 — 10 = —4*. One more than *—4* is *—3*, so there are *3* zeros immediately after the decimal point in the answer, and it is 0.000697.

PRACTICE PROBLEMS

    Now determine the antilog of each of these numbers. Be especially careful when the characteristic is negative. Then, check your answers with the correct answers in the back of the book.

1. 1.375	**6.** 8.275 — 10
2. 2.430	**7.** 1.627
3. 0.743	**8.** 3.112
4. 9.182 — 10	**9.** 0.925
5. 3.520	**10.** 7.670 — 10

REVIEW PROBLEMS

    The answers to these Review Problems are not given in the back of the book, but you can check them by referring to tables of logs.

What is the log of each of these numbers to the base 10?

1. 488		**6.** 4.38
2. 127		**7.** 21.9
3. 91.5		**8.** 0.0676
4. 0.742		**9.** 2890
5. 56000		**10.** 1.715

What is the antilog of each of these numbers?

11. 1.592		**16.** 2.356
12. 3.640		**17.** 1.966
13. 9.235 — 10		**18.** 0.820
14. 0.367		**19.** 7.468 — 10
15. 8.727 — 10		**20.** 1.111

LOGARITHMS TO THE BASE e**.** The logarithm of a number to the base e is the power to which e must be raised to equal the number. The value of e is *2.7183———*. This base is very convenient for work in higher mathematics. Since many formulae used in engineering and shop work are derived by the use of higher mathematics, the logarithm of a number to the base e appears in many formulae. You cannot find the logarithm to the base e directly from the ordinary slide rule, but can find the logarithm to the base 10 and convert it to the base e by using this equation,

logarithm of a number to the base e =
2.3026 × logarithm of the number to the base 10

First find the logarithm of the number to the base 10. Then multiply this logarithm by *2.3026** and you will have the logarithm of the number to the base e.

ILLUSTRATIVE EXAMPLES

7. *Find the logarithm of 3.81 to the base* e*.*

1) The logarithm of *3.81* to the base 10 is *0.581.*
2) Multiply *0.581* by *2.3026.* The result is *1.34,* which is the logarithm of *3.81* to the base e.

---

*You will make this multiplication on the slide rule, using the C and D scales. The number *2.3026* will have to be set as *2.30* since you cannot represent the last two digits of the number on the slide rule.

8. *Find the logarithm of 145.4 to the base **e**.*

1) The logarithm of *145.4* to the base 10 is *2.163*.
2) Multiply *2.163* by *2.3026*. The result is *4.98*, so the logarithm of *145.4* to the base *e* is *4.98*.

The logarithm of any number less than one is negative. This is true whether the base of the logarithm is 10 or *e*. The logarithm of *0.208* to the base 10 is

$$9.318 - 10$$

In this case each part of the logarithm is to be multiplied by *2.3026* in order to find the logarithm to the base *e*. This would give,
$$21.47 - 23.026$$

When the indicated subtraction is carried out, the result is (*— 1.556*). The logarithm of *0.208* to the base *e* is (*—1.556*).

9. *Find the logarithm of 0.0871 to the base **e**.*

1) the logarithm of *0.0871* to the base 10 is *8.940 — 10*.
2) Multiply *8.940 — 10* by *2.3026*. The result is *20.60 — 23.026*, or (*— 2.426*). The logarithm of *0.0871* to the base *e* is (*— 2.426*).

PRACTICE PROBLEMS

After you have worked all of the following problems, check your answers with the correct answers in the back of the book.

Find the logarithm of each of the following numbers to the base *e*.

1. 203	**3.** 37.3	**6.** 0.0569	**9.** 1.792
2. 5.42	**4.** 0.617	**7.** 137	**10.** 876
	5. 10	**8.** 20,000	

THE ANTILOG FOR A GIVEN LOGARITHM TO THE BASE *e*. In many calculations it is necessary to be able to find the number which has a given logarithm to the base *e*. This number is called the antilog. The easiest way to find it with the ordinary slide rule is to convert the logarithm of the number to the base *e* into the logarithm of the same number to the base 10. This conversion can be accomplished by dividing the logarithm to the base *e* by

2.3026. Then when you know the logarithm of the number to the base 10, you can find the number by the method already given in this chapter.

ILLUSTRATIVE EXAMPLES

10. *Find the number which has 3.05 for its logarithm to the base e.*

1) Divide *3.05* by *2.3026.* The result is *1.324.*
2) *1.324* is the logarithm of the number to the base 10. The number which has this logarithm is 21.1.

11. *Find the number which has 0.527 for its logarithm to the base e.*

1) Divide *0.527* by *2.3026.* This gives *0.229.*
2) The logarithm of the answer to the base 10 is *0.229.* The answer is *1.694.*

It is necessary to pay particular attention to cases when the logarithm of the number to the base *e* is negative. This will be the case for any number less than one. When such a logarithm to the base *e* is divided by *2.3026,* the result must also be a negative number. For example, if the logarithm of a numer to the base *e* is $(- 0.783)$, the logarithm of the number to the base 10 is equal to $(- 0.783)$ divided by *2.3026,* which is $(- 0.340)$. However, this logarithm to the base 10 is not expressed in the form to which you are accustomed. You must change it to the usual form by adding ten and subtracting ten. First add ten, which in this case would give *9.660,* since

$$10 + (- 0.340)$$

can be rewritten as

$$10 - 0.340 = 9.660$$

Then subtract ten and leave the result in this form:

$$9.660 - 10$$

This is the standard form for the logarithm of a number less than one to the base 10. The method of finding the number corresponding to it has already been described.

ILLUSTRATIVE EXAMPLES

12. *Find the number which has $(- 1.932)$ for its logarithm to the base e.*

1) Divide (-1.932) by 2.3026. The result is (-0.838).
2) Add ten to (-0.838). This is,

$$10 + (-0.838)$$

which can be written as,

$$10 - 0.838 = 9.162$$

3) Subtract ten from 9.162 and leave the result as

$$9.162 - 10$$

4) The logarithm of the answer is $9.162 - 10$ to the base 10. The answer is 0.1452.

13. *Find the number which has (-5.52) for its logarithm to the base e.*

1) Divide (-5.52) by 2.3026. The result is (-2.40).
2) Add ten to (-2.40). This is

$$10 + (-2.40)$$

or,

$$10 - 2.40 = 7.60$$

3) Subtract ten from 7.60 and leave it as $7.60 - 10$.
4) The logarithm of the answer to the base 10 is $7.60 - 10$. The answer is 0.00398.

PRACTICE PROBLEMS

After you have worked all of the following problems, check your answers with the correct answers shown in the back of the book.

Regard each of the following quantities as the logarithm of a number to the base *e* and find the number.

1. 4.18	**3.** 1.272	**6.** -2.3026	**9.** -0.667
2. 0.715	**4.** -3.30	**7.** 2.950	**10.** 3.72
	5. 2.3026	**8.** 1.787	

REVIEW PROBLEMS

Answers to Review Problems are not given in the back of the book. Readers who are working alone may check their answers if desired by using tables of logarithms.

Find the logarithm of each of the following numbers to the base 10.

1. 15.6
2. 832
3. 0.757
4. 6.28

5. 25,600
6. 96.7
7. 58.5
8. 1.254

9. 0.00382
10. 193.5
11. 5280
12. 4.43

13. 0.283
14. 327
15. 64.4

Find the number corresponding to each of the following logarithms to the base 10.

16. 3.462
17. 1.789
18. 0.317
19. 2.549

20. 1.018
21. 8.242 — 10
22. 2.052
23. 9.163 — 10

24. 1.633
25. 1.995
26. 0.447
27. 0.500

28. 5.393
29. 1.837
30. 0.618

CHAPTER 12

THE SPLIT SCALES FOR THE SQUARE AND SQUARE ROOT

This chapter is for the benefit of people who own slide rules which have two split scales for use with the **D** scale in calculating the square or square root of a number. This type of slide rule does not usually have the **A** and **B** scales, which are on the older and less expensive slide rules, and which are used with the **D** scale to obtain squares and square roots, as explained in Chapter 7.

THE SPLIT SCALES. The split scales are on the lower part of the front of the stock of the slide rule. Sometimes they are designated as **R₁** and **R₂** and sometimes they just have the square root symbol $\sqrt{}$ in front of them. The upper one of the split scales ranges from 1 (the lefthand index) to the sequence of numbers 318; except for the last mark at the righthand end, this scale has the same range as the lefthand half of the **D** scale. The lower split scale runs from the sequence 316 to 1 at the righthand index, the same range of numbers as the righthand half of the **D** scale. The two split scales together cover the same range of numbers as the **D** scale but are twice as long.

The only thing new about the marking of the split scales is in the lefthand portion of the upper one. Here, each of the ten sections between the lefthand index and the division (about 3/5 of the whole scale) is divided into twenty spaces. The first digit of any number in this portion is 1, the second digit is given by the number (1 to 9) designating the section, the third digit is the number of long marks to the right of the lefthand section boundary, and the fourth digit is estimated as 1/5 of a space. Each space represents 5 in the fourth digit of the number. Let's try locating a number in this range.

ILLUSTRATIVE EXAMPLE

1. *Locate the number 1237 in the upper split scale. Fig. 12-1* shows this sequence of numbers.

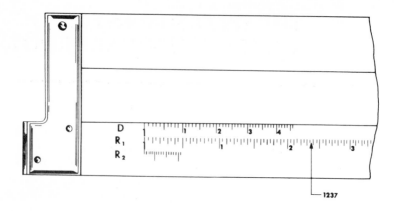

Fig. 12-1. Location of the number 1237 on the upper (R₁) split scale.

1) The first digit is *1,* so the number is in the lefthand portion of the scale.

2) The second digit is *2,* so the number is on the righthand side of the numeral *2.*

3) The third digit is *3,* so three long marks are counted on the right-hand side of the numeral *2.*

4) The fourth digit is *7,* so the number is one short mark and *2/5* of the next space farther to the right.

THE SQUARE OF A NUMBER. The square of a number is the product of the number by itself. The easy way to square a number is (1) to set the hairline of the runner to the number on whichever of the split scales it appears, and (2) read the square on the **D** scale under the hairline.

Location of the Decimal Point. The decimal point in the square of a number can be located by determining the digit count* of the number. The digit count of a number is the number of digits to the left of the decimal point of the number. Thus, the digit count for 23.9 is two. There are two cases to consider, depending on whether the number is on the upper or lower of the split scales.

---

*Digit counts are explained in Chapter 4.

Case 1. When the number is on the upper scale, multiply the digit count of the number by 2 and subtract 1 to get the digit count of the square.

Case 2. When the number is on the lower split scale, multiply the digit count of the number by 2 to get the digit count of the square.

ILLUSTRATIVE EXAMPLES

2. *Square 13.6.*

1) *13.6* is on the upper split scale. Set the hairline of the runner to it.
2) Read the digits of the square of *13.6* as *185* on the **D** scale under the hairline.
3) The digit count for *13.6* is two, so multiply two by two and subtract one, following Case 1. This gives three for the digit count of the square, so the square is *185*.

3. *Square 6.33.*

1) *6.33* is on the lower split scale. Set the hairline of the runner to it.
2) Read the digits in the square as *4* on the **D** scale under the hairline.
3) The digit count for *6.33* is one, so multiply one by two, following Case 2. This gives two for the digit count of the square, so the square of *6.33* is *40*.

4. *A square plot of land is 228 feet on a side. What is the area of the plot?* The answer is the square of 228.

1) Set the hairline of the runner to *228,* on the upper split scale.
2) Read the digits of the square as 52 on the **D** scale under the hairline.
3) The digit count for *228* is three, so multiply three by two and subtract one, following Case 1. This gives five for the digit count of the square, so it is *53000*. The area is *53,000* square ft.

5. *A square bar is 0.042 inches on a side. What is the area of the cross section?*

1) *0.042* is on the lower split scale. Set the hairline of the runner to it.

2) Read the digits of the square as *1764* on the **D** scale under the hairline.

3) The digit count for *0.042* is minus one, so multiply minus one by two, following Case 2. This gives minus two for the digit count of the answer, so the answer is *0.001764* square inches.

PRACTICE PROBLEMS

Do these problems to get enough practice to remember this process, and then check your answers with the correct answers in the back of the book.

Square each of the following numbers:

1. 32.5		6. 732	
2. 1.155		7. 0.0128	
3. 0.921		8. 21.7	
4. 67.5		9. 5.23	
5. 4.28		10. 0.00617	

11. What is the area of a square which is 17.3 inches on a side?

12. The area of a circle is 3.14 times the square of the radius. What is the area of a circle of 2.32 inch radius?

13. The volume of a rectangular block is equal to the product of the height and the area of the base. What is the volume of a block which is 8.5 inches high and has a square base 3.5 inches on a side?

14. A certain type of plastic sheet costs 82 cents per square foot. What is the cost of a square sheet which is 2.6 feet on a side?

15. A square hole in a plate is 0.0718 inches on a side. What is the area of the hole?

THE SQUARE ROOT OF A NUMBER. The square root of a number is a second number, which when multiplied by itself will give the original number. Thus, the square root of 9 is 3, because $3 \times 3 = 9$.

The easy way to calculate the square root of a number is (1) to set the hairline of the runner to the number on the **D** scale, and (2) read the square root on the upper split scale under the hairline if the digit count for the original number is odd, and read the square root on the lower split scale if the digit count for the original number is even.

Location of the Decimal Point. There are two cases to consider here, depending on whether the digit count for the original number is odd or even.

Case 1. When the digit count for the original number is odd, add one to the digit count and divide by two. This will give the digit count for the square root, which will be read from the upper split scale.

Case 2. When the digit count for the original number is even, just divide the digit count by two. This will give the digit count for the square root, which will be read from the lower split scale.

Here are examples to show how it is done.

ILLUSTRATIVE EXAMPLES

6. *What is the square root of 827?*
1) Set the hairline of the runner to *827* on the **D** scale.
2) The digit count for *827* is three, and three is an odd number, so read the digits of the answer as *2877* on the upper split scale under the hairline.
3) Add one to three to get four, and divide four by two, following Case 1. The result is two, and this is the digit count for the answer, so the answer is *28.77.*

7. *What is the square root of 6770?*
1) Set the hairline of the runner to *6770* on the **D** scale.
2) The digit count for *6770* is four, and four is an even number, so read the digits of the square root as *823* on the lower split scale under the hairline.
3) Divide four by two to get the digit count for the square root, following Case 2. The result is two, so the answer is *82.3.*

8. *What is the square root of 0.00378?*
1) Set the hairline of the runner to the sequence *378* on the **D** scale.
2) The digit count for *0.00378* is minus two, and minus two is an even number, so read the sequence of digits in the answer as *615* on the lower split scale under the hairline.
3) Divide minus two by two, following Case 2, to get the digit count for the square root. The result is minus one, so the answer is *0.0615.*

9. *Calculate the square root of 0.000172.*

1) Set the hairline of the runner to *0.000172* on the **D** scale.
2) The digit count for *0.000172* is minus three, which is an odd number, so read the digits of the square root as *1312* on the upper split scale under the hairline.
3) Add one to minus three to get minus two, and divide minus two by two, following Case 1. The result is minus one. This is the digit count for the answer so the answer is *0.01312*.

PRACTICE PROBLEMS

Practice will help you remember what you have just learned. After you have worked the problems, check your answers with the correct answers in the back of the book.

Calculate the square root of each of the following numbers:

1. 234	**6.** 154
2. 1.16	**7.** 0.00191
3. 0.515	**8.** 27300
4. 3000	**9.** 1956
5. 0.0747	**10.** 4.93

11. How large must a square room be to have an area of 600 square feet?

12. What size of square bar will have an area of cross section of 1.5 square inches.

13. What must be the length of side of a square plot of land which has an area of 30,000 square feet?

14. What is the radius of a circle which has an area of 2 square inches? (*Hint:* divide 2 by π and take the square root.)

15. How big must a square hole be to have an area of 0.036 square inches?

Basis of the Process. The basis of the process of using the slide rule to calculate square and square root is explained in Chapter 7, which shows how to do this sort of calculation with the **A** and **D** scales. The explanation is so much the same for the split scales that it will not be repeated here.

OTHER TYPES OF SLIDE RULES. The only other arrangement of scales for calculating square and square root is explained in Chapter 7.

REVIEW PROBLEMS

Answers to Review Problems are not given in the back of the book. One way of checking answers to problems is to work a problem backward, starting with the answer and seeing if you can get the original data of the problem.

Some of these problems have the process of squaring or taking the square root as a part of a more comprehensive problem. This is the way it often occurs in practical work.

1. $(21.6)^2 = ?$ **6.** $\sqrt{0.73} = ?$

2. $(0.583)^2 = ?$ **7.** $\sqrt{353} = ?$

3. $(9.14)^2 = ?$ **8.** $\sqrt{14.2} = ?$

4. $(4.5)^2 = ?$ **9.** $\sqrt{7800} = ?$

5. $(0.062)^2 = ?$ **10.** $\sqrt{0.059} = ?$

11. The solution of a quadratic equation leads to this sort of computation. Calculate x:

$$x = \frac{8.4 + \sqrt{(8.4)^2 - 52}}{2}.$$

12. The square of the hypotenuse of a right triangle is equal to the sum of the squares of the altitude and base. How long is the hypotenuse of a right triangle of which the altitude is 8 inches and the base is 9.5 inches.

13. What is the hypotenuse of a right triangle of which the altitude is 324 feet and the base is 263 feet?

14. What is the altitude of a right triangle if the hypotenuse is 1.73 inches and the base is 1.52 inches?

15. What is the base of a right triangle if the hypotenuse is 32 inches and the altitude is 25 inches?

16. The area of a circle is πr^2, where $\pi = 3.14$ and r is the radius. What is the area of a circle which has a radius of 129 feet?

17. What is the area of a circle which has a radius of 3.42 inches?

18. What is the radius of a circle which has area of 11.5 square inches?

19. What is the radius of a circle which has an area of 98.5 square feet?

20. The volume of a circular cylinder is equal to the product of the altitude and the area of the base. What is the volume of a cylindrical tank which has a radius of 4 feet and is 12 feet high?

21. Brass weighs approximately 0.0319 pounds per cubic inch. Calculate the weight of a circular brass rod which has a radius of 0.6 inches and a length of 3.45 inches.

22. It is desired to make a cylindrical tank which has a diameter of 12 feet (diameter is twice radius) and a volume of 1800 cubic feet. How tall must the tank be?

23. The equation of a certain ellipse is,

$$\frac{x^2}{9} + \frac{y^2}{25} = 1.$$

What is x when y = 4.16?

24. The equation of a certain parabola is $y = 0.4x^2$. What is y when x = 3.9?

25. The equation of a certain circle is $x^2 + y^2 = 72$. What is x when y = 5?

CHAPTER 13

THE RECIPROCAL SCALE

Most slide rules have a **CI** inverted, or reciprocal scale. This scale is on the front of the slide and is designated by the letters *CI* at its left end. It differs from the **C** scale in that it reads from right to left instead of from left to right. Otherwise it is identical with the **C** scale.

For a given position of the runner on the slide rule, the number on the **CI** scale that is under the hairline is the reciprocal* of the number on the **C** scale that is under the hairline. (It is for this reason that the **CI** scale is often called the reciprocal scale.) This is illustrated by the following examples.

ILLUSTRATIVE EXAMPLES

1. *Find the reciprocal of 4.*

1) Set the hairline of the runner to *4* on the **C** scale. The slide can be in any position for this setting.
2) Read the reciprocal of *4* on the **CI** scale under the hairline. The reciprocal of *4* is 0.25.

2. *Find the reciprocal of 17.*

1) Set the hairline of the runner to *17* on the **C** scale.
2) Read the reciprocal of *17* on the **CI** scale under the hairline. The reciprocal of *17* is 0.0589.

3. *Find the reciprocal of 0.65.*

1) Set the hairline of the runner to *0.65* on the **C** scale.
2) Read the reciprocal of *0.65* as *1.54* on the **CI** scale under the hairline.

---

*The reciprocal of a number x is $\dfrac{1}{x}$. Thus the reciprocal of 2 is $\dfrac{1}{2}$, the reciprocal of 5 is $\dfrac{1}{5}$, the reciprocal of 30 is $\dfrac{1}{30}$, etc.

4. *Find the reciprocal of 0.866.*

1) Set the hairline of the runner to *0.866* on the **C** scale.
2) Read the reciprocal of *0.866* as *1.154* on the **CI** scale under the hairline.

Advantages of using the **CI** scale are that it enables many problems to be done with fewer movements of the slide, and in many cases it makes possible a more precise calculation. These advantages will be discussed in greater detail in subsequent examples.

The **CI** scale can be used with the **D** scale for multiplication and division. In doing so, however, you must keep in mind when you set the hairline of the runner to a number on the **CI** scale, that the number with which you are actually calculating is its reciprocal.

MULTIPLICATION WITH THE CI SCALE. The problem is to multiply one number, the multiplicand, by a second, the multiplier, using the **D** scale and the **CI** scale.

STEPS IN THE PROCESS — MULTIPLICATION WITH CI SCALE

1) Set the hairline of the runner to the first number, or multiplicand, on the **D** scale.
2) Move the slide so that the second number, or multiplier, on the **CI** scale is under the hairline.
3) Read the answer on the **D** scale under whichever index of the **C** scale is between the ends of the **D** scale.
4) Locate the decimal point in the answer. Use the rules given in the following paragraph.

Be very careful in **Step 2** that you read the **CI** scale from right to left. This may require care after your experience in using the other scales of the slide rule.

Locating the Decimal Point. Locate the decimal point by using one of the following rules. Only one can apply for a particular calculation.

1. *If the slide extends to the right of the stock during the calculation, the digit count* for the answer is exactly the sum of the digit count for the multiplicand and the digit count for the multiplier.*

---

*Digit counts are explained in Chapter 4. An alternate method of decimal location, based on powers of ten, is explained in Chapter 16.

2. *If the slide extends to the left of the stock during the calculation, the digit count for the answer is one less than the sum of the digit count for the multiplicand and the digit count for the multiplier.*

The following examples will demonstrate the entire process.

ILLUSTRATIVE EXAMPLES

5. *Use the CI scale to multiply 18.8 by 6.15.* Fig. 13-1 shows the proper setting of the slide and runner for this problem. It should be done in the following steps.

1) Set the hairline of the runner to *18.8* on the **D** scale.
2) Move the slide so that *6.15* on the **CI** scale is under the hairline.
3) Read the numerals in the answer as *1155* on the **D** scale under the left index of the **C** scale.
4) The digit count for *18.8* is two, and the digit count is one for *6.15*. The sum of two and one is three. The slide extends to the right of the stock during the calculation so three is the digit count for the answer, which is *115.5*.

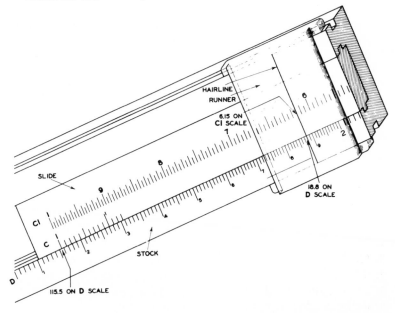

Fig. 13-1. Correct setting of slide and runner to multiply 6.15 × 18.8 = 115.5, using the CI scale.

6. *Use the* **CI** *scale to multiply 718 by 133.*

1) Set the hairline of the runner to *718* on the **D** scale.
2) Move the slide so that *133* on the **CI** scale is under the hairline.
3) Read the numerals in the answer as *954* on the **D** scale under the right index of the **C** scale.
4) The digit count is three for each of the numbers *718* and *133*. Three plus three is six. Since the slide extends to the left of the stock, you are to subtract one from six, leaving five. This is the digit count for the answer, so it is *95400*.

In a decimal fraction such as *0.00438,* remember that each zero between the decimal point and the first digit of the number counts as a negative digit. Thus, the digit count for *0.00438* is minus two.

7. *Use the* **CI** *scale to multiply 0.00438 by 0.0503.*

1) Set the hairline of the runner to *0.00438* on the **D** scale.
2) Bring *0.0503* on the **CI** scale under the hairline.
3) Read the numerals of the answer as *22* on the **D** scale under the left index of the **C** scale.
4) The digit count for *0.00438* is minus two, and minus one for *0.0503*. The sum of minus two and minus one is minus three. Since the slide extends to the right of the stock, there is nothing to be subtracted from this sum and the digit count for the answer is minus three. This means that there must be three zeros between the decimal point and the first digit of the answer, so the answer is *0.00022*.

PRACTICE PROBLEMS

After you have worked all of the following problems, check your answers with the correct answers shown in the back of the book. Perform each multiplication by using the **CI** scale.

1. 1.53 × 6.92 = ?
2. 45.5 × 17 = ?
3. 0.707 × 58 = ?
4. 0.023 × 6560 = ?
5. 8.4 × 1230 = ?
6. 0.693 × 0.521 = ?
7. 10.20 × 73.5 = ?

8. 9.98 × 11.3 = ?
9. 37.5 × 0.866 = ?
10. 0.402 × 0.197 = ?
11. 56.4 × 4900 = ?
12. 804 × 119 = ?
13. 386 × 212 = ?
14. 184.8 × 0.775 = ?

15. 62.4 × 313 = ?

Basis of the Process. Whenever we set out to explain why a certain slide rule manipulation gives the correct answer, we must resort to logarithms. The scales of the ordinary slide rule are based on logarithms to the base 10. The logarithm of a number to the base 10 is the power to which 10 must be raised to equal the number. Thus the logarithm of *16* to the base 10 is *1.2041* since 10 must be raised to the power *1.2041* to equal *16*. The part of the logarithm to the left of the decimal point is called the *characteristic* and is one less than the digit count for the original number. (Since there are two digits to the left of the decimal point in *16*, the digit count is two and the characteristic of its logarithm is *1*.) The part of the logarithm to the right of the decimal point is called the *mantissa* and it depends only on the sequence of digits in the number. Thus, the mantissa is *2041* for the numbers *16, 160, 1600,* etc.

Multiplication of two numbers can be accomplished by adding the logarithms of the two numbers, and this sum of the logarithms of the two numbers is the logarithm of the product of the two numbers. As an example, suppose we use logarithms to multiply *16* by *12*. The characteristic of each logarithm is *1,* since the digit count for each number is two. The mantissa for each can be found from a table of logarithms. Then

$$\text{Logarithm of } 16 = 1.2041$$
$$\text{Logarithm of } 12 = 1.0792$$
$$\text{Sum} \dots\dots\dots = 2.2833$$

The logarithm of the product of *16* and *12* is *2.2833*. The mantissa of the logarithm of the product is *2883* and a table of ·logarithms shows that the sequence of numbers in the product must be *192*. The characteristic is *2,* so there must be three digits to the left of the decimal point. Hence, the answer is *192*.

The mantissa is the only part of the logarithm that can be represented on the slide rule. The distance from the left index of the **D** scale to the location of a number represents the mantissa of the logarithm of the number. However, on the **CI** scale, the distance from the right index to the location of a number represents the mantissa of the logarithm of the number. If we multiply *16* by *12,* using the **CI** scale, it will be evident that we have actually added the mantissae for the two numbers. The problem would be done in the following steps:

1) Set the hairline of the runner to *16* on the **D** scale.
2) Bring *12* on the **CI** scale under the hairline.
3) Read the answer, *192,* on the **D** scale under the right index of the **C** scale.

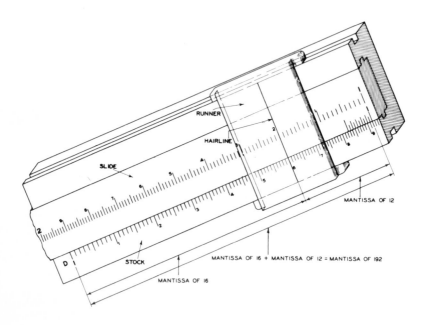

Fig. 13-2. Multiplication of 16 x 12 with the CI scale, illustrating the basis of the process

Fig. 13-2 shows the proper setting of the slide and runner for this problem. It also shows that the operation actually adds the mantissae of *16* and *12* to give the mantissa of *192.* The slide rule gives the sequence of digits in the answer by using mantissae. The decimal point can be located by using characteristics. When the slide extends to the left of the stock during such a problem, the characteristics add without any carry-over from the mantissae. Thus the characteristic of the product of two numbers is equal to the characteristic of the multiplicand plus the characteristic of the multiplier. As an equation, this is

characteristic of product =characteristic of multiplicand + characteristic of multiplier

Since the characteristic for a number is one less than the digit count for the number, this equation can be changed to

(digit count for product — 1) = (digit count for multiplicand — 1) + (digit count for multiplier — 1)

On each side a — 1 can be canceled, leaving

digit count for product = (digit count for multiplicand + digit count for multiplier) — 1

Hence the rule that when the slide extends to the left of the stock during a multiplication with the **CI** scale, the digit count for the product is equal to one less than the sum of the digit count for the multiplicand and the digit count for the multiplier.

When the slide extends to the right of the stock during such a problem, there is a carry-over of 1 from the mantissae to the characteristics when adding the logarithms. Thus the characteristic of the answer is one more than the sum of the characteristics of the multiplicand and multiplier. As an equation, this is

characteristic of product = (characteristic of multiplicand + characteristic of multiplier) + 1

When this equation is expressed in terms of digit counts, it becomes

(digit count for product — 1) = (digit count for multiplicand — 1) + (digit count for multiplier — 1) + 1

All the 1's can be canceled, leaving

digit count for product = digit count for multiplicand + digit count for multiplier

Thus the rule, that when the slide extends to the right of the stock during a multiplication with the **CI** scale, the digit count for the product is equal to the sum of the digit count for the multiplicand and the digit count for the multiplier.

A shorter justification of the process of multiplication with the **CI** scale can be given by comparing it with the ordinary process of division (see chapter on Division). The comparison will show that in multiplying one number by a second with the **CI** scale, you are really dividing the first number by the reciprocal of the second.

This gives the same result as multiplying the first number by the second.

DIVISION WITH THE CI SCALE. One number can be divided by a second by using the **D** scale and the **CI** scale. The first number is called the dividend and the second the divisor. The problem is worked in four steps.

STEPS IN THE PROCESS — DIVISION WITH CI SCALE
1) Place one index of the **C** scale to the dividend on the **D** scale.
2) Set the hairline of the runner to the divisor on the **CI** scale.
3) Read the answer on the **D** scale under the hairline.
4) Locate the decimal point.

Remember in carrying out Step 2 that the **CI** scale must be read from right to left.

Location of the Decimal Point. Here are the rules for locating the decimal point in the answer. They give the digit count for the answer.

1. *If the side extends to the right of the stock, the digit count for the answer is equal to the digit count for the dividend minus the digit count for the divisor.*

2. *If the slide extends to the left of the stock, the digit count for the answer is one more than the digit count for the dividend minus the digit count for the divisor.*

ILLUSTRATIVE EXAMPLES

8. *Use the CI scale to divide 127 by 8.63.* Fig. 13-3 shows the proper setting of the slide and runner for this problem.

1) Set the left index of the **C** scale over *127* on the **D** scale.
2) Set the hairline of the runner to *8.63* on the **CI** scale.
3) Read the numerals in the answer as *1472,* on the **D** scale under the hairline.
4) The digit count is three for the dividend, *127,* and one for the divisor, *8.63.* Three minus one is two. Since the slide extends to the right of the stock, there is nothing to add to two, and it is the digit count for the answer. Hence the answer is *14.72.*

9. *Use the CI scale to divide 0.062 by 5.27.*

1) Set the right index of the **C** scale to *0.062* on the **D** scale.
2) Set the hairline of the runner to *5.27* on the **CI** scale.
3) Read the numerals in the answer as *1175,* on the **D** scale.

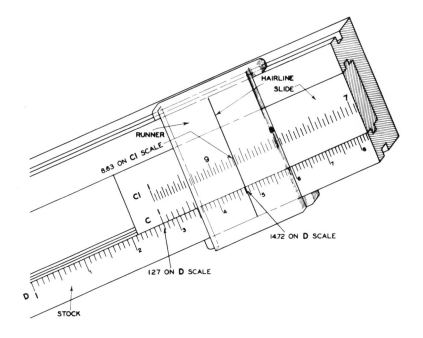

Fig. 13-3. Division of 127 by 8.63 with the CI scale.

4) In making a digit count for such a number as *0.062,* each zero immediately following the decimal point is counted as a negative digit. Thus the digit count is minus one for *0.062,* the dividend. The digit count is one for the divisor, *5.27.* One subtracted from minus one leaves minus two.* The slide projects to the left of the stock when solving the problem so one must be added to minus two, leaving minus one as the number of digit count for the answer. This means that there must be one zero immediately following the decimal point, so the answer is *0.01175.*

You must be careful in starting such a division to use the proper index of the **C** scale to locate the dividend on the **D** scale. If you use the wrong index, the divisor on the **CI** scale will not be between the ends of the **D** scale, and so you cannot complete the operation.

---

* Negative numbers are explained in Appendix A.

When this happens, you must start over, using the other index of the **C** scale. The following example shows how this works.

    10. *Use the **CI** scale to divide 33.7 by 1.17.*

1) Set the left index of the **C** scale to *33.7,* the dividend, on the **D** scale.

2) Try to set the hairline of the runner to *1.17,* the divisor, on the **CI** scale. You cannot because *1.17* on the **CI** scale is beyond the end of the **D** scale.

3) Therefore, set the right index of the **C** scale to *33.7* on the **D** scale.

4) Set the hairline of the runner to *1.17* on the **CI** scale.

5) Read the answer on the **D** scale under the hairline. It is *28.8.*

    It is always possible to divide one number by another using the **CI** scale. If starting with the right index of the **C** scale will not let

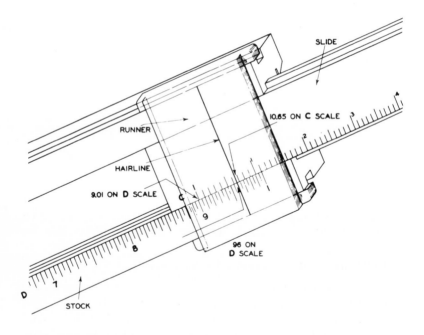

Fig. 13-4. Correct setting of slide and runner to divide 96 by 10.65 with the C scale, reading the answer as 9.01 on the D scale.

you complete the problem, starting with the left index will. One or the other will always work.

Sometimes the ordinary process of division, using the **C** and **D** scales (see chapter on Division for this method), results in an awkward setting of the slide rule. This is demonstrated in Example 11.

11. *Divide 96 by 10.65 using the* **C** *and* **D** *scales.* Fig. 13-4 shows the setting of the slide and runner for this problem. The steps in the operation are:

1) Set the hairline of the runner to *96* on the **D** scale.
2) Bring *10.65* on the **C** scale under the hairline.
3) Read the answer on the **D** scale under the left index of the **C** scale. Notice that only a small part of the slide is held within the stock. In this position the slide is likely to wobble and may slip while you are trying to read the answer.

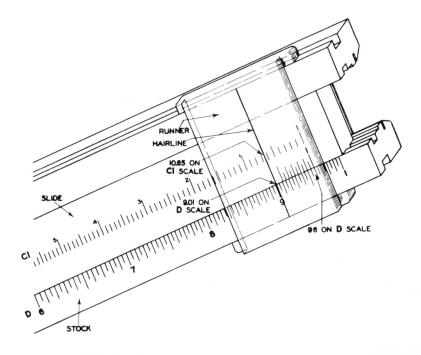

Fig. 13-5. Correct setting of slide and runner to divide 96 by 10.65 using the CI scale for this division. The answer, 9.01, is read on the D scale under the hairline.

The situation encountered in Example 11 can be avoided by performing the division with the **CI** scale. Example 12 shows how this is done.

12. *Use the CI scale to divide 96 by 10.65.* Fig. 13-5 shows the setting of the slide and runner. Do the problem in the following steps:

1) Set the right index of the **C** scale to *96* on the **D** scale.
2) Set the hairline of the runner to *10.65* on the **CI** scale.
3) Read the answer as *9.01* on the **D** scale under the hairline. Notice that nearly all of the slide is within the stock, held securely so that it cannot wobble and is not likely to slip while you are reading the answer.

Using the **CI** scale relieves you of making calculations with an awkward position of the slide. This advantage is demonstrated by Example 12. This may seem a little thing, but mastery of enough little things results in real skill in using the slide rule.

PRACTICE PROBLEMS

After you have worked all of the following problems, check your answers with the correct answers shown in the back of the book. Make each division by using the **CI** scale.

1. $5280 \div 22.7 = ?$	8. $0.042 \div 3.84 = ?$
2. $201 \div 17.32 = ?$	9. $0.707 \div 0.051 = ?$
3. $0.693 \div 4.91 = ?$	10. $922 \div 305 = ?$
4. $83400 \div 397 = ?$	11. $19.32 \div 16 = ?$
5. $8.07 \div 128 = ?$	12. $17,000 \div 29,600,000 = ?$
6. $13 \div 93 = ?$	13. $0.345 \div 78.5 = ?$
7. $2.77 \div 0.148 = ?$	14. $60.9 \div 23.7 = ?$
	15. $112 \div 51.5 = ?$

Basis of the Process. Here come the logarithms again. A quotient is equal to a dividend divided by a divisor. The logarithm of the quotient is equal to the logarithm of the dividend minus the logarithm of the divisor. Suppose we divide *150* by *12,* using logarithms to the base 10. The mantissa of the logarithm of each number can be obtained from a table of logarithms. (The *mantissa* is the part of the logarithm to the right of the decimal point of the logarithm.) The characteristic of the logarithm of a number can be found by using the rule that it is always one less than the digit count for the number. (The *characteristic* is the part of the logarithm to the left of the decimal point of the logarithm. The characteristic of *150* is 2 and that of *12* is *1*. After finding the mantissae of the logarithms from a set of tables, we can write

$$\text{Logarithm of } 150 = 2.1761$$
$$\text{Logarithm of } 12 = 1.0792$$
$$\overline{\text{Difference} \ldots \ldots = 1.0969}$$

The logarithm of the quotient is *1.0969*. The mantissa is *0969* and the tables show that the digits of the quotient are *125*. Since the characteristic of the quotient is *1*, the digit count must be two. Hence the quotient is *12.5*.

On the slide rule, only the mantissa of the logarithm is represented. The distance from the left index of the **D** scale to the location of a number on the **D** scale represents the mantissa of the logarithm of the number. But on the **CI** scale, the distance from the right index to the location of a number represents the mantissa of the logarithm of the number. If *150* is divided by *12* on the slide rule, the operation actually subtracts the mantissa of *12* from the mantissa of *150* to give the mantissa of the quotient, *12.5*. The problem is done in the following steps, using the **CI** scale:

1) Set the right index of the **C** scale to *150* on the **D** scale.
2) Set the hairline of the runner to *12* on the **CI scale.**
3) Read the answer, *12.5,* on the **D** scale under the hairline.

Fig. 13-6 shows the setting of the slide and runner for this problem and demonstrates that the operation actually does subtract one mantissa from another.

Since only the mantissa of the logarithm of a number can be represented on the slide rule, and the mantissa represents only the sequence of digits of the number, only the sequence of digits in the answer can be read from the slide rule. However, the decimal point in the answer can be located by considering characteristics. If the slide projects to the left of the stock during a division in which the **CI** scale is used, the mantissae of the logarithms subtract without any carry-over to the characteristics. Thus the characteristics can be subtracted separately, and the characteristic of the quotient is

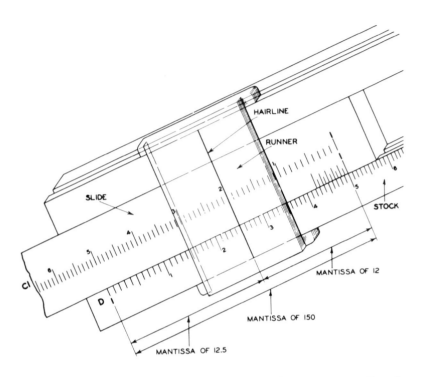

Fig. 13-6. In dividing 150 by 12 with the CI scale, we are actually sub-tracting the mantissa of log 12 from the mantissa of log 150, as illustrated here. The antilog of this difference, 1.0969, is 12.5.

equal to the characteristic of the dividend minus the characteristic of the divisor. As an equation, this is,

characteristic of quotient = characteristic of dividend —
characteristic of divisor

This can be written in a more convenient form in terms of digit counts, remembering that the characteristic for a number is one less than the digit count for the number. Then

(digit count for quotient — 1) = (digit count for dividend — 1) —
(digit count for divisor — 1)

or,

digit count for quotient — 1 = digit count for dividend — 1 —
digit count for divisor + 1

After a (— 1) is canceled from each side, there remains,

digit count for quotient = (digit count for dividend —
digit count for divisor) + 1

Hence the rule that when the slide projects to the left of the stock during a division with the **CI** scale, the digit count for the quotient is one more than the digit count for the dividend minus the digit count for the divisor.

When the slide projects to the right beyond the stock during such a division, there is a carry-over of — 1 from the mantissae to the characteristics in subtracting logarithms, and so the characteristic of the quotient is one less than the characteristic of the dividend minus the characteristic of the divisor. As an equation, this statement is,

characteristic of quotient = (characteristic of dividend —
characteristic of divisor) — 1

When this equation is written in terms of digit counts, it becomes,

(digit count for quotient — 1) = (digit count for dividend — 1) —
(digit count for divisor — 1) —1

All of the — 1's will cancel, leaving,

digit count for quotient = digit count for dividend —
digit count for divisor

And so, when the slide extends to the right of the stock during the process of division with the **CI** scale, the digit count for the quotient is equal to the digit count for the dividend minus the digit count for the divisor.

Another basis of this process can be given by comparing with the ordinary process of multiplication (see chapter on Multiplication). The comparison will show that when you use the **CI** scale to divide one number by a second, you are really multiplying the first number by the reciprocal of the second, which gives the same result as dividing the first number by the second.

MULTIPLICATION OF THREE NUMBERS. Three numbers can be multiplied conveniently by using the **D, C,** and **CI** scales in combination. The problem is to find the product of $a \times b \times c$. We will refer to the first number, a, as the multiplicand; to the second number, b, as the first multiplier; and to the third number, c, as the second multiplier. The procedure is to multiply a by b in the ordinary way, using the **C** and **D** scales, (see chapter on

Multiplication) and then to multiply their product by c with the **CI** scale. The steps in the operation of the slide rule are:

1) Place one index of the **C** scale over the multiplicand on the **D** scale.

2) Multiply by the first multiplier by setting the hairline of the runner to the first multiplier on the **C** scale. The product of the multiplicand and the first multiplier is then located on the **D** scale under the hairline, but do not bother to write it down.

3) Multiply by the second multiplier by bringing the second multiplier on the **CI** scale under the hairline. This step multiplies the product of Step 2 by the second multiplier.

4) Read the answer on the **D** scale under whichever index of the **C** scale is between the ends of the **D** scale. Only one index of the **C** scale can be between the ends of the **D** scale at one time.

5) Locate the decimal point as described in the following paragraphs.

This process is efficient and will enable you to save time. It requires fewer movements of the slide and runner than the method described in the chapter on Multiplication with the **C** and **D** scales.

Locating the Decimal Point.* It is desirable to know a method for locating the decimal point in the answer. As you carry out the foregoing operations, apply the following rules:

1. *If the slide projects to the right of the stock in multiplying the multiplicand by the first multiplier with the C scale, jot down — 1. If the slide projects to the left, there is nothing to jot down.*

2. *If the slide projects to the right of the stock in multiplying by the second multiplier with the CI scale, there is nothing to jot down. If the slide projects to the left, jot down — 1.*

As you jot down the — 1's, carry them in a horizontal row, which will hereafter be called the *digit summation*. In a typical problem, you might have at this point, in the digit summation,

$$- 1$$

As soon as you finish the manipulation of the slide rule, read the digits in the answer and write them down. Then return to the digit summation. Add to it the digit count for each of the original numbers of the problem. These original numbers are the multiplicand,

---

*Another method of locating the decimal point, based on powers of ten, is explained in Chapter 16.

the first multiplier, and the second multiplier. As an example, suppose they are *12.4, 275* and *5.13*, respectively. The digit count is two for the multiplicand, *12.4;* three for the first multiplier, *275;* and one for the second multiplier, *5.13*. The completion of the digit summation in this case would give.

$$- 1 + 2 + 3 + 1 = 5$$

The final result of the digit summation is the digit count for the answer. A few examples will illustrate the entire process.

ILLUSTRATIVE EXAMPLES

13. *Find the result of 580 × 4.27 × 32.*

1) Place the right index of the **C** scale over the multiplicand, *580,* on the **D** scale.

2) Multiply by the first multiplier, *4.27,* by setting the hairline of the runner to *4.27* on the **C** scale. Notice that the slide projects to the left of the stock, so there is nothing to jot down for the digit summation.

3) Multiply by the second multiplier, *32,* by sliding *32* on the **CI** scale under the hairline. The slide projects to the left when this is done, so jot down − *1* in the digit summation.

4) Read the digits in the answer as *792* on the **D** scale under the right index of the **C** scale.

5) At this point the digit summation is,

$$- 1$$

Add to it the digit count for each of the original numbers of the problem, *580, 4.27,* and *32*. The numbers to be addel to the digit summation are, respectively, *3, 1,* and *2*. Thus the digit summation becomes,

$$- 1 + 3 + 1 + 2 = 5$$

The final result, *5,* is the digit count for the answer. You must add two zeros to *792*. The result is *79,200*.

In the next example, there are numbers similar to 0.00224 in which there are several zeros after the decimal point and before the first digit of the number. Remember that each such zero is counted as a negative digit, so the digit count for *0.00224* is minus two.

14. *Find the result of 0.0137 × 6.67 × 0.0048.*

1) Start by setting the left index of the **C** scale to the multiplicand, *0.0137,* on the **D** scale.

2) Multiply by the first multiplier, *6.67,* by setting the hairline of the runner to *6.67* on the **C** scale. The slide projects to the right beyond the stock when you have done this, so start the digit summation by jotting down — *1.*

3) Multiply by the second multiplier, *0.0048,* by sliding *0.0048* on the **CI** scale under the hairline. The slide projects to the right of the stock for this setting, so there is no contribution to the digit summation.

4) Read the digits of the answer as *439* on the **D** scale under the left index of the **C** scale.

5) At this point the digit summation is,

$$- 1$$

Now add to the digit summation the digit count for each of the original numbers of the problem, *0.0137, 6.67* and *0.0048.* The numbers to add are respectively, — *1, 1,* and — *2.* This makes the digit summation

$$- 1 + (- 1) + 1 + (- 2)$$

or,

$$- 1 - 1 + 1 - 2 = - 3$$

The final result, — *3,* is the digit count for the answer, so you must insert three zeros after the decimal point and before the first digit of the answer, so it is *0.000439.*

Occasionally you will find it desirable to interchange the multiplicand and the first multiplier. For eqample, suppose the problem is to find the result of 91 × 1.05 × 32.2. You would start by setting the left index of the **C** scale to *91* on the **D** scale, since *91* is the multiplicand. Then you would set the hairline of the runner to *1.05,* the first multiplier, on the **C** scale. But this is an awkward setting of the slide and runner, as you can see when you try it on your own slide rule. Most of the slide projects to the right of the stock so that it may wobble or slip in the stock. See how much better it is if you interchange *91* and *1.05.* Then you would start by setting the left index of the **C** scale over *1.05* on the **D** scale, using *1.05* as the multiplicand. Next you would set the hairline of the runner to the first multiplier, *91,* on the **C** scale. This setting is much better, since most of the slide remains within the stock and is held more securely. It is better to do the problem in the order *1.05 × 91 × 32.3* than in the order *91 × 1.05 × 32.2.*

PRACTICE PROBLEMS

This procedure cannot be learned without practice. Do these problems carefully. Write out the digit summation for each one.

After you have worked all of the following problems check your answers with the correct answers in the back of the book.

1. 22.5 × 4.12 × 47 = ?
2. 1.93 × 29 × 0.707 = ?
3. 0.866 × 0.495 × 558 = ?
4. 6.28 × 1024 × 3 = ?
5. 99 × 88 × 77 = ?
6. 12.5 × 0.071 × 46 = ?
7. 201 × 0.0033 × 3.97 = ?

8. 5.21 × 47 × 0.618 = ?
9. 3.14 × 95 × 0.206 = ?
10. 0.0073 × 4.62 × 15.5 = ?
11. 1.078 × 301 × 0.84 = ?
12. 18.86 × 0.595 × 17 = ?
13. 6.07 × 291 × 4.1 = ?
14. 0.932 × 7.8 × 1.65 = ?

15. 57.7 × 0.0038 × 2.5 = ?

Basis of the Process. This process merely combines the ordinary method of multiplication (see chapter on Multiplication), with the method which uses the **CI** scale. The basis of each has been explained previously, so no further comments are necessary here.

DIVISION OF ONE NUMBER BY TWO OTHER NUMBERS. The **CI** scale can be used efficiently in combination with the **C** and **D** sales when dividing one number by two other numbers.

Such an operation can be written as, $\dfrac{a}{b \times c}$. The number *a* is the dividend, *b* is the first divisor and *c* is the second divisor. The operation combines the ordinary method of division (see chapter on Division) with the method which uses the **CI** scale. It can be performed with the following manipulations of the slide rule:

1) Set the hairline of the runner to the dividend on the **D** scale.
2) Divide by the first divisor by bringing the first divisor on the **C** scale under the hairline.
3) Divide by the second divisor by setting the hairline of the runner to the second divisor on the **CI** scale.
4) Read the answer on the **D** scale under the hairline.

This process requires fewer settings of the slide and runner than the ordinary process which was explained in the chapter on Division.

Locating the Decimal Point.* In many problems it would be difficult to locate the decimal point in the answer by inspection. It is desirable, therefore, to know a method for doing this. As you operate the slide and runner, follow these rules:

1. *When you divide the dividend by the first divisor, jot down + 1 if the slide projects to the right of the stock. If the slide projects to the left of the stock there is nothing to jot down.*

2. *When you divide by the second divisor, there is nothing to jot down if the slide projects to the right of the stock. If the slide projects to the left of the stock jot down + 1.*

Carry the + 1's in a horizontal line, as for instance,

$$+ 1 + 1$$

This line will hereafter be called the digit summation. As soon as you finish manipulating the slide rule, read the digits in the answer and write them down. Then return to the digit summation and complete it in order to know where to locate the decimal point in the answer. Add to the digit summation the digit count for the dividend. Subtract from it the digit count for each of the divisors. For example, if the problem is to find the result of

$$\frac{27.5}{1.24 \times 3.79}$$

you would add to the digit summation the digit count for the dividend, *27.5*. This is two, so the digit summation started above would become,

$$+ 1 + 1 + 2$$

Then you would subtract the digit count for each of the divisors, *1.24* and *3.79*. The digit count is one for each of these numbers, so you would subtract one twice, completing the digit summation as

$$+ 1 + 1 + 2 - 1 - 1 = 2$$

The final result of the digit summation, two in this case, is the digit count for the answer.

Follow the examples closely. This process is worth knowing.

---

*Another method of locating the decimal point, based on powers of ten, is explained in Chapter 16.

ILLUSTRATIVE EXAMPLES

15. *Find the result of* $\dfrac{396}{19.5 \times 5.92}$

1) Set the hairline of the runner to the dividend, *396,* on the **D** scale.

2) Divide by the first divisor, *19.5,* by bringing *19.5* on the **C** scale under the hairline. The slide projects to the right beyond the stock during this setting. Hence, you must start the digit summation by jotting down + *1.*

3) Divide by the second divisor, *5.92,* by setting the hairline of the runner to *5.92* on the **C** scale. The slide projects to the right beyond the stock so there is no contribution to the digit summation.

4) Read the digits of the answer as *344* on the **D** scale under the hairline.

5) At this point the digit summation is,

$$+ \; 1$$

Add to it the digit count for the dividend, *396.* This is three, so the digit summation becomes,

$$+ \; 1 + 3$$

Now subtract from the digit summation the digit count for each of the divisors, *19.5* and *5.92.* For these numbers, you subtract, respectively, two and one. This completes the digit summation as,

$$+ \; 1 + 3 - 2 - 1 = 1$$

The final result of the digit summation, one, is the digit count for the answer. Hence the answer is *3.44.*

Be careful when you are dealing with such a number as *0.00423,* which has a digit count of minus two. Remember that each zero immediately following the decimal point is counted as a negative digit.

16. *Find the result of* $\dfrac{2.12}{0.07 \times 0.0022}$

1) Start by setting the hairline of the runner to the dividend, *2.12,* on the **D** scale.

2) Divide by the first divisor, *0.07,* by bringing *0.07* on the **C** scale under the hairline. The slide projects to the left beyond the stock, so there is no contribution to the digit summation.

3) Divide by the second divisor, *0.0022*, by setting the hairline of the runner to *0.0022* on the **CI** scale. The slide projects to the left so start the digit summation by jotting lown + 1.

4) Read the digits of the answer as *1375* on the **D** scale under the hairline.

5) At this point the digit summation is,

$$+ 1$$

Add to it the digit count for the dividend, *2.12*, that is, add one. This gives,

$$+ 1 + 1$$

Now subtract from the digit summation, the digit count for each of the divisors, *0.07* and *0.0022*. The numbers to be subtracted are, respectively, minus one and minus two, since each zero after the decimal point and before the first digit of the number counts as a negative digit. This completes the digit summation as,

$$+ 1 + 1 - (- 1) - (- 2)$$
$$\text{or,}$$
$$+ 1 + 1 + 1 + 2 = 5$$

Thus the digit count for the answer is five, so you must add a zero to *1375* and the answer is *13,750*.

Occasionally, when you are ready to divide by the second divisor, you will find that the second divisor on the **CI** scale is beyond the end of the **D** scale. When this happens, it is best to complete the problem by making the second division in the ordinary way (see chapter on Division). Move the hairline of the runner to whichever index of the **C** scale is within the ends of the **D** scale. Leave the runner in this position while sliding the second divisor on the **C** scale under the hairline. Read the answer on the **D** scale under whichever index of the **C** scale is between the ends of the **D** scale. Since each division in such a problem is done with the **C** scale, use the rule given in the chapter on Division for the calculations which lead to the location of the decimal point.

ILLUSTRATIVE EXAMPLE

17. *Find the result of* $\dfrac{54.4}{2.56 \times 1.3}$

1) Set the hairline of the runner to the dividend, *54.4,* on the **D** scale.

2) Divide by the first divisor, *2.56,* by sliding *2.56* on the **C** scale under the hairline. The slide projects to the right beyond the stock when you have done this, so start the digit summation with + *1.*

3) Try to divide by the second divisor, *1.3,* by setting the hairline of the runner to *1.3* on the **CI** scale. You cannot do this because *1.3* on the **CI** scale is beyond the right end of the **D** scale.

4) Therefore, move the hairline of the runner to the left index of the **C** scale.

5) Now divide by *1.3* by sliding *1.3* on the **C** scale under the hairline. The slide extends to the right beyond the stock so follow the first rule and add + *1* to the digit summation.

6) Read the digits of the answer as *1637* on the **D** scale under the left index of the **C** scale. You know that you must read the answer under the left index of the **C** scale because the right index is beyond the end of the **D** scale.

7) At this point the digit summation is,

$$+ 1 + 1$$

Add to it the digit count for the dividend, *54.4.* This is two, which makes the digit summation

$$+ 1 + 1 + 2$$

Next subtract from the digit summation the digit count for each of the divisors, *2.56* and *1.3.* The digit count is one for each, so the digit summation is completed as

$$+ 1 + 1 + 2 - 1 - 1 = 2$$

This is the digit count for the answer. There are, then, two digits to the left of the decimal point in the answer, so it is *16.37.*

PRACTICE PROBLEMS

After you have worked all of the following problems, check your answers with the correct answers shown in the back of the book. Use the **C** scale for the first division and the **CI** scale for the second.

1. $\dfrac{74.8}{37.5 \times 5.30} = ?$

2. $\dfrac{1.81}{0.62 \times 1.19} = ?$

3. $\dfrac{14,500,000}{17,600 \times 732} = ?$

4. $\dfrac{0.000549}{0.0000065 \times 24} = ?$

5. $\dfrac{2.75}{4.3 \times 0.0178} = ?$ 10. $\dfrac{39,300}{72 \times 51.5} = ?$

6. $\dfrac{61.4}{3.71 \times 47.5} = ?$ 11. $\dfrac{938}{0.00812 \times 29} = ?$

7. $\dfrac{29,600,000}{1.25 \times 9,800} = ?$ 12. $\dfrac{1.37}{82.7 \times 161} = ?$

8. $\dfrac{120}{32.2 \times 11.1} = ?$ 13. $\dfrac{144}{17 \times 11} = ?$

9. $\dfrac{768}{14.7 \times 6.14} = ?$ 14. $\dfrac{748}{9,500 \times 0.031} = ?$

15. $\dfrac{5.03}{0.044 \times 0.75} = ?$

Basis of the Process. This process combines the ordinary method of division (see chapter on Division) with the method which uses the **CI** scale. Each of these methods has been justified in previous pages, so no further explanation is given here.

PRACTICE PROBLEMS

Use the **CI** scale in making the calculations. *After* you have worked all of the following problems, check your answers with the correct answers shown in the back of the book.

1. $34.5 \times 27.3 = ?$

2. $0.947 \times 6.84 = ?$

3. $23.4 \times 1.78 \times 780 = ?$

4. $5280 \times 17 = ?$

5. $83.5 \times 0.682 = ?$

6. $3720 \div 6.28 = ?$

7. $0.866 \div 3.42 = ?$

8. $256 \div 13 = ?$

9. $14.4 \div 0.085 = ?$

10. $8.72 \div 2.7 = ?$

11. $\dfrac{5280}{45 \times 66} = ?$

12. $\dfrac{1750 \times 6.28}{60} = ?$

13. $\dfrac{43.5}{0.707 \times 0.386} = ?$

14. $\dfrac{28 \times 15 \times 12}{32.2 \times 17} = ?$

15. $\dfrac{65}{28.3 \times 1.64} = ?$

16. $37.7 \times 0.0243 = ?$

17. $15.6 \div 48.7 = ?$

18. $1.88 \times 63.5 \times 0.105 = ?$

19. $\dfrac{2.54}{6.28 \times 53} = ?$

20. $\dfrac{364,000}{1250 \times 4.17} = ?$

OTHER TYPES OF SLIDE RULES. On most slide rules the reciprocal scale is marked **CI** (**I** standing for *inverted,* which has essentially the same meaning). On other slide rules you may find this scale marked **R** (**R** standing for *reciprocal*). However this scale is marked, the numbers on it will increase from right to left, it will be located on the slide, and will be used in the manner described in this chapter.

REVIEW PROBLEMS

Answers to Review Problems are not given in the back of the book. Readers who are working alone may check their answers by working problems longhand or by using the **C** and **D** scales only.

Practice using the reciprocal scale on these problems. As you acquire experience, you will find that you work faster and with greater precision.

1. An orchard containing 112 pear trees produces 1350 bushels of pears. What is the average yield per tree?

2. A machine shop contracts to finish 520 gears at a price of 84 cents per gear. What is the price for the whole job?

3. Water weighs 8.33 pounds per gallon and there are 7.48 gallons of water in one cubic foot. How much will 2.7 cubic feet of water weigh?

4. A gross of a certain size of machine screw costs $3.12. How much does one dozen cost? (There are twelve dozen in one gross.)

5. A certain type of truck uses 0.22 gallons of gasoline per mile. How much gasoline will 17 such trucks use while each travels 484 miles?

6. In a construction gang, 75 men receive a total of $2710 for 35 hours, each, of work. What is the average hourly pay?

7. An airplane travels 410 miles in 2.3 hours. What is its average speed?

8. A contractor plans to pour 12 concrete foundations, each requiring 4.85 cubic yards of concrete. The concrete will cost $9.60 per cubic yard in place. What is the total cost?

9. A shop buys 120 iron castings, each weighing 5.35 pounds, for $42.60. What is the average cost per pound?

10. Storage space is required for 820 cubic feet of material. An area 9.5 feet wide is available, but the material cannot be stored to a greater depth than 7 feet. How long a space is needed?

11. $37.3 \times 0.0519 = ?$

12. $1.28 \div 60.9 = ?$

13. $9.7 \times 11.4 \times 0.805 = ?$

14. $5280 \times 19.5 \times 27 = ?$

15. $\dfrac{0.702}{2.17 \times 0.041} = ?$

16. $\dfrac{62.4}{3.14 \times 28} = ?$

17. $\dfrac{16,200}{258 \times 39.5} = ?$

18. $7.11 \times 493 \times 0.00145 = ?$

19. $0.866 \times 0.741 \times 28 = ?$

20. $\dfrac{913}{0.64 \times 0.437} = ?$

CHAPTER 14

MULTIPLICATION AND DIVISION WITH THE FOLDED SCALES AND THE C, D AND CI SCALES

Just as you have done before in studying the slide rule, you should have the slide rule in your hands as you study this chapter, and actually perform each operation as it is described.

WHAT THE FOLDED SCALES ARE. Nearly all modern slide rules of the duplex type (with scales on both sides of stock and slide), including log log rules, have the *folded* scales, as they are called.

There are three folded scales altogether, and these are designated as **CF**, **DF**, and **CIF**. The **F** stands for *folded*. The **CIF** scale often has numerals in red. The **I** in **CIF** stands for *inverted*, because this scale is like the **CI** scale in that its numbers increase from right to left; it is an inverted, folded **C** scale. The folded scales are all on the front of the slide rule.

In the usual arrangement the **CF** scale is on the upper part of the slide. The **DF** scale is on the upper part of the stock, just above the **CF** scale. The **CIF** scale is on the slide, just below the **CF** scale.

The **CF** scale is a variation of the **C** scale and has the same markings as the **C** scale, but the markings are in a different order. If you were to cut the **C** scale in two at the mark π (pi = 3.14), then move the righthand part to the left and the lefthand part to the right, and join the two parts you would have the **CF** scale with a center index. The index is the mark by the large number 1. The **CF** scale starts at the sequence of numbers in π (3.14) at the lefthand end, goes through the divisions 4, 5, 6, 7, 8, and 9 to the center index, then goes through the divisions 2 and 3 to the sequence of numbers in π at the righthand end.

The **DF** scale is identical with the **CF** scale in its markings.

Because the **CIF** scale is an inverted or reciprocal scale, it is read from right to left. It is keyed to the **CF** and **DF** scales. If you set the hairline of the runner to a given sequence of numbers, say 865, on the **CF** scale, you will see the sequence of numbers of the reciprocal of 865 under the hairline on the **CIF** scale. This is 1157, reading from right to left. Try this one for yourself.

WHAT YOU CAN DO WITH THE FOLDED SCALES. You can perform all the operations of multiplication and division with the folded scales, including multiplication of one number by another, multiplication of a sequence of numbers, division of one number by another, and combinations of multiplication and division. You can perform these operations with the folded scales alone, but it is most efficient to use the folded scales in combination with the **C** and **D** scales.

HOW TO LOCATE NUMBERS ON THE CF AND DF SCALES. Anyone who knows how to use the **C** and **D** scales can learn to locate numbers on the **CF** and **DF** scales, because the **CF** and **DF** scales have the same markings as the **C** and **D** scales. The only difference is in the order of the markings.

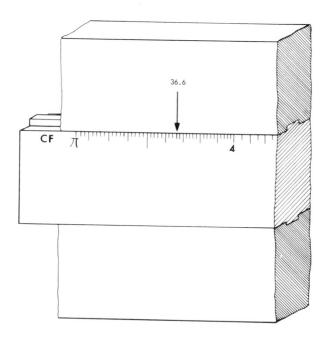

Fig. 14-1. Location of 36.6 on the CF scale.

The **CF** and **DF** scales each have the divisions 4, 5, 6, 7, 8, and 9 in the lefthand portion and the divisions 2 and 3 in the righthand portion. *There is only one index and it is a center index.*

ILLUSTRATIVE EXAMPLE

1. *Locate the number 36.6 on the* **CF** *scale.*

1) The first digit is *3* so the number is on the lefthand side of the division *4*.
2) The longest mark between the lefthand end of the scale and the division *4* represents the sequence of numbers *35*, so count one section to the right from this longest mark, because the second digit is *6*.
3) Then, since each space in this portion of the scale has a value of *2* in the third digit, count three more spaces to the right to represent *6* in the third digit.
4) Fig. 14-1 shows the location of 36.6 on the **CF** scale.

MULTIPLICATION WITH THE CF AND DF FOLDED SCALES AND THE C AND D SCALES. The problem now is to use the folded scales, with the **C** and **D** scales, to multiply one number, the multiplicand, by a second number, the divisor.

STEPS IN THE PROCESS — MULTIPLICATION WITH THE FOLDED SCALES

1) Set one index of the **C** scale to the first number, or multiplicand, on the **D** scale.
2) Set the hairline of the runner to the second number, or multiplier, on the **CF** scale.
3) Read the numbers in the answer on the **DF** scale under the hairline.
4) Locate the decimal point in the answer by using good judgment, the powers of ten method,* or by using the rules given in the following paragraph.

Locating the Decimal Point. Locating the decimal point by rules is a little more complicated when you use the folded scales for

---

*The powers of ten method for decimal point location is explained in Chapter 16.

multiplication, but you can learn it if you work at it. These are the rules.

1. If the slide extends to the right during the multiplication, the digit count** for the answer is *usually* one less than the sum of the digit count for the multiplicand and the digit count for the multiplier, but there is an exception to the rule. If the multiplier is located in the lefthand half of the **CF** scale and the answer is located in the righthand half of the **DF** scale, then the digit count for the answer is exactly equal to the sum of the digit count for the multiplicand and the digit count for the multiplier.

2. If the slide extends to the left during the multiplication, the digit count for the answer is *usually* exactly equal to the sum of the digit count for the multiplicand and the digit count for the multiplier, but there is one exception to this rule. If the multiplier is located in the righthand half of the **CF** scale and the answer is located in the lefthand half of the **DF** scale, the digit count for the answer is one less than the sum of the digit count for the multiplier and the digit count for the multiplicand.

It may help in remembering these exceptions to notice that they apply whenever the answer is in the opposite half of the **DF** scale from the multiplier in the **CF** scale.

Now, here are some examples to demonstrate the process of multiplication.

ILLUSTRATIVE EXAMPLES

2. *Use the folded scales to multiply 11.4 by 415.* Fig. 14-2 shows the setting of the slide and runner for this calculation. It should be done in the following steps:

1) Set the lefthand index of the **C** scale to *11.4* on the **D** scale.
2) Set the hairline of the runner to *415* on the **CF** scale.
3) Read the digits in the answer as *473* on the **DF** scale under the hairline.
4) The digit count for *11.4* is two and the digit count for *415* is three. The sum of two and three is five. Since the slide extends to the right during the calculation, the digit count for the answer is one less than five, and this is four. The answer is *4730*.

Sometimes the slide must extend to the left during this kind of

---
**Digit counts are explained in Chapter 4.

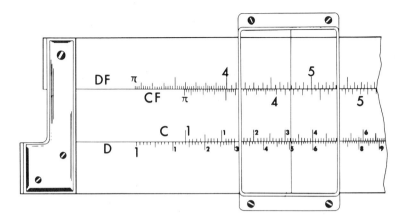

Fig. 14-2. Multiplication of 11.4 x 415.

multiplication. If you can't do it with the slide extending to the right, then just go the other way.

3. *Use the folded scales to multiply 9.53 by 37.9.*

1) Set the righthand index of the **C** scale to *9.53* on the **D** scale.
2) Set the hairline of the runner to *37.9* on the **CF** scale.
3) Read the sequence of numbers in the answer as *361* on the **DF** scale.
4) The digit count for *9.53* is one and the digit count for *37.9* is two. The sum of one and two is three. The slide extends to the left during the calculation so the digit count for the answer is three, and the answer is *361*.

In a decimal fraction such as *0.00123,* remember that each zero between the decimal point and the first digit of the number counts as a negative digit. The digit count for *0.00123* is minus two.

4. *Use the folded scales to multiply 0.00123 by 943.*

1) Set the lefthand index of the **C** scale to *0.00123* on the **D** scale.
2) Set the hairline of the runner to *943* on the **CF** scale.
3) Read the sequence of numbers in the answer as *116* on the **DF** scale.
4) The digit count for *0.00123* is minus two and the digit count for *943* is three. The sum of three and minus two is one. The slide

extends to the right during this calculation, *but* the multiplier is in the lefthand half of the **CF** scale and the answer is in the righthand half of the **DF** scale, so the digit count for the answer is one. The answer is *1.16.*

PRACTICE PROBLEMS

Now you should work these problems to get enough experience so that you will remember how to multiply with the folded scales. Check your answers with the correct answers in the back of the book.

1. $21.7 \times 0.618 = ?$ 6. $12 \times 17 = ?$
2. $1.85 \times 120 = ?$ 7. $78000 \times 3.87 = ?$
3. $568 \times 0.0314 = ?$ 8. $62.4 \times 5.5 = ?$
4. $8.14 \times 32.2 = ?$ 9. $144 \times 7.5 = ?$
5. $0.47 \times 44.8 = ?$ 10. $5150 \times 0.866 = ?$

11. There are 5280 feet in a mile. How many feet are there in 4.5 miles?

12. If a car can run 21.5 miles on one gallon of gasoline, how far can it run on 28 gallons?

13. What is the area of a rectangle which is 6.75 inches by 4.25 inches?

14. If one screw costs 2.12 cents, how much does a gross cost? (A gross is 144.)

15. What is 78% of 4200? (*Hint:* multiply 4200 by 0.78.)

Basis of the Process of Multiplication With the Folded Scales. This explanation of the process of multiplication with the folded scales is for the benefit of two classes of students:

1. Those who want a thorough enough understanding to formulate their own methods for special problems they may encounter.

2. Those who enjoy a firm understanding of the theoretical basis for their work.

However, it is possible to use the folded scales to multiply any number by any other number without understanding the basis of the process.

The **C, D, CF,** and **DF** scales are all based on the logarithm of a number to the base 10, so it is necessary to base the explanation on logarithms.

As you probably remember, the logarithm of a number to the base 10 is the power to which 10 must be raised to equal the number. For example, the logarithm of 100 to the base 10 is 2, because 10 must be raised to the power 2 to equal 100.

The logarithm of a number to the base 10 has two parts, as can be illustrated by the logarithm of 11.4, which is 1.057. The characteristic of the logarithm is the number to the left of the decimal point and it is 1 in this case. The characteristic of the logarithm of a number to the base 10 is always one less than the number of digits to the left of the decimal point in the number. There are two digits to the left of the decimal point in the number 11.4, and one less than two is one, so the characteristic of its logarithm is 1.

The mantissa of the logarithm of a number to the base 10 is the part of the logarithm to the right of the decimal point. The mantissa of the logarithm of 11.4 is .057*. The mantissa depends only on the sequence of numbers in the number and not on the location of the decimal point so the mantissa would be .057 for all numbers which have the sequence 114, for example, 0.114, 1.14, 114, 11400, etc.

The logarithm of 415 is 2.618. The number 415 has three digits to the left of the decimal point, so the characteristic is one less than three, or two. The mantissa for the sequence of numbers 415 is read from the slide rule as .618.

The process of multiplication with the slide rule is based on the fact that the logarithm of the product of two numbers is equal to the sum of the logarithms of the two numbers. Thus,

$$A \times B = C.$$
$$\log A + \log B = \log C.$$

Now, look at Fig. 14-3 which shows the multiplication of 11.4 by 415. The **C** and **D** scales are laid out in such a way that the distance from the lefthand end of each of these scales to a number is equal to the mantissa of the logarithm of the number. Notice the designation of the mantissa of 11.4 on the **D** scale in Fig. 14-3.

The **CF** and **DF** scales start with the sequence of numbers in π (3.14), so the lefthand end of each of these scales already represents the mantissa of 3.14. Consequently, the distance from the lefthand end to a number represents "the mantissa of the number *minus* the

---

*Obtained from the slide rule.

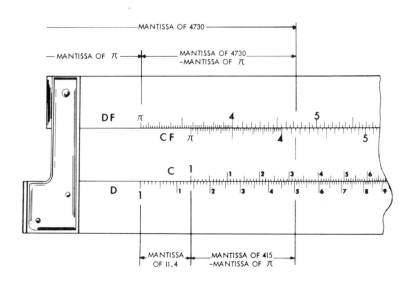

Fig. 14-3. Multiplication of 11.4 x 415, illustrating the basis of the process.

mantissa of 314". Notice the designation of "the mantissa of 415 minus the mantissa of 314" in Fig. 14-3.

The product of 11.4 and 415 is 4730, as we saw in Illustrative Example 2, so on the **DF** scale we see the distance from the lefthand end of the scale to the sequence of numbers 4730 designated as "the mantissa of 4730 minus the mantissa of 314". What we have really done in making this multiplication is to add logarithms in this way,

mantissa of 11.4 + mantissa of 415 — mantissa of 314 = mantissa of 4730 — mantissa of 314.

We can cancel the two negative terms and have,

mantissa of 11.4 + mantissa of 415 = mantissa of 4730.

The mantissa of 4730 can be read from the slide rule as 675 (the characteristic is 3), so the numbers in the last equation are,

$$057 + 618 = 675.$$

Only the mantissa of the logarithm of a number is represented on the slide rule in performing multiplication.

If you are willing to use judgment to determine the location of the decimal point in an answer, you can stop here. But if you want to develop a rule for the location of the decimal point, you must consider the characteristics of the logarithms of the numbers. In this example,

$$11.4 \times 415 = 4730.$$
$$\log 11.4 = 1.057$$
$$\log 415 = 2.618$$
$$\overline{\log 4730 = 3.675}$$

This addition gives 3 for the characteristic of the logarithm of the answer, so there must be four digits to the left of the decimal point, so the answer is 4730.

When the sum of the mantissae of the multiplicand and multiplier is less than one, there is no carryover to the characteristic column in the addition, and so the characteristic of the product is the sum of the characteristics of the multiplicand and the multiplier. This is the case when the multiplier is in the lefthand half of the **CF** scale and the answer is also in the lefthand end of the **DF** scale. Then,

characteristic of multiplicand + characteristic of multiplier = characteristic of answer.

Since the characteristic of the logarithm of a number is one less than the digit count of the number, we could change this equation to,

digit count of multiplicand − 1 + digit count of multiplier − 1 = digit count of answer − 1.

Here, we can cancel −1 on each side and rewrite the equation as:

digit count of answer = digit count of multiplicand + digit count of multiplier − 1,

and this is the rule stated previously.

However, if the multiplier is in the lefthand half of the **CF** scale and the answer is in the righthand half of the **DF** scale, we have gone past the center index of the **DF** scale, which means that the sum of the mantissae of the multiplicand and the multiplier is more than one and there is a carryover of one to the characteristic column in adding the logarithms, so the characteristic of the answer is one more than the sum of the characteristics of the multiplicand and the multiplier. Thus,

characteristic of multiplicand + characteristic of multiplier + 1
= characteristic of answer.

When we replace each characteristic by its digit count minus one, we have,

digit count of multiplicand − 1 + digit count of multiplier
− 1 + 1 = digit count of answer − 1.

Here, all of the −1's cancel to leave,

digit count of answer = digit count of multiplicand
+ digit count of multiplier.

This is the reason for the exception to the rule for locating the digit count in the answer.

DIVISION WITH THE FOLDED SCALES AND THE C AND D SCALES. The next problem is to use the folded scales, with the **C** and **D** scales, to divide one number, the dividend, by another number, the divisor.

STEPS IN THE PROCESS—DIVISION WITH
THE FOLDED SCALES

1) Set the hairline of the runner to the dividend on the **DF** scale.
2) Bring the divisor on the **CF** scale under the hairline.
3) Read the numbers in the answer on the **D** scale under whichever index of the **C** scale is between the ends of the **D** scale. Also, if the center index of the **CF** scale is between the ends of the **DF** scale, the answer will be on the **DF** scale above this index.
4) Locate the decimal point in the answer using the rules given in the following paragraph.

Locating the Decimal Point.* Here are the rules for locating the decimal point in the answer by means of the digit count.

1. If the slide extends to the right during the process of division, the digit count for the answer is *usually* one more than the digit count for the dividend minus the digit count for the divisor, with the exception that if the dividend is located in the righthand half of the **DF** scale and the divisor is located in the lefthand half

_____
*Another method of locating the decimal point, using powers of 10, is explained in Chapter 16.

of the **CF** scale, the digit count for the answer is exactly equal to the digit count for the dividend minus the digit count for the divisor.

2. If the slide extends to the left during the division, the digit count for the answer is *usually* exactly equal to the digit count for the dividend minus the digit count for the divisor, with the exception that if the dividend is located in the lefthand half of the **DF** scale and the divisor is located in the righthand half of the **CF** scale, the digit count for the answer is one more than the digit count for the dividend minus the digit count for the divisor.

A convenient way to remember about these exceptions is that they occur whenever the dividend is in the opposite half of the **DF** scale from the divisor in the **CF** scale.

Now, let's try some examples of division.

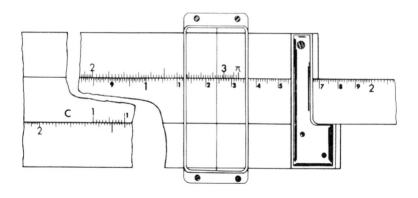

Fig. 14-4. Division of 293 by 12.4 with CF, C, and D scales.

ILLUSTRATIVE EXAMPLES

5. *Use the folded scales to divide 293 by 12.4.* Fig. 14-4 shows the setting of the slide rule for this calculation. Do it this way.

1) Set the hairline of the runner to 293 on the **DF** scale.
2) Bring 12.4 on the **CF** scale under the hairline.

3) Read the digits in the answer as 236 on the **D** scale under the lefthand index of the **C** scale, *or,* on the **DF** scale over the center index of the **CF** scale.

4) The slide extends to the right during the calculation. The digit count for the dividend is three and the digit count for the divisor is two. Three minus two is one. The digit count for the answer is one more than one, so it is two, and the answer is 23.6.

    6. *Use the folded scales to divide 5.65 by 0.00683.*

1) Set the hairline of the runner to *5.65* on the **DF** scale.
2) Bring *0.00683* on the **CF** scale under the hairline of the runner.
3) Read the digits of the answer as *828* on the **D** scale under the righthand. index of the **C** scale, *or,* on the **DF** scale over the center index of the **CF** scale.
4) The slide extends to the left. The digit count for the dividend *5.65* is one and the digit count for the divisor *0.00683* is minus two. The result of subtracting minus two from one is three. This is the digit count for the answer, so the answer is *828.*

    7. *Use the folded scales to divide 0.223 by 96.2.*

1) Set the hairline of the runner to *0.223* on the **DF** scale.
2) Bring *96.2* on the **CF** scale under the hairline.
3) Read the digits of the answer as *232* on the **D** scale under the lefthand index of the **C** scale *or* on the **DF** scale over the center index of the **CF** scale.
4) The slide extends to the right, *but* the dividend is located in the righthand half of the **DF** scale and the divisor is located in the lefthand half of the **CF** scale, so here we have an exception to the rule. The digit count for the answer is exactly equal to the digit count for the dividend minus the digit count for the divisor.

This is:

$$0 - 2 = -2.$$

The answer is *0.00232.*

PRACTICE PROBLEMS

    Work these problems and then check your answers with the correct answers in the back of the book. Use the folded scales.

1. 48.4 ÷ 2.72 = ?   6. 37.8 ÷ 983 = ?
2. 1155 ÷ 324 = ?   7. 217 ÷ 17.5 = ?
3. 8.57 ÷ 12 = ?   8. 1.48 ÷ 22 = ?
4. 0.634 ÷ 26 = ?   9. 58.7 ÷ 417 = ?
5. 788 ÷ 31.6 = ?   10. 915 ÷ 2270 = ?

11. Water weighs 62.4 pounds per cubic foot. What does a cubic inch of water weigh? (There are 1728 cubic inches in a cubic foot.)

12. If the total cost for 72 screwdrivers is $39.60, what is the cost of one screwdriver?

13. A total force of 68600 pounds is applied to an area one foot square. What is the force per square inch?

14. If 2860 cars pass a given point in 53 minutes, how many cars is this per minute?

15. The area of the base of a steel block is 66 square inches and the volume of the block is 938 cubic inches. What is the height of the block?

Basis of the Process of Division With the Folded Scales. You can use the folded scales to divide any number by any other number without understanding the basis of the process, but here is an explanation for those who want it.

The explanation is based on the logarithm of a number to the base 10, because the **C, D, CF,** and **DF** scales are all laid off so that the location of each number represents the mantissa of the logarithm of that number.

We explained logarithms in an earlier part of this chapter in showing the basis of the process of multiplication with the folded scales, so we will assume now that you know something about logarithms.

The process of division with the slide rule is based on the fact that the logarithm of the quotient of two numbers is equal to the difference of the logarithms of the two numbers. Thus,

$$A \div B = C.$$
$$\log A - \log B = \log C.$$

Fig. 14-5 shows the setting of the slide rule to divide 455 by 4.05. The answer is 112.2. The distance from the lefthand end of the **DF** scale to 455 is the mantissa of 455 minus the mantissa of π. Then, the distance from the lefthand end of the **CF** scale to 4.05 is

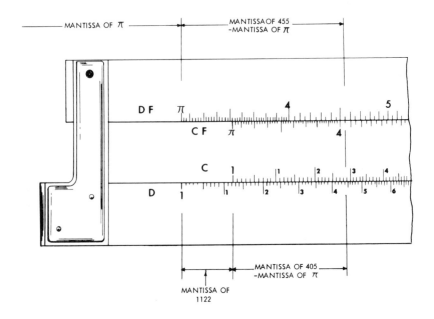

Fig. 14-5. Division of 455 by 4.05, illustrating the basis of the process.

the mantissa of 4.05 minus the mantissa of π. And, the distance from the lefthand end of the **D** scale to 112.2 is the mantissa of 112.2. So,

(mantissa of 455 — mantissa of π) — (mantissa of 4.05 — mantissa of π = mantissa of 112.2

Here, the mantissa of π can be canceled to leave,

mantissa of 455 — mantissa of 4.05 = mantissa of 112.2.

This explanation shows how the process of division with the folded scales leads to the correct sequence of digits in the answer. If we want to know how to locate the decimal point in the answer, we must go further.

The mantissa of the logarithm of 455 can be read from the slide rule as 658. The characteristic is 2 so the logarithm of 455 is 2.658.

The mantissa of the logarithm of 4.05 can be read from the slide rule as 608. The characteristic is zero so the logarithm of 4.05 is 0.608.

The mantissa of the logarithm of 112.2 can be read from the slide rule as 050. The characteristic is 2 so the logarithm is 2.050.

In this example,

$$455 \div 4.05 = 112.2$$
$$\log 455 - \log 4.05 = \log 112.2$$
$$2.658 - 0.050 = 2.608.$$

The subtraction leaves 2 as the characteristic of the logarithm of the answer, so there are 3 digits to the left of the decimal point. This verifies the location of the decimal point in the answer of 112.2.

When the difference between the mantissa of the dividend and the mantissa of the divisor is less than one, there is no carryover to the characteristic column in the subtraction, so the characteristic of the answer is equal to the characteristic of the dividend minus the characteristic of the divisor. This is the case when the slide extends to the right during the division, and the dividend is in the lefthand half of the **DF** scale, and the divisor is in the lefthand half of the **CF** scale. Then,

characteristic of dividend — characteristic of divisor
= characteristic of answer.

Since the characteristic of logarithm of a number is one less than the digit count for the number, we can change the equation to,

(digit count of dividend — 1) — (digit count of divisor — 1)
= digit count of answer — 1.

Here, we can cancel —1 on each side, and rewrite the equation as,

digit count of answer = digit count of dividend —
digit count of divisor + 1,

which is the rule stated previously.

However, if the dividend is in the righthand half of the **DF** scale and the divisor is in the lefthand half of the **CF** scale, for example in dividing 18 by 6, the mantissa of the divisor is greater than the mantissa of the dividend, and there is a carryover of —1 to the characteristic column in the subtraction. Thus, using logs of 18 and 6 as read from the slide rule,

$$\log 18 - \log 6 = \log 3.$$
$$1.255 - 0.778 = 0.477.$$

Then, the characteristic of the answer is equal to one less than the characteristic of the dividend minus the characteristic of the divisor.

characteristic of dividend — characteristic of divisor — 1
= characteristic of answer.

When each characteristic in this equation is replaced by a digit count minus 1, it becomes,

(digit count of dividend — 1) — (digit count of divisor — 1) —1
= (digit count of answer — 1)

All of the — 1's cancel, leaving:

digit count of answer = digit count of dividend
— digit count of divisor.

This is the basis of the exception to the previous rule.

COMBINATIONS OF MULTIPLICATION AND DIVISION WITH THE CF AND DF SCALES AND THE C AND D SCALES. There are many practical formulae that lead to such involved calculations as,

$$\frac{72000 \times 47.8}{336 \times 1.72}.$$

This sort of thing can be done very efficiently by using the **CF** and **DF** folded scales with the **C** and **D** scales. The way to do it is to alternate multiplications and divisions until the calculation has been completed. Then, just write down the answer. Follow these examples with your own slide rule and you will learn the method.

The advantage of using the folded scales in this way is that you can nearly always avoid the slide reversals that were sometimes necessary when using only the **C** and **D** scales for combinations of multiplication and division, as you learned in Chapter 6. But, there is a minor disadvantage that goes along with this advantage. The rules for locating the decimal point are so numerous and complicated that it isn't really worth your while to memorize them. It is better to locate the decimal point by using good judgment about approximate numerical values or by using the powers of ten method explained in Chapter 16. Fortunately, people who make this type of calculation usually know the problem well enough to have a pretty good feeling for the size of the answer.

ILLUSTRATIVE EXAMPLES

8. *Calculate* $\dfrac{72000 \times 47.8}{336 \times 1.72}$.

1) Set the hairline of the runner to the first number of the numerator, *72000,* on the **DF** scale.
2) Bring the first number of the denominator, *336,* on the **CF** scale under the hairline.
3) Leave the slide stationary and set the hairline of the runner to the second number of the numerator, *47.8,* on the **CF** scale.
4) Bring the second number of the denominator, *1.72,* on the **CF** scale under the hairline.
5) Read the answer as *5960* on the **D** scale under the righthand index of the **C** scale *or* on the **DF** scale over the center index of the **CF** scale.

You can decide that the answer is *5960* instead of *596* or *59600* in this way. First, *72000 ÷ 336* is about *200.* Then, *200 × 47.8* is about *9400.* Finally, *9400 ÷ 1.72* would have to be *5960,* rather than *596* or *59600.*

If the calculation ends with a division, the answer is read on the **D** scale under an index of the **C** scale *or* on the **DF** scale over the center index of the **CF** scale. If the calculation ends with a multiplication, the answer is read on the **DF** scale under the hairline of the runner.

9. *Compute* $\dfrac{328 \times 11.27 \times 1.83}{63.2 \times 27.8}$

1) Set the hairline of the runner to *328* on the **DF** scale.
2) Bring *63.2* on the **CF** scale under the hairline.
3) Set the hairline to *11.27* on the **CF** scale.
4) Bring *27.8* on the **CF** scale under the hairline.
5) Set the hairline to *1.83* on the **CF** scale.
6) Read the answer as *3.85* on the **DF** scale under the hairline.

Locate the decimal point by this sort of thinking. First, *328 ÷ 63.2* is about *5.* Then, *5 × 11.27* is about *55.* Next, *55 ÷ 27.8* is about *2.* Finally, *2 × 1.83* is about *3.6* so the answer is *3.85,* rather than *0.385* or *38.5.*

10. *What is the result of* $\dfrac{10.52 \times 67.8 \times 453}{21.6 \times 3.27 \times 7.16}$?

1) Set *10.52* on the **DF** scale under the hairline of the runner.
2) Bring *21.6* on the **CF** scale under the hairline.
3) Move the hairline to *67.8* on the **CF** scale.
4) Bring *3.27* on the **CF** scale under the hairline.
5) Move the hairline to *453* on the **CF** scale
6) Bring *7.16* on the **CF** scale under the hairline.
7) Read the answer as *638* on the **D** scale under the righthand index of the **C** scale *or* on the **DF** scale over the center index of the **CF** scale.

Here is the way to locate the decimal point. First, *10.52 ÷ 21.6* is about ½. Then, ½ × *67.8* is about *34*. Next, *34 ÷ 3.27* is about *10*. And, *10 × 453* is *4530*. Finally, *4530 ÷ 7.16* is about *600,* so the answer must be *638*.

These examples have gone very smoothly, but sometimes a number of the numerator will be outside of the **DF** scale when you want to move the hairline of the runner to it on the **CF** scale to multiply by the number. Then, you have two choices for the next action.

1. You can reverse the slide, by moving the hairline to whichever index of the **C** scale is between the ends of the **D** scale, and then moving the slide to bring the other index of the **C** scale under the hairline.

2. You can make the next multiplication on the **C** scale by setting the hairline of the runner to the number on the **C** scale. Then, you can divide by the next number of the denominator by bringing that number on the **C** scale under the hairline. There is one point to remember in this kind of maneuver. *If you make a multiplication with the **C** scale, you must make the next division with the **C** scale. When you make a multiplication with the **CF** scale, you must make the next division with the **CF** scale.*

Now, let's try this procedure.

ILLUSTRATIVE EXAMPLES

11. *Calculate* $\dfrac{63.2 \times 4.87 \times 571}{288 \times 15.6 \times 37.7}$.

1) Set the hairline of the runner to *63.2* on the **DF** scale.

2) Bring *288* on the **CF** scale under the hairline.

3) The number *4.87* on the **CF** scale is outside of the **DF** scale, but you *can* set the hairline of the runner to *4.87* on the **C** scale.

4) Now you *must* use the **C** scale next. Bring *15.6* on the **C** scale under the hairline.

5) Set the hairline to *571* on the **CF** scale.

6) Bring *37.7* on the **CF** scale under the hairline.

7) Read the answer as *1.040* on the **D** scale under the lefthand index of the **C** scale or on the **DF** scale over the center index of the **CF** scale. How do you know the location of the decimal point in the answer? First, *63.2 ÷ 288* is about *1/4*. Next, *1/4 × 4.87* is about *1*. Then, *1 ÷ 15.6* is about *1/15*. And, *1/15 × 571* is about *40*. Finally, *40 ÷ 37.7* is a little more than *1,* so the answer must be *1.040*.

12. *What is the result of* $\dfrac{13.65 \times 30.4 \times 19.6}{53.8 \times 21.9 \times 74}$ *?*

1) Set the hairline of the runner to *13.65* on the **DF** scale.

2) Bring *53.8* on the **CF** scale under the hairline.

3) Set the hairline to *30.4* on the **C** scale.

4) Bring *21.9* on the **C** scale under the hairline.

5) Set the hairline to *19.6* on the **C** scale.

6) Bring *74* on the **C** scale under the hairline.

7) Read the answer as *0.0933* on the **D** scale under the righthand index of the **C** scale.

The decimal point can be located by this sort of thinking. First, *13.65 ÷ 53.8* is about *1/4*. Then, *1/4 × 30.4* is about *7*. Next, *7 ÷ 21.9* is about *1/3*. And, *1/3 × 19.6* is about *6*. Finally, *6 ÷ 74* is a little less than *0.1,* so the answer is *0.0933*.

PRACTICE PROBLEMS

Now you should work all of these problems to become proficient in this type of calculation. Locate the decimal point by making approximate mental calculations as we showed you in the Illustrative Examples.

After you have worked the problems, check your answers with the correct answers in the back of the book.

1. $\dfrac{53.5 \times 72.4}{29.5} = ?$ 2. $\dfrac{14.4 \times 38.2}{6.51 \times 7.5} = ?$

3. $\dfrac{818 \times 1.52 \times 98}{20.6 \times 473} = ?$ 4. $\dfrac{67.5 \times 37.3 \times 0.25}{4.26 \times 8.61 \times 3.48} = ?$

5. $\dfrac{0.798 \times 29.9 \times 6.14}{11.52 \times 3.65 \times 42.7} = ?$ 6. $\dfrac{958 \times 27.1 \times 52}{42.5 \times 7.88 \times 23} = ?$

7. $\dfrac{23.6 \times 15.7 \times 67.5}{72.5 \times 3.63 \times 295} = ?$ 8. $\dfrac{1.87 \times 1.13 \times 415}{45.5 \times 2.85 \times 31.8} = ?$

9. $\dfrac{358 \times 9.33 \times 11.5}{2.32 \times 0.404 \times 217} = ?$ 10. $\dfrac{0.477 \times 45.8 \times 24.9}{0.832 \times 19.5 \times 652} = ?$

MULTIPLICATION WITH THE CIF SCALE. The **CIF** scale is a reciprocal folded scale and is read from right to left. It is located on the slide, just under the **CF** scale. The letters **CIF** and the numbers are sometimes marked in red. The **CIF** scale is keyed to the **CF** scale, in that whatever number is under the hairline of the runner on the **CIF** scale is the reciprocal of the number on the **CF** scale under the hairline. This is the way to multiply with the **CIF** scale.

STEPS IN THE PROCESS—MULTIPLICATION WITH THE CIF SCALE

1) Set the hairline of the runner to the multiplicand on the **DF** scale.
2) Bring the multiplier on the **CIF** scale under the hairline.
3) Read the answer on the **D** scale under whichever index of the **C** scale is between the ends of the **D** scale, *or* on the **DF** scale over the center index of the **CF** scale, if this index is between the ends of the **DF** scale.

Now, let's try a few examples.

ILLUSTRATIVE EXAMPLES

13. *Multiply 28.2 by 1.37.*

1) Set the hairline of the runner to *28.2* on the **DF** scale.
2) Bring *1.37* on the **CIF** scale under the hairline.
3) Read the answer as *38.6* on the **D** scale under the lefthand index of the **C** scale.

14. *Calculate 6.28 × 33.*

1) Set the hairline of the runner to *6.28* on the **DF** scale.
2) Bring *33* on the **CIF** scale under the hairline.
3) Read the answer as *207* on the **D** scale under the righthand index of the **C** scale.

15. *What is 958 × 14.5?*

1) Set the hairline of the runner to *958* on the **DF** scale.
2) Bring *14.5* on the **CIF** scale under the hairline.
3) Read the answer as *13900* on the **D** scale under the lefthand index of the **C** scale, *or* on the **DF** scale over the center index of the **CF** scale.

PRACTICE PROBLEMS

This is a tricky sort of calculation. You need to practice it in order to learn it well. Check your answers with the correct answers in the back of the book after you have worked the problems.

1. $11.5 \times 39 = ?$	**6.** $0.817 \times 51.6 = ?$
2. $27.8 \times 2.12 = ?$	**7.** $428 \times 15.7 = ?$
3. $54.7 \times 19.5 = ?$	**8.** $32.2 \times 2.91 = ?$
4. $60.7 \times 0.920 = ?$	**9.** $25.8 \times 0.616 = ?$
5. $7.15 \times 248 = ?$	**10.** $0.925 \times 18.4 = ?$

11. A cubic foot of steel weighs 490 pounds. What is the weight of 2.87 cubic feet of steel?

12. There are 231 cubic inches in a gallon. How many cubic inches are there in 14 gallons?

13. What is the area of a rectangle which is 27 inches long and 12.5 inches wide?

14. How many hours are there in 365 days?

15. If an aluminum alloy can withstand a force of 17500 pounds on an area of 1 square inch, how large a force can be applied to an area of 3.23 square inches?

MULTIPLICATION OF A SEQUENCE OF NUMBERS WITH THE CIF SCALE. Possibly the best use of the **CIF** scale is in multiplying a sequence of numbers, for example, 27.2 × 1.88 × 0.516. This is the way to do it.

STEPS IN THE PROCESS—MULTIPLICATION OF A SEQUENCE OF NUMBERS WITH THE CIF SCALE

1) Set the hairline of the runner to the first number on the **DF** scale.
2) Bring the second number on the **CIF** scale under the hairline.
3) Move the hairline of the runner to the third number on the **CF** scale.

The process can be continued for as many numbers as there are in the sequence. If there is an odd number of numbers in the sequence, read the answer on the **DF** scale under the hairline of the runner. If there is an even number of numbers in the sequence, read the answer on the **D** scale under whichever index of the **C** scale is between the ends of the **D** scale, *or* on the **DF** scale over the center index of the **CF** scale.

ILLUSTRATIVE EXAMPLES

16. *Calculate 27.2 × 1.88 × 0.516.*
1) Set the hairline of the runner to *27.2* on the **DF** scale.
2) Bring *1.88* on the **CIF** scale under the hairline.
3) Move the hairline to *0.516* on the **CF** scale.
4) Read the answer as *26.4* on the **DF** scale under the hairline.

17. *What is 7.28 × 5.38 × 11.7?*
1) Set the hairline of the runner to *7.28* on the **DF** scale.
2) Bring *5.38* on the **CIF** scale under the hairline.
3) Move the hairline to *11.7* on the **CF** scale.
4) Read the answer as *458* on the **DF** scale under the hairline.

18. *Compute 4.27 × 19.2 × 0.61 × 3.15.*
1) Set the hairline of the runner to *4.27* on the **DF** scale.
2) Bring *19.2* on the **CIF** scale under the hairline.
3) Move the hairline to *0.61* on the **CF** scale.
4) Bring *3.15* on the **CIF** scale under the hairline.
5) Read the answer as *157.5* on the **D** scale under the lefthand index of the **C** scale.

PRACTICE PROBLEMS

This is the type of calculation that requires real concentration to be sure that you use the correct scale at each step. Do these problems for experience and then check your answers with the correct answers in the back of the book.

1. $28 \times 32 \times 45 = ?$

2. $1.6 \times 5.5 \times 19 = ?$

3. $0.98 \times 73 \times 1.15 = ?$

4. $45.4 \times 0.52 \times 31 = ?$

5. $66 \times 1.27 \times 21 = ?$

6. $8.15 \times 24.2 \times 0.59 = ?$

7. $37.1 \times 1.52 \times 0.68 \times 4 = ?$

8. $2.95 \times 0.37 \times 16 \times 7.4 = ?$

9. $71.5 \times 2.43 \times 0.16 \times 3.2 = ?$

10. $0.922 \times 27 \times 4.18 \times 63 = ?$

11. What is the volume of a rectangular box which is 9.5 inches by 11 inches by 6.5 inches?

12. What is the volume of a room which is 21 feet long, 13 feet wide and 8.5 feet high?

13. A certain type of steel sheet costs 22 cents per square foot. What is the cost of a sheet which is 7.5 feet wide and 9.5 feet long?

14. A certain steel casting has a volume of 41.5 cubic inches and the steel weighs 0.282 pounds per cubic inch. What is the weight of 528 such castings?

15. How many minutes are there in 54 days?

The process isn't always this simple, and here is why. While you can always set the hairline of the runner to the first number on the **DF** scale, and you can always bring the second number on the **CIF** scale under the hairline, the third number on the **CF** scale may be outside the **DF** scale. If this happens, you can probably find the third number on the **C** scale between the ends of the **D** scale and set the hairline to it. The answer at this point would be read on the **D** scale under the hairline. If there is a fourth number, you can bring the fourth number on the **CI** scale under the hairline and read the answer on the **D** scale under one index of the **C** scale. Let's try it.

ILLUSTRATIVE EXAMPLES

19. *Calculate 38 $\times$ 13 $\times$ 0.42.*

1) Set the hairline of the runner to *38* on the **DF** scale.

2) Bring *13* on the **CIF** scale under the hairline.

3) Set the hairline of the runner to *0.42* on the **C** scale.

4) Read the answer as *208* on the **D** scale under the hairline.

20. *25.4 × 1.27 × 15.3 × 0.233 = ?*
1) Set the hairline of the runner to *25.4* on the **DF** scale.
2) Bring *1.27* on the **CIF** scale under the hairline.
3) Set the hairline of the runner to *15.3* on the **C** scale.
4) Bring *0.233* on the **CI** scale under the hairline.
5) Read the answer as *115.7* on the **D** scale under the lefthand index of the **C** scale.

PRACTICE PROBLEMS

A few problems now to help you really learn this procedure. You know where the answers are.

1. $7.54 \times 2.72 \times 1.6 = ?$ 6. $48 \times 0.8 \times 3.2 = ?$
2. $12.5 \times 52 \times 0.311 = ?$ 7. $11 \times 12 \times 22 \times 24 = ?$
3. $38.3 \times 9.1 \times 0.8 = ?$ 8. $0.61 \times 21 \times 3.5 \times 7.2 = ?$
4. $5.5 \times 5.6 \times 5.7 = ?$ 9. $82 \times 0.57 \times 4.1 \times 21 = ?$
5. $9.3 \times 3.6 \times 2.5 = ?$ 10. $1.02 \times 29 \times 1.17 \times 23 = ?$

DIVISION WITH THE CIF SCALE. The **CIF** scale can be used with the **C, D,** and **DF** scales in the process of division. This is the way.

STEPS IN THE PROCESS—DIVISION WITH THE CIF SCALE

1) Set the proper index of the **C** scale over the dividend on the **D** scale.
2) Move the hairline of the runner to the divisor on the **CIF** scale.
3) Read the answer on the **DF** scale under the hairline of the runner.

Sometimes you must start with the lefthand index of the **C** scale and sometimes the righthand index. Only one will enable you to move the hairline of the runner to the divisor on the **CIF** scale. Try one way and if it doesn't work, then go the other way.

These examples will help you in learning the calculation.

ILLUSTRATIVE EXAMPLES

21. *Calculate 258 ÷ 12.7.*
1) Set the lefthand index of the **C** scale to the dividend *258* on the **D** scale.

2) Move the hairline of the runner to *12.7* on the **CIF** scale.

3) Read the answer as *20.3* on the **DF** scale under the hairline.

22. *What is 115 ÷ 46.5?*

1) Set the lefthand index of the **C** scale over *115* on the **D** scale.

2) Move the hairline of the runner to *46.5* on the **CIF** scale.

3) Read the answer as *2.48* on the **DF** scale under the hairline.

23. $\dfrac{97.5}{1.88} = ?$

1) Here you must set the righthand index of the **C** scale over the number *97.5* on the **D** scale.

2) Move the hairline of the runner to *1.88* on the **CIF** scale.

3) Read the answer as *51.9* on the **DF** scale under the hairline.

PRACTICE PROBLEMS

1. $515 \div 156 = ?$
2. $1.058 \div 1.033 = ?$
3. $228 \div 482 = ?$
4. $16.5 \div 3.57 = ?$
5. $7.28 \div 3.42 = ?$
6. $0.848 \div 7 = ?$
7. $64.7 \div 2.12 = ?$
8. $192 \div 3.5 = ?$
9. $12.8 \div 49.2 = ?$
10. $389 \div 51.7 = ?$

11. If a motorist drives 273 miles on 14.8 gallons of gasoline, how many miles is he getting per gallon?

12. What per cent of 8400 is 525. (*Hint:* divide 525 by 8400 and multiply by 100.)

13. If an electric bill is $16.93 and 628 kilowatt hours of energy were used, what is the cost per killowatt-hour?

14. What is the length of a rectangle which is 3.5 feet wide and has an area of 20 square feet?

15. What is the average speed of a car which travels 5400 feet in 48.6 seconds?

DIVISION OF ONE NUMBER BY A SEQUENCE OF NUMBERS WITH THE CIF SCALE. The **CIF** scale can be used very effectively to divide one number by a sequence of numbers, for example,

$$\frac{26}{21 \times 1.15 \times 3.7}$$

STEPS IN THE PROCESS—DIVISION OF ONE NUMBER BY A SEQUENCE OF NUMBERS WITH THE CIF SCALE

1) Set one index of the **C** scale over the dividend on the **D** scale.
2) Set the hairline of the runner to the first number of the divisor on the **CIF** scale.
3) Bring the second number of the divisor on the **CF** scale under the hairline.
4) Set the hairline of the runner to the third number of the divisor on the **CIF** scale.

The process can be continued for as many numbers as there are in the divisor. If there is an even number of numbers in the divisor, read the answer on the **D** scale under an index of the **C** scale. *If there is an odd number of numbers in the divisor, read the answer on the **DF** scale under the hairline.* Now for some examples.

ILLUSTRATIVE EXAMPLES

24. *Calculate* $\dfrac{26}{21 \times 1.15}$.

1) Set the lefthand index of the **C** scale over *26* on the **D** scale.
2) Move the hairline of the runner to *21* on the **CIF** scale.
3) Bring *1.15* on the **CF** scale under the hairline.
4) Read the answer as *1.08* on the **D** scale under the lefthand index of the **C** scale.

25. $\dfrac{353}{15.5 \times 2.02 \times 7} = ?$

1) Set the lefthand index of the **C** scale over *353* on the **D** scale.
2) Move the hairline of the runner to *15.5* on the **CIF** scale.
3) Bring *2.02* on the **CF** scale under the hairline.
4) Move the hairline of the runner to *7* on the **CIF** scale.
5) Read the answer as *1.61* on the **DF** scale under the hairline.

26. *What is* $\dfrac{9.28}{37.7 \times 2.33 \times 0.417}$?

1) Set the righthand index of the **C** scale over *9.28* on the **D** scale.
2) Move the hairline of the runner to *37.7* on the **CIF** scale.
3) Bring *2.33* on the **CF** scale under the hairline.
4) Move the hairline of the runner to *0.417* on the **CIF** scale.
5) Read the answer as *0.254* on the **DF** scale under the hairline.

PRACTICE PROBLEMS

This kind of calculation requires some care and you need practice in order to learn it. After you have worked these problems, check your answers against the correct answers in the back of the book.

1. $\dfrac{72}{13 \times 17 \times 19} = ?$ 2. $\dfrac{195}{9.3 \times 0.515 \times 2.32} = ?$

3. $\dfrac{3400}{27.5 \times 8.3 \times 6} = ?$ 4. $\dfrac{2.34}{0.8 \times 6.7 \times 3.1} = ?$

5. $\dfrac{55.5}{3.33 \times 17 \times 22} = ?$ 6. $\dfrac{483}{95 \times 4.3 \times 6.2} = ?$

7. $\dfrac{63700}{19 \times 87.5 \times 4.20} = ?$ 8. $\dfrac{1560}{2.1 \times 10.4 \times 41} = ?$

9. $\dfrac{847}{20.2 \times 72 \times 4.8} = ?$ 10. $\dfrac{94.7}{7 \times 5.5 \times 23} = ?$

There is another facet to this problem. Suppose you get to the third number in the divisor, and you want to move the hairline of the runner to this number on the **CIF** scale, but the number is outside the **DF** scale. Then, you can probably transfer to the **CI** scale, set the hairline to this number on the **CI** scale, and read the answer on the **D** scale under the hairline. Let's try it.

ILLUSTRATIVE EXAMPLES

27. *Calculate* $\dfrac{123}{47 \times 1.4 \times 5.5}$.

1) Set the lefthand index of the **C** scale to *123* on the **D** scale.
2) Move the hairline of the runner to *47* on the **CIF** scale.
3) Bring *1.4* on the **CF** scale under the hairline.
4) The number *5.5* on the **CIF** scale is outside the **DF** scale so transfer to the **CI** scale, and move the hairline of the runner to *5.5* on the **CI** scale.
5) Read the answer as *0.340* on the **D** scale under the hairline.

28. *What is* $\dfrac{2780}{66 \times 9.4 \times 2.52}$?

1) Set the righthand index of the **C** scale to *2780* on the **D** scale.

2) Move the hairline of the runner to *66* on the **CIF** scale.
3) Bring *9.4* on the **CF** scale under the hairline.
4) Move the hairline to *2.52* on the **CI** scale.
5) Read the answer as *1.78* on the **D** scale under the hairline.

     29. *Calculate* $\dfrac{638}{21.7 \times 1.59 \times 4.13}$.

1) Set the lefthand index of the **C** scale to *638* on the **D** scale.
2) Move the hairline of the runner to *21.7* on the **CIF** scale.
3) Bring *1.59* on the **CF** scale under the hairline.
4) Move the hairline to *4.13* on the **CI** scale.
5) Read the answer as *1.78* on the **D** scale under the hairline.

PRACTICE PROBLEMS

    Now, try it for yourself and check your answers with the correct answers in the back of the book.

1. $\dfrac{1188}{4.37 \times 62.7 \times 8.5} = ?$ 2. $\dfrac{57.2}{1.65 \times 9.5 \times 3.08} = ?$

3. $\dfrac{44000}{1250 \times 9.1 \times 1.75} = ?$ 4. $\dfrac{772}{21 \times 10.5 \times 2.95} = ?$

5. $\dfrac{84.7}{44 \times 49 \times 0.7} = ?$ 6. $\dfrac{332}{3.15 \times 2.78 \times 19} = ?$

7. $\dfrac{2660}{11 \times 47 \times 9} = ?$ 8. $\dfrac{6.27}{1.81 \times 1.26 \times 1.3} = ?$

9. $\dfrac{98}{43 \times 0.75 \times 0.81} = ?$ 10. $\dfrac{1055}{39 \times 9.42 \times 3.5} = ?$

    OTHER TYPES OF SLIDE RULES. Most modern slide rules of the duplex type have the folded scales. They are the same on all of the slide rules which have them.

REVIEW PROBLEMS

Answers to Review Problems are not given in the back of the book. However, if you have really studied this book, you can work each of these problems by more than one method. An excellent way to check a problem is to do it another way.

1. $38 \times 72 = ?$
2. $11.56 \times 27.3 = ?$
3. $6.2 \times 12.5 = ?$
4. $728 \times 3.55 = ?$
5. $0.92 \times 18.4 = ?$
6. $63.7 \times 84.5 = ?$
7. $5.25 \div 1.92 = ?$
8. $475 \div 23 = ?$
9. $227 \div 15.9 = ?$
10. $71.5 \div 33.2 = ?$
11. $53.4 \div 9.6 = ?$
12. $845 \div 61 = ?$

13. $\dfrac{38.7 \times 25.5}{6.25 \times 11.6} = ?$
14. $\dfrac{21.5 \times 4.1}{8.4 \times 27} = ?$

15. $\dfrac{12.75 \times 37}{7.7 \times 23} = ?$
16. $\dfrac{63.9 \times 9.1 \times 8.3}{4.72 \times 27 \times 15} = ?$

17. $\dfrac{58 \times 39 \times 18}{62 \times 75 \times 34} = ?$
18. $\dfrac{4.35 \times 22.5 \times 61.4}{82 \times 19 \times 38.7} = ?$

19. $35 \times 27 = ?$
20. $10.7 \times 62 = ?$
21. $78.7 \times 1.23 = ?$
22. $428 \times 0.922 = ?$
23. $5.85 \times 6.52 = ?$
24. $337 \times 0.625 = ?$
25. $21 \times 16 \times 4.1 = ?$
26. $7.9 \times 3.5 \times 8.2 = ?$
27. $41.5 \times 0.91 \times 2.5 = ?$
28. $17.8 \times 0.57 \times 7 = ?$
29. $337 \times 1.56 \times 0.18 = ?$
30. $0.63 \times 2.9 \times 53 = ?$

31. $\dfrac{28}{17 \times 13} = ?$
32. $\dfrac{37.5}{5.7 \times 16.1} = ?$

33. $\dfrac{928}{31.5 \times 26 \times 9} = ?$
34. $\dfrac{5.27}{1.3 \times 1.72 \times 0.63} = ?$

35. $\dfrac{2890}{33.4 \times 19.2 \times 5.72} = ?$
36. $\dfrac{4000}{74 \times 5.16 \times 2.27} = ?$

CHAPTER 15

THE LOG LOG SCALES

HOW TO STUDY. The best way to study this chapter is to have a log log slide rule in hand, and to follow each instruction with it. Each operation should be performed as it is described .

WHAT THE LOG LOG SCALES ARE. The log log scales are special scales on the more expensive duplex type slide rules, which also have the simpler scales described earlier in the book, The inclusion of these log log scales greatly expands the range of calculations that can be performed without reference to tables or computations with logarithms.

Up to this point you have learned how to calculate squares and square roots, using either the **A** and **D** scales or the R_1 and R_2 scales in conjunction with the **C** and **D** scales. You have also learned how to calculate cubes and cube roots, using the **K** and **D** scales. These particular powers and roots occur so frequently in everyday problems that one forgets they are special cases among thousands of other powers and roots that appear in scientific and engineering formulas and equations.

Powers and roots may also be obtained by actual calculation with logarithms found on the **L** scale, but the process is not mechanical. The work is therefore rather slow and tedious. The log log scales, based on logarithms of logarithms, make it possible to find any power of any number or any root of any number, and solve related problems, almost as easily as multiplying or dividing numbers. The main difficulty associated with the log log scales is the initial one of learning to read them.

Now we are going to describe the log log scales and show you how to locate numbers on them. However, there is so much variation from one make of slide rule to another that you may expect to find a few minor differences between your slide rule and the one used as a model in writing and illustrating this chapter.

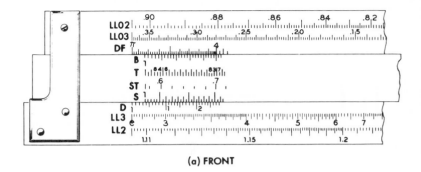

(a) FRONT

Fig. 15-1. Typical log log slide rule with four log log scales (LL2, LL3, LL02, and LL03) on front.

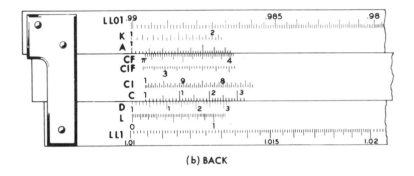

(b) BACK

Fig. 15-2. Back of same slide rule shown in Fig. 15-1, with two log log scales (LL1 and LL01) on lower and upper stocks.

The log log scales can be recognized easily because each has the letters LL in front of a numerical designation. For example, Fig. 15-1 shows the log log scales LL02, LL03, LL3, and LL2 as they appear on the front of a popular make of slide rule. Fig. 15-2 shows the LL01 and LL1 scales on the back of this slide rule.

A slightly different arrangement is seen in another popular make of slide rule, Fig. 15-3. Here, the log log scales are marked as LL1, LL2, LL3, and LL4. Various methods are used to designate

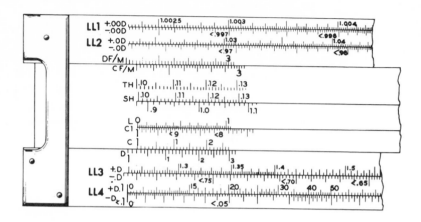

Fig. 15-3. Some log log slide rules have four log log scales (LL1, LL2, LL3, and LL4) on front, as shown, and corresponding reciprocal scales on back.

the comparable reciprocal scales. A fourth LL scale (1.001 to 1.01) and its reciprocal counterpart (.999 to .990) on some types of slide rules meet the need of certain special applications.

The use of the log log scales is essentially the same for each of these slide rules. If a person learns to work with the log log scales on one of them, he can easily transfer to another.

HOW TO LOCATE NUMBERS
ON THE LOG LOG SCALES

THE LL1 SCALE. The LL1 scale is shown at the bottom of the slide rule in Fig. 15-2. The numbers marked on it extend from 1.01 at the left hand end to 1.15 at the right hand end. In the type of marking between 1.01 and 1.02, each space (the distance between consecutive marks) represents 0.0001 which is an increase of 1 in the fourth digit after the decimal point. The long marks, at intervals of 10 spaces, each represent 0.001, which is an increase of 1 in the third digit after the decimal point.

ILLUSTRATIVE EXAMPLE

1. Locate the number 1.0173 on the LL1 scale.

1) The third digit after the decimal point is 7, so the number is located between the seventh and eighth long marks to the right of 1.01.
2) The fourth digit after the decimal point is 3, so the number is 3 spaces to the right of the seventh long mark.
3) Fig. 15-4 shows the location of the number *1.0173*.

In the portion of the **LL1** scale between 1.02 and 1.05 each space between consecutive marks represents 0.0002, which is an increase of 2 in the fourth digit after the decimal point of the number. Half a space can be estimated here for an increase of 1 in the fourth digit after the decimal point.

Fig. 15-4. Lefthand portion of typical LL1 scale, reading from 1.01 to a little beyond 1.02. Log log scales, unlike others on slide rule, show decimal location.

ILLUSTRATIVE EXAMPLES

*2. Locate the number 1.0337 on the **LL1** scale.*

1) The third digit after the decimal point is 3, so the number is located to the right of the third long mark past 1.03.
2) The fourth digit after the decimal point is 7, which represents three and one-half spaces past the long mark.
3) Fig. 15-5 shows the location of the number 1.0337.

In the portion of the **LL1** scale on the right hand side of 1.05, each space between consecutive marks represents 0.0005, which is an increase of 5 in the fourth digit after the decimal point. Also, each double space represents 0.001, which is an increase of one in the third digit after the decimal point. It is possible to estimate one-fifth of a space for an increase of 1 in the fourth digit after the decimal point.

Fig. 15-5. Location of the number 1.0337 on the LL1 scale. Each number on log log scales has a unique location based on decimal location as well as digits.

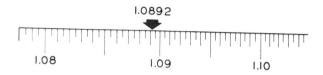

Fig. 15-6. Location of the 1.0892 on the LL1 scale. Learning to read log log scales is critical because the values of markings changes widely with the magnitudes of the numbers.

3. *Locate the number 1.0892 on the* **LL1** *scale.*

1) The number is located 9 double spaces to the right of 1.08, since the third digit after the decimal point is 9.

2) The fourth digit after the decimal point is 2, so the number is two-fifths of a space further to the right. The two-fifths of a space is estimated.

3) Fig. 15-6 shows the number 1.0892 on the **LL1** scale.

THE LL01 SCALE (ALSO KNOWN AS LL/1 SCALE). The **LL01** scale is reversed, in that the numbers diminish from left to right. (In this book, all **LL** scales which contain the symbol 0 in their designations are reversed. The reason for the reversal becomes evident when we come to the use of these scales in making calculations.) The **LL01** escale extends from about .99 at the left hand end to about .905 at the right hand end.

The easiest way to read the **LL01** scale is to read from right to left. The marking is of one type from the right hand end to .98;

Fig. 15-7. Location of number marked "A" on the LL01 scale is .9464. All scales with an "0" in the designation are reciprocals of those without the "0", and therefore read from right to left.

here, each space between consecutive marks represents .0005, and each double space represents .001 in the number. One-fifth of a space can be estimated and represents .0001.

ILLUSTRATIVE EXAMPLE

4. *Read the number marked A in Fig. 15-7.*

1) The number is located more than 6 double spaces to the left of .94, so the first three digits of the number are .946.
2) The fractional part of the space is estimated as four-fifths, so the last digit is 4 and the number is .9464.

In the left hand portion of the **LL01** scale, each space represents 0.0001, an increase of 1 in the fourth digit after the decimal point. This is the same kind of marking as in the left hand portion of the **LL1** scale, except that the numbers are reversed and read from right to left. There are 10 spaces between the long marks, and each space represents .0001.

ILLUSTRATIVE EXAMPLE

5. *Locate the number .9886 on the **LL01** scale.*

1) Reading from right to left, the number must be three long marks past .985, and
2) Six spaces further to the left.
3) Fig. 15-8 shows the location of the number.

THE LL2 SCALE. The **LL2** scale extends from 1.105 at the left hand end to e (e is a number which is approximately equal to 2.718) at the right hand end. The **LL2** scale reads from left to right.

From the left hand end of the **LL2** scale to 1.2, each space between consecutive marks represents 0.001, which is an increase of 1 in the third digit after the decimal point. Thus, since the mark at

Fig. 15-8. Location of the number .9886 on the LL01 scale. Remember the "0" in the designation of this scale.

the left hand end of the scale represents 1.105, the second mark represents 1.106, the third mark 1.107, etc.

Between 1.2 and 1.4, each space represents 0.002, which is an increase of 2 in the third digit after the decimal point.

Then from 1.4 to 1.8, each space represents 0.005, which is an increase of 5 in the third digit after the decimal point.

Finally, in the portion of the **LL2** scale to the right of 1.8, each space represents 0.01, which is an increase of 1 in the second digit after the decimal point.

ILLUSTRATIVE EXAMPLES

6. Locate the number 1.169 on the **LL2** *scale.*

1) The first long mark to the right of 1.15 is read as 1.16, or 1.160.
2) The number is located 9 more marks to the right, since the third digit after the decimal point is 9. (This is a total of nineteen spaces beyond 1.15.)

7. Locate the number 2.23 on the **LL2** *scale.*

1) Each of the longest marks beyond 2 represents 0.1, so the number is beyond the second of the longest marks on the right hand side of 2.
2) The second digit after the decimal point is 3, so the number is located 3 more spaces to the right.

THE LL02 SCALE (ALSO KNOWN AS LL/2 SCALE). The **LL02** scale reads from right to left as do all log log scales which have the symbol 0 in their designations. It extends from .368 at the right hand end to .91 at the left hand end.

Between the right hand end and the .80 mark of the **LL02** scale, each space between consecutive marks represents 0.002, which is an increase of 2 in the third digit after the decimal point. If the third digit after the decimal point is odd, the number is located halfway between two consecutive marks.

From .80 to the left hand end of the **LL02** scale, each space represents 0.001, which is a increase of one in the third digit after the decimal point.

ILLUSTRATIVE EXAMPLE

8. *Locate the number .625 on the* **LL02** *scale.*

1) The number is on the left hand side of .60.
2) The second digit after the decimal point is 2, so 2 long marks are counted to the left of .6.
3) The third digit is 5, so the number is halfway between the second and third marks further to the left as shown in Fig. 15-9.

THE LL3 SCALE. The **LL3** scale reads from left to right. It extends from e ($e = 2.718$) at the left hand end to about 22000 at the right hand end. The numbers increase rapidly on the **LL3** scale, so there are frequent changes in the manner of marking. It is especially desirable to have the slide rule in hand in reading the explanation which follows.

From the left hand end to 4, each space between consecutive marks represents 0.02, which is an increase of 2 in the second digit after the decimal point.

Between 4 and 6, each space represents 0.05.

Between 6 and 10, each space represents 0.1.

From 10 to 15, each space between consecutive marks represents 0.2.

Between 15 and 30, each space represents 0.5.

From 30 to 50 on the **LL3** scale, each space represents 1.

Between 50 and 100, each space between consecutive marks represents 2.

From 100 to 200, each space represents 5.

Between 200 and 500, each space represents 10.

From 500 to 1000, each space represents 50.

Between 1000 and 2000, each space represents 100.

From 2000 to 5000, each space represents 200.

From 5000 to 10,000, each space represents 500.

Beyond 10,000, each space represents 1000.

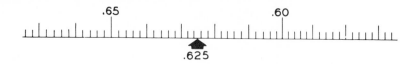

Fig. 15-9. Location of the number .625 on the LL02 scale. Again, remember to read the scale from right to left as numbers increase.

THE LL03 SCALE (ALSO KNOWN AS LL/3 SCALE). The **LL03** scale reads from right to left. It extends from .0000455 at the right hand end to .368 at the left hand end. Here, too, the markings change frequently and one should look at the slide rule often while studying the following explanations.

From the right hand end of the **LL03** scale to .0002, each space between consecutive marks represents 0.00001. For example, the first mark on the right hand side of .0001 is the number .0001 — .00001 = .00009.

From .0002 to .0005, each space represents .00002, which is an increase of 2 in the fifth digit after the decimal point.

Between .0005 and .002, each space represents .0001.

From .002 to .01, each space between consecutive marks represents 0.0002.

Between .01 and .02, each space represents 0.0005. Thus, the first mark on the left hand side of .01 is the number .0105.

From .02 to .10, each space represents 0.001.

Between .10 and .368 at the left hand end of the **LL03** scale, each space represents 0.002, which is an increase of 2 in the third digit after the decimal point.

REVIEW QUESTIONS

You should be sure that you can answer these review questions before you go on to study the rest of the chapter. Read the questions with the slide rule in your hands and refer to it. If you find a question which you cannot answer, look at the first part of the chapter again to find the answer.

1. Which log log scales read from left to right?
2. Which log log scales read from right to left?

3. On which scale is the number 1.46 located?

4. On which scale is the number .912 located?

5. On which scale is the number 3.65 located?

6. On which scale is the number .0026 located?

7. On which scale is the number 1.033 located?

8. On which scale is the number .777 located?

9. How much does each space represent between 10 and 15 on the **LL3** scale?

10. How much does each space represent between .70 and .75 on the **LL02** scale?

11. How much does each space represent between .97 and .98 on the **LL01** scale?

12. How much does each space represent between 0.15 and .20 on the **LL03** scale?

13. How much does each space represent between 1.25 and 1.3 on the **LL2** scale?

14. How much does each space represent between 1.06 and 1.07 on the **LL1** scale?

15. What is the number which is located six and one-half marks to the right hand side of 1.02 on the **LL1** scale?

16. What is the number which is located seven marks on the left hand side of .55 on the **LL02** scale?

17. What is the number which is located two marks to the left of .97 on the **LL01** scale?

18. What is the number which is located one and one-half marks to the right hand side of 30 on the **LL3** scale?

19. What is the number which is located three marks to the right hand side of 2.1 on the **LL2** scale?

20. What is the number which is located eight marks to the left of .002 on the **LL03** scale?

POWERS AND ROOTS OF NUMBERS

WHAT A POWER OF A NUMBER IS. You recall that a power of a number is the number obtained when the number is multiplied by itself; it may be multiplied by itself once, or twice, or some other number of times. For example, the square of a number is obtained when the number is multiplied by itself once; the square is the second power of the number. If the number is 2, the square is written as $(2)^2$ and is just

$$2 \times 2 = 4.$$

The cube of 2 is the third power of 2, and is equal to 2 multiplied by itself twice; it is written as $(2)^3$ and is,

$$2 \times 2 \times 2 = 8.$$

In some engineering calculations, it is necessary to calculate a number to a fractional power, such as 1.39. So a person might want to know the value of $(2)^{1.39}$, for example. It may not be easy to visualize $(2)^{1.39}$, but this quantity does have a numerical value. It can be calculated by means of the log log slide rule, and we are going to show you how to do it.

HOW TO CALCULATE A NUMBER GREATER THAN ONE TO A POSITIVE POWER. The material which follows is not especially difficult, but it does require your careful attention. Follow the instructions and illustrative examples on your own slide rule.

A helpful theorem for powers of numbers is this: *any number greater than one remains greater than one when calculated to a positive power.*

STEPS IN CALCULATING A NUMBER GREATER THAN ONE TO A POSITIVE POWER.

1. Set the hairline of the runner to the number on whichever of the **LL1, LL2,** or **LL3** scales it is located.

2. Move the slide so that one index of the **C** scale is under the hairline.

3. Set the hairline of the runner to the power on the **C** scale.

4. Read the answer under the hairline of the runner on either the **LLl, LL2,** or **LL3** scales.

(All numbers on the **LL1, LL2,** and **L3** scales are greater than one; so both the beginning number and the answer are located on these scales in calculating a number greater than one to a positive power.)

ILLUSTRATIVE EXAMPLES

9. *Calculate* $(3.22)^{1.87}$.

1) This is the 1.87th power of the number 3.22.

2) Set the hairline of the runner to the number 3.22 which is located on the **LL3** scale. (Note: each number appears on only one log log scale.)

3) Set the left hand index of the **C** scale under the hairline of the runner. (You may have to do this by turning the slide rule over and using the hairline on the other side of the runner, because

there may not be a **C** scale on the same face of the slide rule as
the **LL3** scale.)

4) Move the runner so that the hairline is over 1.87 (the power) on
the **C** scale.

5) The answer is 8.92 under the hairline of the runner on the **LL3**
scale.

    10. *Calculate* $(1.014)^{2.36}$

1) This is the 2.36th power of 1.014.

2) Set the hairline of the runner to the number 1.014 on the **LL1**
scale. (Note: this is at the first of the longest marks on the left
hand side of 1.015.)

3) Set the left index of the **C** scale under the hairline of the runner.

4) Move the hairline of the runner to the power 2.36 on the **C** scale.

5) The answer is 1.0333 under the hairline of the runner on the
LL1 scale.

It may happen that the power on the **C** scale is beyond the
stock of the slide rule when the left hand index of the **C** scale is
under the hairline of the runner. (You should remember that this
sort of thing also happens in multiplication.) If it does happen, the
thing to do is to reverse the slide and set the right hand index of
the **C** scale under the hairline of the runner.

ILLUSTRATIVE EXAMPLE

    11. *Calculate* $(2)^{0.762}$.

1) This is the 0.762nd power of 2.

2) Set the hairline of the runner to the number 2, on the **LL2** scale.

3) Bring the right hand index of the **C** scale under the hairline of
the runner.

4) Set the hairline of the runner to 0.762 on the **C** scale.

5) The answer is 1.696 under the hairline of the runner on the **LL2**
scale.

It is easiest to learn just one thing at a time, so one question
has been postponed until this point. This is the question: Which
log log scale is to be used in reading the answer? The time has
come to settle this question.

When a number greater than one is calculated to a positive
power, the answer is always greater than one, so the answer must
be on one of three scales—**LL1, LL2** or **LL3**. The easiest way to

determine which of these three scales is to "round off" the numbers of the problem and make a mental calculation of about what the answer should be. Then, choose the scale on which the number under the hairline of the runner is somewhere near the result of the mental calculation. To "round off" means to take a simpler number of about the same size. For example, $(1.96)^{3.12}$ could be "rounded off" to $(2)^3$, by replacing 1.96 by 2, and replacing 3.12 by 3. The gain from the "rounding off" is that it can easily be calculated mentally that $(2)^3$ is 8, so $(1.96)^{3.12}$ is approximately equal to 8.

ILLUSTRATIVE EXAMPLES

12. *Calculate* $(1.96)^{3.12}$.

1) Set the hairline of the runner to 1.96, on the **LL2** scale.
2) Bring the right hand index of the **C** scale under the hairline of the runner.
3) Set the hairline of the runner to 3.12 on the **C** scale.
4) See what numbers are under the hairline of the runner on the **LL1, LL2,** and **LL3** scales. These are 1.0212 on the **LL1** scale, 1.234 on the **LL2** scale, and 8.17 on the **LL3** scale.
5) The correct answer is 8.17.

13. *Calculate* $(5.32)^{0.407}$.

1) Set the hairline of the runner to 5.32 on the **LL3** scale.
2) Bring the left hand index of the **C** scale under the hairline of the runner.
3) Set the hairline of the runner to 0.407 on the **C** scale.
4) "Round off" the numbers of the problem to $(5)^{0.5}$, which is the square root of 5, and equal to 2.24. The answer is somewhere near 2.24.
5) Notice that the hairline of the runner is at 1.0704 on the **LL1** scale, 1.973 on the **LL2** scale, and 900 on the **LL3** scale.
6) The correct answer is 1.973.

14. *Calculate* $(1.095)^{1.47}$.

1) Set the hairline of the runner to 1.095 on the **LL1** scale.
2) Bring the right hand index of the **C** scale under the hairline of the runner.
3) Set the hairline of the runner to 1.47 on the **C** scale.

4) "Round off" the numbers of the problem to $(1.10)^{1.5}$. The result will be greater than 1.10, which is $(1.10)^1$ but less than 1.21 which is $(1.10)^2$.

5) Notice that the numbers under the hairline of the runner are 1.0134 on the **LL1** scale, 1.143 on the **LL2** scale, and 3.80 on the **LL3** scale.

6) Choose the correct answer as 1.143.

PRACTICE PROBLEMS

Here is a chance to practice what you have just learned, so that you can master it thoroughly. You can check with the answers in the back of the book.

1. $(500)^{0.3}$	6. $(2.78)^{1.5}$
2. $(1.64)^{1.64}$	7. $(1.075)^{1.56}$
3. $(1.25)^{2.1}$	8. $(4.44)^{2.52}$
4. $(615)^{0.82}$	9. $(1.13)^{0.6}$
5. $(1.01)^{3.16}$	10. $(1.023)^{0.465}$

HOW TO CALCULATE A NUMBER LESS THAN ONE TO A POSITIVE POWER. The best way to learn this material is to follow it carefully with your own slide rule also.

A useful theorem for numbers less than one is: *any number less than one remains less than one when calculated to a positive power.* Since both the original number and the answer are less than one, both must be located on the **LL01**, **LL02**, or **LL03** scales. (Note that the numbers on these scales are all less than one.)

STEPS IN CALCULATING A NUMBER LESS THAN ONE TO A POSITIVE POWER.

1. Set the hairline of the runner to the number on whichever of the **LL01**, **LL02**, or **LL03** scales it is located.

2. Move the slide so that one index of the **C** scale is under the hairline.

3. Set the hairline of the runner to the power on the **C** scale.

4. Read the answer under the hairline of the runner on either the **LL01**, **LL02**, or **LL03** scale.

ILLUSTRATIVE EXAMPLES

15. *Calculate* $(0.763)^{0.632}$.

1) This is the 0.632nd power of 0.763.

2) Set the hairline of the runner to the number 0.763, which is on the **LL02** scale. (You recall that the log log scales which have the symbol 0 in their designations read from right to left.)
3) Bring the right hand index of the **C** scale under the hairline.
4) Set the hairline of the runner to the power 0.632 on the **C** scale.
5) The answer, 0.843, is under the hairline of the runner on the **LL02** scale.

  16. *Calculate $(0.327)^{2.34}$.*

1) Set the hairline of the runner to the number 0.327 on the **LL03** scale.
2) Bring the left hand index of the **C** scale under the hairline of the runner.
3) Set the hairline of the runner to the power 2.34, on the **C** scale.
4) Read the answer as 0.0735 under the hairline of the runner on the **LL03** scale.

  The time has come to face the question: On which of the log log scales is the answer located? As before, the way to find out is to "round off" the numbers and make a mental calculation first; then, the nearest number which is under the hairline of the runner is the desired answer.

ILLUSTRATIVE EXAMPLES

  17. *Calculate $(0.863)^{1.78}$*

1) Set the hairline of the runner to the number 0.863 on the **LL02** scale.
2) Bring the left hand index of the **C** scale under the hairline of the runner.
3) Set the hairline of the runner to the power 1.78 on the **C** scale.
4) "Round off" the calculation to $(0.8)^2$, the result of which is just 0.64. The answer to the problem should be somewhere near 0.64.
5) Notice that the numbers under the hairline of the runner are 0.974 on the **LL01** scale, 0.769 on the **LL02** scale, and 0.0725 on the **LL03** scale.
6) Choose the answer as 0.769, because this is the only one which is anywhere near the approximate result obtained by "rounding off" the calculation.

18. *Calculate* $(0.0573)^{0.335}$.

1) Set the hairline of the runner to the number 0.0573 on the **LL03** scale.

2) Bring the left hand index of the **C** scale under the hairline of the runner.

3) Set the hairline of the runner to the power 0.335 on the **C** scale.

4) "Round off" the calculation to $(0.05)^{1/3}$, which would be the cube root of 0.05. (This cube root can be found to be 0.368, by using the **K** scale and the **C** scale.)

5) Notice that the numbers under the hairline of the runner are 0.9085 on the **LL01** scale, 0.383 on the **LL02** scale, and 0.000069 on the **LL03** scale.

6) Choose the correct answer as 0.383 from the **LL02** scale, because it is the only one of the three numbers which is anywhere near the approximate answer obtained by "rounding off."

PRACTICE PROBLEMS

This kind of calculation requires practice to master. It will help you to work these problems. Answers to them are in the back of the book.

1. $(0.162)^{1.44}$	**6.** $(0.895)^{0.82}$
2. $(0.989)^{3.46}$	**7.** $(0.0623)^{1.27}$
3. $(0.577)^{0.6}$	**8.** $(0.925)^{0.377}$
4. $(0.735)^{0.785}$	**9.** $(0.467)^{1.17}$
5. $(0.253)^{1.68}$	**10.** $(0.950)^{1.83}$

NUMBERS OUTSIDE THE RANGE OF THE LOG LOG SCALES. It is possible that you may want to calculate a power of a number when the answer is outside the range of the log log scales. We'll show you how to do it. First, you need to be able to recognize that the answer is outside the range of the log log scales, so now pick up your own slide rule and see what happens when you try to calculate $(7.5)^{6.6}$, You begin by setting the hairline of the runner to 7.5 on the **LL3** scale. Next, you bring the lefthand index of the **C** scale under the hairline. Then, you notice that 6.6 on the **C** scale is beyond the righthand end of the **LL3** scale, so this isn't going to work.

The six log log scales have a total range from 0.0000455 to 22,026. If this range isn't enough for you, you must use special methods.

If you are raising a number to a power and the answer is outside the range of the log log scales, you can use the law for exponents that you can divide an exponent by any number and write what is left as raised to that number as a power. Thus, if you had $7.5^{6.6}$, you could divide 6.6 by 2 to get 3.3, and write $7.5^{6.6} = (7.5^{3.3})^2$. Or, you could divide 6.6 by 3 to get 2.2, and write $7.5^{6.6} = (7.5^{2.2})^3$. You could calculate $7.5^{3.3}$ in the usual way and square what you found to get $7.5^{6.6}$. Or, you could calculate $7.5^{2.2}$ and cube it.

Now, follow these examples on your own slide rule.

ILLUSTRATIVE EXAMPLES

19. *Calculate $7.5^{6.6}$.*

1) Divide *6.6* by 2 to get *3.3* and write $7.5^{6.6} = (7.5^{3.3})^2$.
2) Calculate $7.5^{3.3}$. First, set the hairline of the runner to *7.5* on the **LL3** scale.
3) Bring the lefthand index of the **C** scale under the hairline.
4) Set the hairline of the runner to *3.3* on the **C** scale.
5) Read $7.5^{3.3}$ as *770* on the **LL3** scale under the hairline.
6) Square *770* to get *592000* as the answer.

20. *Calculate $0.024^{4.5}$.*

1) Divide *4.5* by *3* to get *1.5* and write $0.024^{4.5} = (0.024^{1.5})^3$.
2) Calculate $0.024^{1.5}$. First, set the hairline of the runner to *0.024* on the **LL03** scale.
3) Bring the lefthand index of the **C** scale under the hairline.
4) Set the hairline of the runner to *1.5* on the **C** scale.
5) Read $0.024^{1.5}$ as *0.00375* on the **LL03** scale under the hairline.
6) Cube *0.00375* to get *0.0000000529* as the answer.

There is another case in which the range of the log log scales isn't enough for direct calculation. Suppose you want to calculate $32000^{1.2}$. You can't even start in the usual way, because *32000* is outside the range of the log log scales. But you can do it this way. You can factor *32000*, say into *80* $\times$ *400*, and write $32000^{1.2} = 80^{1.2} \times 400^{1.2}$. Now, you can easily calculate $80^{1.2}$ and $400^{1.2}$ and multiply them to get the answer. Try it for yourself in these examples.

ILLUSTRATIVE EXAMPLES

21. *Calculate $32000^{1.2}$.*

1) Factor *32000* into *80* × *400*. Write $32000^{1.2} = 80^{1.2} \times 400^{1.2}$.
2) Calculate $80^{1.2}$. This is *192*.
3) Calculate $400^{1.2}$. This is *1320*.
4) Multiply *192* by *1320* to get *254000* for the answer.

22. *Calculate $0.000018^{0.72}$.*

1) Factor *0.000018* into *0.009* × *0.002*. Write $0.000018^{0.72} = 0.009^{0.72} \times 0.002^{0.72}$.
2) Calculate $0.009^{0.72}$. This is *0.0337*.
3) Calculate $0.002^{0.72}$. This is *0.0114*.
4) Multiply *0.0337* × *0.0114* to get *0.000384* for the answer.

PRACTICE PROBLEMS

This sort of calculation is pretty tricky, so you should do these problems for practice and then check your answers with the correct answers in the back of the book.

1. $32^{3.6} = ?$
2. $4^{8.4} = ?$
3. $160^{2.8} = ?$
4. $0.005^{2.6} = ?$
5. $0.076^{3.4} = ?$
6. $28000^{1.6} = ?$
7. $42000^{0.52} = ?$
8. $96000^{0.3} = ?$
9. $0.00003^{0.8} = ?$
10. $0.00002^{0.65} = ?$

WHAT A ROOT OF A NUMBER IS. A root of a number, such as 4 for example, is a second number of such a size that when multiplied by itself, the result is the first number. The square root of 4 is 2; when 2 is multiplied by itself, the result is 4.

The root may have to be multiplied by itself more than once to obtain the original number. For example, the cube root of 8 is 2, so,

$$2 \times 2 \times 2 = 8.$$

The symbol which indicates that a root is to be calculated is $\sqrt{}$, placed over the number; this symbol is called a *radical*. For example,

$$\sqrt{36},$$

means the square root of 36. *Always remember that the square root is meant when there is no additional number over the radical.*

A root different from the square root is indicated by writing the number of the root over the radical. For example,

$$\sqrt[3]{78} \text{ is the third root of 78,}$$

$$\sqrt[4]{52} \text{ is the fourth root of 52,}$$

$$\sqrt[1.5]{107} \text{ is the 1.5th root of 107,}$$

$$\sqrt[0.342]{0.967} \text{ is the 0.342nd root of 0.967,}$$

$$\sqrt[0.73]{3.79} \text{ is the 0.73rd root of 3.79.}$$

HOW TO CHANGE A ROOT TO A POWER. A certain root of a number can be expressed as some other power of the number, by using a rule of algebra. The rule is: *the power is the reciprocal of the root.* Thus,

$$\sqrt[4]{34} = (34)^{1/4},$$

that is, the fourth root of 34 is equal to the one-fourth power of 34. *Always remember that the power is the reciprocal of the root. The reciprocal of a number is equal to one divided by the number, as pointed out previously.*

HOW TO CALCULATE THE ROOT OF A NUMBER. Anyone can learn to calculate roots of numbers if he will follow the following instructions.

STEPS IN CALCULATING THE ROOT OF A NUMBER.
1. Calculate the power of the number by calculating the reciprocal of the root.
2. Set the hairline of the runner to the number on whichever of the log log scales it is located.
3. Move the slide so that one index of the **C** scale is under the hairline.
4. Set the hairline of the runner on the power on the **C** scale.
5. Read the answer under the hairline of the runner on one of the log log scales.
(Remember that any number greater than one remains greater than one when calculated to a power; if the calculation starts on the **LL1**, **LL2**, or **LL3** scale, it ends on one of these scales. Any number less than one remains less than one when calculated to a power; if the calculation starts on the **LL01**, **LL02**, or **LL03** scale, it ends on one of these scales.)

ILLUSTRATIVE EXAMPLES

23. *Calculate* $^{1.73}\sqrt{2.58}$.

1) The power is obtained by dividing one by 1.73, and is 0.578. The quantity to be calculated is $(2.58)^{0.578}$.
2) Set the hairline of the runner to 2.58 on the **LL2** scale.
3) Move the right hand index of the **C** scale under the hairline of the runner.
4) Set the hairline of the runner to the power 0.578 on the **C** scale.
5) Read the answer as 1.73 under the hairline of the runner on **LL3** scale.

24. *Calculate* $^{0.246}\sqrt{3.05}$.

1) Calculate the power by dividing one by 0.246; it is 4.07.
2) Set the hairline of the runner to 3.05 on the **LL3** scale.
3) Move the left hand index of the **C** scale under the hairline of the runner.
4) Set the hairline of the runner to the power 4.07 on the **C** scale.
5) Read the answer as 93 under the hairline of the runner on the **LL3** scale.

25. *Calculate* $^{0.732}\sqrt{0.638}$.

1) Calculate the power by dividing one by 0.732; it is 1.366.
2) Set the hairline of the runner to 0.638 on the **LL02** scale.
3) Move the left hand index of the **C** scale under the hairline of the runner.
4) Set the hairline of the runner to the power 1.366 on the **C** scale.
5) Read the answer as 0.541 under the hairline of the runner on the **LL02** scale.

26. *Calculate* $^{2.43}\sqrt{0.267}$.

1) Calculate the power by dividing one by 2.43; it is 0.412.
2) Set the hairline of the runner to 0.267 on the **LL03** scale.
3) Move the left hand index of the **C** scale under the hairline of the runner.
4) Set the hairline of the runner on the power 0.412 on the **C** scale.
5) Read the answer as 0.580 under the hairline of the runner on the **LL03** scale.

PRACTICE PROBLEMS

The best way to really learn how to calculate the root of a number is to practice on these problems. Calculate the roots as indicated:

1. $\sqrt[3.5]{458}$ 6. $\sqrt[0.55]{73}$

2. $\sqrt[2.5]{0.207}$ 7. $\sqrt[2.92]{1.95}$

3. $\sqrt[0.6]{3.75}$ 8. $\sqrt[0.43]{0.108}$

4. $\sqrt[0.3]{0.443}$ 9. $\sqrt[1.15]{0.833}$

5. $\sqrt[0.8]{112}$ 10. $\sqrt[1.78]{0.95}$

LOGARITHMS TO THE BASE e
WHAT A LOGARITHM TO THE BASE e IS.

As previously defined, the logarithm of a number to the base e ($e = 2.718$) is the power to which e must be raised to equal the number. For example, since the square of e is,

$$(2.718)^2 = 7.40,$$

the log of 7.40 to the base e is 2. (Logarithm is often abbreviated as log.)

STEPS IN FINDING THE LOG OF A NUMBER TO THE BASE e:

1. Set the hairline of the runner on the number on whichever of the log log scales it is located.

2. Read the digits of the log of the number to the base e on the **D** scale, under the hairline of the runner.

3. Place the decimal point in the log as follows:

a. If the number is on the **LL1** scale, the log is between 0.01 and 0.1.

b. If the number is on the **LL2** scale, the log is between 0.1 and 1.

c. If the number is on the **LL3** scale, the log is between 1 and 10.

d. If the number is on the **LL01** scale, the log is between −0.01 and −0.1.

e. If the number is on the **LL02** scale, the log is between −0.1 and −1.

f. If the number is on the **LL03** scale, the log is between −1 and −10.

ILLUSTRATIVE EXAMPLES

27. *Determine the log of 15.5 to the base e.*

1) Set the hairline of the runner to 15.5 on the **LL3** scale.
2) Read the digits of the log as 274 on the **D** scale under the hairline of the runner.
3) The log is between 1 and 10, because the number 15.5 is located on the **LL3** scale, so the answer is 2.71.

28. *Determine the log of 1.21 to the base e.*

1) Set the hairline of the runner to 1.21, on the **LL2** scale.
2) Read the digits of the log as 190 on the **D** scale, under the hairline of the runner.
3) The log is between 0.1 and 1, because the number 1.21 is located on the **LL2** scale, so the answer is 0.190.

29. *Determine the log of 0.487 to the base e.*

1) Set the hairline of the runner to 0.487 on the **LL02** scale.
2) Read the digits of the log as 717 on the **D** scale, under the hairline of the runner.
3) The log is between −0.1 and −1, because the number 0.487 is on the **LL02** scale, so the answer is −0.717.

30. *Determine the log of 0.0153 to the base e.*

1) Set the hairline of the runner to 0.0153 on the **LL03** scale.
2) Read the digits of the log as 418 on the **D** scale, under the hairline of the runner.
3) The log is between −1 and −10, because the number 0.0153 is on the **LL03** scale, so the answer is −4.18.

PRACTICE PROBLEMS

Here are problems for practice in finding logs to the base *e*. Just determine the log of each of these numbers to the base *e*.

1. 234		**6.** 105	
2. 0.168		**7.** 0.079	
3. 73.7		**8.** 0.92	
4. 1.52		**9.** 6.48	
5. 0.216		**10.** 0.555	

Basis of the Process. Logarithms are the basis of the process of using the log log scales to obtain a power of a number. In fact, the explanation of the basis involves both logarithms to the base 10 and natural logarithms, but don't let this discourage you if you are really interested in understanding the basis of this process.

If you are doing work on an advanced enough level to need to use the log log scales, you have probably studied logarithms already. So, we will just remind you of what you already know. The log of a number to the base 10 is the power to which 10 must be raised to equal the number. We'll write it as log 100, for example, which means the power to which 10 must be raised to equal 100. You know that 100 is the second power, or square, of 10, so we could write log $100 = 2$.

The natural logarithm of a number is the power to which e ($e = 2.718\ldots$) must be raised to equal the number. We use *In* as an abbreviation for "natural logarithm of." So, you can use the **LL3** scale on your slide rule to find that the natural logarithm of 3.5 is 1.253, and write it as ln $3.5 = 1.253$.

Let's review the **C** and **D** scales a bit. You probably remember that the distance from the lefthand end of one of these scales to any number on the scale represents the log of the number to the base 10. Thus, in Fig. 15-10 you can see the distance designated as log 2.

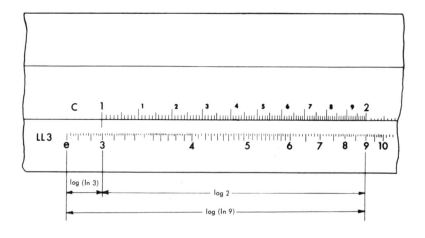

Fig. 15-10. Squaring with the log log scales.

Each log log scale is laid out so that the distance from the left-hand end of the scale to a number represents the logarithm to the base 10 of the natural logarithm of the number. Notice this in Fig. 15-10, where you can see the distance designated as log (ln 3).

Now, we are going to use a simple set of numbers to explain the basis of the process of raising a number to a power with the log log scales. We are going to square 3, that is, raise 3 to the second power. You know that $3^2 = 9$. We'll show you this in Fig. 15-10, and you can follow it on your own slide rule.

We set the hairline of the runner to 3 on the **LL3** scale, and bring the lefthand index of the **C** scale under the hairline. Then we move the hairline of the runner to 2 on the **C** scale, and read 9 on the **LL3** scale under the hairline. Notice the distance from the lefthand end of the **LL3** scale to 9, which is designated as log (ln 9) in Fig. 15-10.

You can see in Fig. 15-10 that
$$\log (\ln 3) + \log 2 = \log (\ln 9).$$
Now we'll use the mathematical law that the sum of the logarithms of two numbers is equal to the logarithm of the product of the two numbers, and change the lefthand side of this equation so that we have,
$$\log (2 \ln 3) = \log (\ln 9).$$
Then, we'll use another law of mathematics, that enables us to write, $2 \ln 3 = \ln 3^2$, to make the equation
$$\log (\ln 3^2) = \log (\ln 9).$$
Since $3^2 = 9$, this establishes the process.

REVIEW PROBLEMS

Now work all of the problems below, so that you will remember what you have learned in this chapter.

Calculate:

1. $(150)^{0.6}$

2. $(73.5)^{1.08}$

3. $(4.27)^{1.15}$

4. $(1.07)^{2.2}$

5. $(2.16)^{0.72}$

6. $(1.75)^{3.5}$

7. $(22)^{0.33}$

8. $(2480)^{0.57}$

9. $(17)^{1.31}$

10. $(1.97)^{0.43}$

11. $(0.336)^{2.12}$

12. $(0.072)^{0.56}$

13. $(0.151)^{1.38}$

14. $(0.782)^{1.93}$

15. $(0.473)^{0.7}$

16. $(0.042)^{0.43}$

17. $(0.206)^{0.48}$

18. $(0.555)^{1.47}$

19. $(0.016)^{0.22}$

20. $(0.283)^{1.56}$

21. $\sqrt[2.1]{333}$

22. $\sqrt[1.06]{1.15}$

23. $\sqrt[0.6]{0.785}$

24. $\sqrt[3.2]{0.05}$

25. $\sqrt[1.7]{38}$

26. $\sqrt[0.47]{5.67}$

27. $\sqrt[1.95]{172}$

28. $\sqrt[1.4]{3620}$

29. $\sqrt[2.7]{0.192}$

30. $\sqrt[1.5]{0.063}$

Determine the log of each of the following numbers to the base *e:*

31. 576

32. 13.9

33. 1.08

34. 0.314

35. 0.067

36. 142

37. 3.19

38. 0.715

39. 0.298

40. 0.873

THE POWERS OF 10 METHOD FOR LOCATING THE DECIMAL POINT

In this chapter, we are going to explain a general method of locating the decimal point in the result of a calculation. We call the method "Powers of 10" because it makes so much use of powers of 10.

The "Powers of 10" method does not conflict with the Digit Count method which is explained earlier in the book. It will give the same result. Many people prefer it to the Digit Count method.

The "Powers of 10" method has one great advantage over the Digit Count method in that there isn't so much to remember. For instance, there is no need to notice the moves of the slide to left or right when making slide rule calculations. Against this, it has the disadvantage that you have to reason on a higher level in order to use it.

It is necessary to know something about exponents in order to use the "Powers of 10" method, so we'll begin by explaining exponents and how to work with them.

EXPONENTS. An exponent is a number or symbol which is written behind another number or symbol, and a bit higher. Thus, when we write 10^2, the number 2 is an exponent of 10.

The exponent of a number is really a direction to raise the number to the power designated by the exponent. Thus, 10^2 means to raise 10 to the second power, that is, to square 10; similarly, 4^3 means to raise 4 to the third power, that is, to cube 4.

POWERS OF 10. Look now at some powers of 10, as listed in the following table:

TABLE 16-1. POWERS OF TEN

$$10^6 = 1,000,000$$
$$10^5 = 100,000$$
$$10^4 = 10,000$$
$$10^3 = 1,000$$
$$10^2 = 100$$
$$10^1 = 10$$
$$10^0 = 1$$
$$10^{-1} = 0.1$$
$$10^{-2} = 0.01$$
$$10^{-3} = 0.001$$
$$10^{-4} = 0.0001$$
etc.

This table can be summarized in two statements:

1) A positive power of 10 is the number of places the decimal point would have to be moved to the left to make the number equal to 1.

2) A negative power of 10 is the number of places the decimal point would have to be moved to the right to make the number equal to 1.

LAWS OF EXPONENTS. There are several mathematical laws of exponents which you should know if you are going to use the "Powers of 10" method to locate decimal points.

LAW NO. 1. *Exponents are added when powers of 10 are multiplied.* Thus,

$$10^1 \times 10^2 = 10^{1+2} = 10^3.$$

Now, since $10^1 = 10$, $10^2 = 100$, and $10^3 = 1,000$, this is just another way of writing $10 \times 100 = 1,000$. As another example,
$$10^3 \times 10^{-2} = 10^{3-2} = 10^1 = 10, \text{ or, } 1000 \times 0.01 = 10.$$

LAW NO. 2. *The exponent of the divisor is subtracted from the exponent of the dividend when one power of 10 is divided by another.* For example,

$$10^3 \div 10^2 = 10^{3-2} = 10^1 = 10,$$
or you could have done it this way, $1000 \div 100 = 10$.

LAW NO. 3. *Exponents are multiplied when a power of 10 is raised to a power,* thus,

$$(10^2)^2 = 10^{2 \times 2} = 10^4,$$

or you might have put it this way, $(100)^2 = 10,000$.

LAW NO. 4. *The exponent of a power of 10 is divided by the root number when a root is calculated.* For example, if you take a square root,

$$\sqrt{10^4} = 10^{4/2} = 10^2.$$

This is the same as, $\sqrt{10^4} = \sqrt{10,000} = 100$.

Or, for an example with the cube root,

$$\sqrt[3]{10^3} = 10^{3/3} = 10^1,$$

which is the same as

$$\sqrt[3]{1000} = 10.$$

SCIENTIFIC NOTATION. Scientific notation is a way of writing any number in the special form of a coefficient (number) between 1 and 10, multiplied by a power of 10. The best way to explain is to illustrate. Thus, 1234 can be written as $1.234 \times 1000 = 1.234 \times 10^3$. This is the coefficient 1.234 multiplied by 10 to the third power. The procedure in changing to scientific notation is to move the decimal point to a new location such that there is only one digit to its left. The power of 10 is positive if you move the decimal point to the left, and is equal to the number of places the decimal point is moved. Thus, you must move the decimal point three places to the left to change 1234 to 1.234, so the power of 10 is 3, and $1234 = 1.234 \times 10^3$.

The power of 10 is negative if you move the decimal point to the right in order to have just one digit to the left of the decimal point, but is still equal to the number of places the decimal point is moved. So, for example, if you have the number 0.01234, you must move the decimal point two places to the right to get 1.234, so the power of 10 is -2, and $0.01234 = 1.234 \times 10^{-2}$. Now try this sort of thing for yourself.

PRACTICE PROBLEMS

Express each of these numbers in scientific notation, and then check your answers with the correct answers in the back of the book.

1. 256		**6.** 0.0722
2. 89.3		**7.** 37,300
3. 0.588		**8.** 0.000347
4. 2800		**9.** 9800
5. 134,000		**10.** 0.0654

MULTIPLICATION. Now, let's see how to use the "Powers of 10" method for locating the decimal point in a multiplication problem. Just do it this way,

1) Write each number of the product in scientific notation.
2) Multiply the coefficients of the powers of 10 to get the coefficient of the power of 10 in the answer.
3) Multiply the powers of 10 in the product by adding their exponents.
4) Write the answer first as the coefficient from step 2 times the power of 10 from step 3.
5) Change the answer to the usual form by moving the decimal point to absorb the power of 10.

Now follow these examples with your own slide rule. Write down each intermediate step.

ILLUSTRATIVE EXAMPLES

1. *What is 378 × 15.6?*

1) Write the product this way, with each number in scientific notation: $3.78 \times 10^2 \times 1.56 \times 10^1$.
2) Multiply the coefficients thus: $3.78 \times 1.56 = 5.90$.
3) Multiply the powers of 10: $10^2 \times 10^1 = 10^3$.
4) Write the answer first in scientific notation as 5.90×10^3.
5) Move the decimal point three places to the right to absorb the 10^3, and write the answer as *5900*.

2. *What is 19800 × 0.00453?*

1) Express each number in scientific notation and write the product this way: $1.980 \times 10^4 \times 4.53 \times 10^{-3}$.
2) Multiply the coefficients: $1.980 \times 4.53 = 8.96$.
3) Multiply the powers of 10: $10^4 \times 10^{-3} = 10^1$.
4) Write the answer first in scientific notation: 8.96×10^1.
5) Change the answer to *89.6*.

3. *Multiply: 262 × 33.6 × 418.*

1) Express each number in scientific notation and write the product this way: *2.62 × 10^2 × 3.36 × 10^1 × 4.18 × 10^2.*
2) Multiply the coefficients: *2.62 × 3.36 × 4.18 = 36.8.*
3) Multiply the powers of 10: *10^2 × 10^1 × 10^2 = 10^5.*
4) Write the answer first as *36.8 × 10^5.*
5) Move the decimal point five places to the right to get the answer as *3,680,000.*

4. *What is 0.00742 × 0.0821?*

1) Express each number in scientific notation and write the product as: *7.42 × 10^{-3} × 8.21 × 10^{-2}.*
2) Multiply the coefficients: *7.42 × 8.21 = 60.9.*
3) Multiply the powers of 10: *10^{-3} × 10^{-2} = 10^{-5}.*
4) Write the answer first as *60.9 × 10^{-5}.*
5) Move the decimal point five places to the left to get the final answer as *0.000609.*

PRACTICE PROBLEMS

The only way to really learn this procedure is to practice it. Calculate each of these products and then check your answers with the correct answers in the back of the book.

1. 35 × 27	**6.** 3420 × 0.00072
2. 0.062 × 0.159	**7.** 818 × 346 × 42
3. 728 × 1156	**8.** 17 × 18 × 19
4. 97.5 × 218	**9.** 424 × 0.0519 × 3.28
5. 456 × 0.00315	**10.** 0.056 × 0.138 × 23

DIVISION. This is the way to use the "Powers of 10" method to locate the decimal point in a division problem.

1) Write the numerator and denominator in scientific notation.
2) Divide the coefficient of the power of 10 in the numerator by the coefficient of the power of 10 in the denominator, to get the coefficient of the power of 10 in the answer.
3) Subtract the power of 10 in the denominator from the power of 10 in the numerator, to get the power of 10 in the answer.
4) Write the answer first as the coefficient from step 2 times the power of 10 from step 3.
5) Change the answer to the usual form.

ILLUSTRATIVE EXAMPLES

5. *What is* $\dfrac{7260}{58}$ *?*

1) Write the expression in scientific notation as: $\dfrac{7.26 \times 10^3}{5.8 \times 10^1}$.

2) Divide: *7.26/5.8 = 1.251.*

3) Subtract: $10^3/10^1 = 10^{3-1} = 10^2$.

4) Write the answer first as *1.251 × 10²*.

5) Rewrite the answer as *125.1.*

    6. *Divide: 227 ÷ 0.0195.*

1) Write it this way in scientific notation: $\dfrac{2.27 \times 10^2}{1.96 \times 10^{-2}}$.

2) Divide: *2.27/1.95 = 1.164.*

3) Subtract −2 from 2, thus: *2 — (−2) = 4.*

4) Write the answer first as *1.164 × 10⁴.*

5) Now, write the answer as *11640.*

    7. *Calculate* $\dfrac{0.385}{6480}$.

1) Write this in scientific notation as: $\dfrac{3.85 \times 10^{-1}}{6.48 \times 10^3}$.

2) Divide: *3.85/6.48 = 0.593.*

3) Subtract 3 from −1: *−1 — 3 = −4.*

4) Write the answer first as *0.593 × 10⁻⁴.*

5) Now move the decimal point four places to the left to absorb the *10⁻⁴* and get *0.0000598* as the answer.

PRACTICE PROBLEMS

Now, practice this method in order to learn it. After you have made each of these calculations, check your answers with the correct answers in the back of the book.

1. 4370 ÷ 27.5 = ?
2. 238 ÷ 0.0622 = ?
3. 34.5 ÷ 1850 = ?
4. 0.756 ÷ 0.00212 = ?
5. 556,000 ÷ 827 = ?

6. 0.913 ÷ 377 = ?
7. 7.85 ÷ 463 = ?
8. 0.00188 ÷ 12.7 = ?
9. 33800 ÷ 595 = ?
10. 2720 ÷ 0.082 = ?

COMBINATIONS OF MULTIPLICATION AND DIVISION. If a calculation is a combination of multiplication and division, you can just put together what you have learned about multiplication and division separately, in order to use the "Powers of 10" method to locate the decimal point in the answer. A typical problem might look like this,

$$\frac{21.8 \times 364 \times 0.757}{65 \times 4.16} \; .$$

Here is the way to apply the "Powers of 10" method.

1) Write the expression with each number in scientific notation.
2) Multiply and divide with the coefficients to get the coefficient in the answer.
3) Add the powers of 10 in the numerator and subtract the powers of 10 in the denominator to get the power of 10 in the answer.
4) Write the answer first as the coefficient from step 2 times the power of 10 from step 3.
5) Move the decimal point in the answer to absorb the power of 10.

ILLUSTRATIVE EXAMPLES

8. *Calculate* $\dfrac{21.8 \times 364 \times 0.757}{65 \times 4.16} \; .$

1) Put each number into scientific notation and write the expression as,

$$\frac{2.18 \times 10^1 \times 3.64 \times 10^2 \times 7.57 \times 10^{-1}}{6.5 \times 10^1 \times 4.16 \times 10^0}$$

2) Multiply and divide with the coefficients,

$$\frac{2.18 \times 3.64 \times 7.57}{6.5 \times 4.16} = 2.22$$

3) Add the powers of 10 in the numerator and subtract the powers of 10 in the denominator: $(1 + 2 - 1) - (1 + 0) = 2 - 1 = 1.$

4) Write the answer first as $2.22 \times 10^1.$

5) Rewrite the answer as *22.2.*

9. *Calculate* $\dfrac{936 \times 33.4 \times 1270}{4720 \times 10.7} \; .$

1) Rewrite the expression with each number in scientific notation:

$$\frac{9.36 \times 10^2 \times 3.34 \times 10^1 \times 1.27 \times 10^3}{4.72 \times 10^3 \times 1.97 \times 10^1}$$

2) Multiply and divide with the coefficients:

$$\frac{9.36 \times 3.34 \times 1.27}{4.72 \times 1.97} = 4.27.$$

3) Add the powers of 10 in the numerator and subtract the powers of 10 in the denominator: $(2 + 1 + 3) - (3 + 1) = 6 - 4 = 2$.
4) Write the answer first as 4.27×10^2.
5) Rewrite the answer as 427.

10. *Calculate* $\dfrac{31.3 \times 0.0526}{248 \times 0.157}$.

1) Put each number into scientific notation and write the expression as:

$$\frac{3.13 \times 10^1 \times 5.26 \times 10^{-2}}{2.48 \times 10^2 \times 1.57 \times 10^{-1}}$$

2) Multiply and divide with the coefficients:

$$\frac{3.13 \times 5.26}{2.48 \times 1.57} = 4.22.$$

3) Add the powers of 10 in the numerator and subtract the powers of 10 in the denominator: $(1 - 2) - (2 - 1) = -1 - 1 = -2$.
4) Write the answer first as 4.22×10^{-2}.
5) Rewrite the answer as 0.0422.

PRACTICE PROBLEMS

This sort of thing requires practice to learn. Carry out the calculations indicated and then check your answers with the correct answers in the back of the book.

1. $\dfrac{26 \times 115 \times 7}{31 \times 71}$

2. $\dfrac{950 \times 38}{216}$

3. $\dfrac{64.8 \times 315}{36 \times 0.820}$

4. $\dfrac{0.474 \times 0.0923}{21.5}$

5. $\dfrac{29700 \times 185}{38.7 \times 44.5}$

6. $\dfrac{0.179 \times 387}{8.16 \times 11.5}$

7. $\dfrac{56.5 \times 0.349 \times 78.4}{0.362 \times 0.127}$

8. $\dfrac{1,200,000 \times 512 \times 0.866}{292 \times 7.65}$

9. $\dfrac{0.0666 \times 39.7 \times 592}{14.4 \times 0.712 \times 19}$ **10.** $\dfrac{136 \times 217 \times 31.9}{0.0632 \times 71.4 \times 827}$

THE SQUARE OF A NUMBER. The square of a number is just the product of a number by itself. Here is the way to use the "Powers of 10" method.

1) Put the number into scientific notation and write the expression for its square.
2) Square the coefficient of the power of 10 to get the coefficient of the square.
3) Double the power of 10 in the number to get the power of 10 in the square.
4) Write the answer first as the coefficient from step 2 times the power of 10 from step 3.
5) Rewrite the answer to put it into the usual form.

Try it with these examples.

ILLUSTRATIVE EXAMPLES

11. *Square 437.*

1) Put the number into scientific notation and square it, thus: $(4.37 \times 10^2)^2$.
2) Square *4.37* to get *19.09*.
3) Double the power of 10: $2 \times 2 = 4$.
4) Write the answer first as 19.09×10^4.
5) Rewrite the answer as *190,900*.

12. *Square 0.00178.*

1) Put the number into scientific notation and square it, thus: $(1.78 \times 10^{-3})^2$.
2) Square *1.78* and get *3.17*.
3) Double the power of 10: $-3 \times 2 = -6$.
4) Write the answer first as 3.17×10^{-6}.
5) Move the decimal point six places to the left and rewrite the answer as *0.00000317*.

PRACTICE PROBLEMS

Practice now by squaring each of these numbers. Then, check your answers against the correct answers in the back of the book.

1. 23.4	**6.** 0.167
2. 119	**7.** 0.0832
3. 4840	**8.** 0.0269
4. 91.8	**9.** 0.00423
5. 1.27	**10.** 0.0356

THE SQUARE ROOT OF A NUMBER. The easy way to use the "Powers of 10" method for locating the decimal point in the square root of a number requires you to vary a bit from the scientific notation for a number. You write the number as a coefficient between 1 and 100, times an *even* power of 10. For example, $117 = 1.17 \times 10^2$, $1170 = 11.7 \times 10^2$, $11700 = 1.17 \times 10^4$, $117000 = 11.7 \times 10^4$, etc. The whole procedure for the square root is,

1) Write the number as a coefficient times an even power of 10 and indicate the process of taking the square root.
2) Take the square root of the coefficient to get the coefficient in the answer.
3) Take half of the power of 10 to get the power of 10 in the answer.
4) Write the answer first as the coefficient from step 2 times the power of 10 from step 3.
5) Rewrite the answer to absorb the power of 10.

ILLUSTRATIVE EXAMPLES

13. *What is the square root of 92800?*

1) Express the square root as $\sqrt{9.28 \times 10^4}$.
2) Take the square root of *9.28*. It is *3.09*.
3) Take half of *4* to get *2*.
4) Write the answer first as 3.09×10^2.
5) Rewrite the answer as *309*.

14. *What is the square root of 0.00348?*

1) Write the number as 34.8×10^{-4} and express the square root as $\sqrt{34.8 \times 10^{-4}}$.
2) Take the square root of *34.8* to get *5.90*.
3) Take half of *−4* to get *− 2*.
4) Write the answer first as 5.90×10^{-2}.
5) Rewrite the answer as *0.0590*.

PRACTICE PROBLEMS

Calculate the square root of each of these numbers, and then check your answers with the correct answers in the back of the book.

1. 658		**6.** 0.0177	
2. 327		**7.** 7,980,000	
3. 7470		**8.** 0.00532	
4. 1833		**9.** 0.00148	
5. 0.193		**10.** 0.000222	

THE CUBE OF A NUMBER. The cube of a number is the result of multiplying the number by itself twice. Thus, the cube of 10, which is written as 10^3, is equal to $10 \times 10 \times 10$. The easy way to use the "Powers of 10" method to locate the decimal point in the cube of a number is,

1) Write the number in scientific notation and indicate the cube of it.
2) Take the cube of the coefficient to get the coefficient in the answer.
3) Multiply the power of 10 by 3 to get the power of 10 in the answer.
4) Write the answer first as the coefficient from step 2, times the power of 10 from step 3.
5) Rewrite the answer in the usual form to absorb the power of 10.

Now, follow this procedure in these examples.

ILLUSTRATIVE EXAMPLES

15. *Calculate the cube of 56.9.*

1) Put the number into scientific notation and cube it, thus: *$(5.69 \times 10^1)^3$*.
2) Cube *5.69* to get *184*.
3) Multiply the power of 10: *$1 \times 3 = 3$*.
4) Write the answer first as *184×10^3*.
5) Move the decimal point three places to the right and rewrite the answer as *184,000*.

16. *What is the cube of 0.0473?*

1) Put the number into scientific notation and cube it, thus: *$(4.73 \times 10^{-2})^3$*.

2) Cube *4.73* to get *106*.
3) Multiply the power of 10: $-2 \times 3 = -6$.
4) Write the answer first as *106 × 10⁻⁶*.
5) Move the decimal point six places to the left and rewrite the answer as *0.000106*.

PRACTICE PROBLEMS

Practice this procedure by cubing each of these numbers, and then check your answers with the correct answers in the back of the book.

1.	26.5	6.	0.178
2.	128	7.	4150
3.	0.919	8.	8.33
4.	0.0637	9.	0.0747
5.	323	10.	0.0322

THE CUBE ROOT OF A NUMBER. There is an easy way to use the "Powers of 10" method to locate the decimal point in the cube root of a number. The first thing to do is to write the number as a coefficient times a power of 10 which has 3 as a factor, that is, 3, 6, 9, etc. For example, 228 can be written as 0.228×10^3, 2280 can be written as 2.28×10^3, 22800 can be written as 22.8×10^3 or 0.0228×10^6, etc. The whole procedure is,

1) Write the number as a coefficient times a power of 10 which has 3 as a factor, and write the expression for the cube root.
2) Take the cube root of the coefficient to get the coefficient in the answer.
3) Divide the power of 10 by 3 to get the power of 10 in the answer.
4) Write the answer first as the coefficient from step 2, times the power of 10 from step 3.
5) Move the decimal point to absorb the power of 10 and rewrite the answer. Here are examples for you to follow.

ILLUSTRATIVE EXAMPLES

17. *What is the cube root of 4920?*

1) Write the number as *4.92 × 10³*, and then write the expression for the cube root: $\sqrt[3]{4.92 \times 10^3}$.
2) Take the cube root of *4.92* to get *1.70*.
3) Divide *3* by *3* to get *1*.

4) Write the answer first as *1.70 × 10¹*.
5) Move the decimal point one place to the right and rewrite the answer as *17.0*.

  18. *What is the cube root of 0.000236.*

1) Write the number as *236 × 10⁻⁶* and the cube root as $^3\sqrt{236 \times 10^{-6}}$.
2) Take the cube root of *236* to get *6.18*.
3) Divide —*6* by *3* to get —*2*.
4) Write the answer first as *6.18 × 10⁻²*.
5) Move the decimal point two places to the left and rewrite the answer as *0.0618*.

PRACTICE PROBLEMS

  Now practice by calculating the cube root of each of these numbers and then check your answers with the correct answers in the back of the book.

1. 1380		**6.** 0.375
2. 33000		**7.** 3,560,000
3. 254000		**8.** 0.00617
4. 0.0793		**9.** 5960
5. 0.0188		**10.** 0.00206

REVIEW PROBLEMS

  Here are problems for review of this chapter. Just perform the calculations indicated. There are no answers supplied for these review problems, but you could check them by using the Digit Count method.

1. 38.5 × 245	**2.** 119 × 387
3. 953 × 0.062	**4.** 4150 × 0.0591
5. 3180 × 2760	**6.** 0.084 × 0.049
7. 0.164 × 0.032	**8.** 9150 × 0.0762
9. 43.8 × 920	**10.** 820 × 13200
11. 16.7 ÷ 232	**12.** 18.5 ÷ 0.0342
13. 9560 ÷ 128	**14.** 24.5 ÷ 726
15. 316 ÷ 0.259	**16.** 72.7 ÷ 0.0422
17. 1,560,000 ÷ 854	**18.** 0.0156 ÷ 0.0388
19. 0.0628 ÷ 42.2	**20.** 0.00347 ÷ 0.0173

21. $\dfrac{56 \times 88}{33}$

22. $\dfrac{3.47 \times 12.5}{224}$

23. $\dfrac{75.9 \times 354}{29.5 \times 0.656}$

24. $\dfrac{0.0588 \times 21.5}{0.136 \times 0.417}$

25. $\dfrac{4420 \times 15.3 \times 0.284}{325 \times 79.2}$

26. $\dfrac{0.959 \times 37.5 \times 427}{185000 \times 0.0637}$

27. $\dfrac{56500 \times 22.7 \times 118}{43.6 \times 1920}$

28. $\dfrac{75.6 \times 0.123 \times 496}{137 \times 0.523}$

29. $\dfrac{6560 \times 227 \times 324}{45.6 \times 0.253 \times 18.5}$

30. $\dfrac{627 \times 91.5 \times 292}{0.781 \times 10.6 \times 108}$

Square each of these numbers:

31. 18.5
32. 327
33. 0.852
34. 0.0216
35. 6170
36. 2780
37. 0.252
38. 0.0725
39. 1230
40. 0.000466

Calculate the square root of each of these numbers:

41. 235
42. 0.0762
43. 1725
44. 18000
45. 0.00246
46. 843000
47. 0.183
48. 0.0359
49. 12,000,000
50. 0.01234

Cube each of these numbers:

51. 12.8
52. 23.7
53. 0.0922
54. 133
55. 0.276
56. 7.85
57. 0.0358
58. 248
59. 0.473
60. 0.0536

Calculate the cube root of each of these numbers:

61. 2720
62. 78000
63. 0.053
64. 37.5
65. 0.168
66. 0.00693
67. 32,000,000
68. 558000
69. 0.0275
70. 0.00147

CHAPTER 17

CHECKING SLIDE RULES

No slide rule, or anything else for that matter, is perfect. Variations in materials and processes, and slight inaccuracies in workmanship, combine to produce an article that is short of perfection. The best of slide rules cannot be exactly right. However, the imperfections do not exist in the same degree in all slide rules. Some are better than others. It is with this in mind that this chapter is written. Before buying a slide rule it is advisable to check it carefully, so as to secure a rule that is quick and sure in operation and that will give results with precision.

Marking. Make sure that the scales of the slide rule stand out distinctly from one another, and that the marking is clear and easy to read. A great deal of time can be wasted and a great deal of eye strain suffered in trying to use a slide rule that cannot be read quickly and easily.

The Runner. Make sure that the runner slides easily so that it can be adjusted with the fingertips. There should be no rough spots noticeable as the runner is moved from one end of the rule to the other. Try moving it, first with the slide entirely within the stock, then with the slide extended to the left, and last with the slide extended to the right. It should move easily but should not be loose enough to wobble.

The Slide. The slide should move freely in the stock. There should be just enough resistance so that it will not fall out when the slide rule is held vertically. In many cases the slide will fit loosely in the stock when one end of the slide projects from the stock and tightly when the other end projects from the stock. This is not desirable. It should require about the same amount of force to push the slide, no matter what its position.

Pull the slide out of the stock and sight along both stock and slide to make sure that neither is warped. The stock is so much heavier than the slide that it will hold the slide straight when engaged, even though the slide is badly warped.

The C and D Scales. The C and D scales are used more than any others on the slide rule. For this reason they should be checked carefully. Place the left index of the C scale over the left index of the D scale and see if each mark on the C scale lines up with the corresponding mark on the D scale.

Try a few multiplications and divisions with the C and D scales and see if you get the correct answers. Use simple numbers so that you can check the answers mentally. For instance, see if *2* times *4* comes out exactly as *8*, if *7* divided by *2* is exactly *3.5*, etc.

The A and D Scales. Place the hairline of the runner over the left index of the D scale and see if it is over the left index of the A scale. Try this also with the right indices. Square a few simple numbers. See if the square of *8* comes out exactly as *64*, the square of *5* as *25*, the square of *3* as *9*, etc. If they do not, you don't want that slide rule.

The B and C Scales. Check the B and C scales together in the same way as the A and D scales.

The K Scale. See that the left index of the K scale lines up with the left index of the D scale. You should be able to set the hairline of the runner so that it will fall exactly on both indices at the same time. Try this also for the right indices. Try cubing a few simple numbers. Make sure that the cube of *2* is obtained exactly as *8*, the cube of *3* as *27*, the cube of *5* as *125*, etc.

The CI Scale. Set the hairline of the runner on the left index of the C scale and see that it falls exactly on the left index of the CI scale. Try this also for the right indices. Remember that when the hairline is set to a number on the C scale, the number on the CI scale that is under the hairline should be the reciprocal of the number on the C scale. See if you read the reciprocal of *2* as *0.5*, and that of *8* as *0.125*.

The S Scale (on rules having the S scale but not the ST scale). Remember that on slide rules having *only* the S scale for finding sines of angles the S scale is keyed to operate in conjunction with the A and B scales, as explained in Part **B** of Chapter 9. Bearing this in mind, check the scale by finding the sine of each of several angles and comparing results with a table of trigonometric functions. For instance, make sure that you read the sine of *30°* as *0.5*, and sine of

$60°$ as *0.866,* etc. The last mark at the right end of the sine scale represents $90°$. See that the sine of $90°$ comes out as *1.*

The S Scale (on rules having both the S and ST scales). Remember that on slide rules having *both* the **S** and **ST** scales for finding sines of angles the **S** scale is keyed to operate in conjunction with the **D** and **C** scales, as explained in Part **A** of Chapter 9. The **S** scale on slide rules of this type is designed for angles from $5.7°$ to $90°$. Bearing these facts in mind, check the scale by finding the sine of each of several angles within this range and comparing results with a table of trigonometric functions, as described' in the preceding paragraph.

The ST Scale (on rules having both the S and ST scales). The **ST** scale on slide rules of this type is used for finding both sines and tangents of small angles in the range from about $0.574°$ to $5.74°$, in which range the sines and tangents are so nearly alike that for practical calculations they are considered identical. Check the **ST** scale by finding the sine (and tangent) of each of several angles, bearing in mind that the **ST** scale is keyed to the **D** and **C** scales. Compare the results with those in a table of trigonometric functions. For instance, both the sine and tangent of $2°$ are *.0349,* and for $1°$ both of these functions are *0.0175.*

The T Scale (on rules having the T scale but not the ST scale). The **T** scale on slide rules of this type is keyed to operate in conjunction with the **C** and **D** scales, as explained in Part **B** of Chapter 10. The range of the **T** scale on such slide rules is from $5°43'$ at the lefthand end to $45°$ at the righthand end. Bearing these facts in mind, try a few angles and compare with the "trig" tables. The tangent of $30°$ is *0.577,* and the tangent of $45°$ is *1,* etc. You cannot secure precise results with an inaccurate slide rule.

The T Scale (on rules having both the T and ST scales). The **T** scale on slide rules of this type is keyed to the **D** and **C** scales, as explained in Part **A** of Chapter 10. The range of the **T** scale on such slide rules is from $5.7°$ at the lefthand end to $45°$ at the righthand end. Bearing these facts in mind, try a few angles and compare results with those in "trig" tables, as described in the preceding paragraph.

The Split Scales. The split scales are used with the **D** scale to calculate squares and square roots, so the easiest way to check them is to check a few squares. First, make sure that the lefthand index

of the R_1 scale lines up with the lefthand index of the **D** scale, and
the righthand index of the R_2 scale lines up with the righthand index of the **D** scale. Then, with the R_1 scale and the **D** scale, try a
few numbers: for example, the square of *14* is *196,* the square of *2* is
4, and the square of *3* is *9.* Make sure that the slide rule actually
gives you these results. Finally, use the R_2 scale with the **D** scale to
check that you get *16* as the square of *4,* and *36* as the square of *6.*

The Folded Scales. First, you might check the **CF** and **DF**
scales to make sure that the marks on one are in exact alignment
with the marks on the other. Then, check the **DF** scale. Here, you
can set the hairline of the runner to any number on the **D** scale, and
the number on the **DF** scale under the hairline should be *3.14* times
the number on the **D** scale. So, if you set the hairline of the runner
to the lefthand index of the **D** scale, you should see π on the **DF**
scale under the hairline. Also, if the number on the **D** scale is *2,* the
number on the **DF** scale should be *6.28;* if the number on the **D**
scale is *5,* the number on the **DF** scale should be *15.7.*

The **CIF** scale is a reciprocal scale, keyed to the **CF** scale. If the
hairline of the runner is set to any number on the **CF** scale, the
reciprocal of that number should be on the **CIF** scale under the
hairline. Thus, if you have the number *5* on the **CF** scale, you should
have *0.2* on the **CIF** scale; also, the center indices should line up for
the **CF** and **CIF** scales.

The Log Log Scales. The log log scales can be checked in two
steps. First, check the **LL1, LL2,** and **LL3** scales by raising small
numbers to integral powers. Then, check the **LL/1, LL/2,** and
LL/3 scales against the **LL1, LL2,** and **LL3** scales.

Here's the way to check the **LL1, LL2,** and **LL3** scales. First set
the hairline of the runner to *1.10* on the **LL1** scale and bring the
righthand index of the **C** scale under the hairline. Then, set the
hairline of the runner to *2* on the **C** scale and see if you can read the
square of *1.10* as *1.21* on the **LL2** scale. If you can't there is something wrong.

Next, set the hairline of the runner to *2* on the **LL2** scale and
bring the righthand index of the **C** scale under the hairline. Then,
set the hairline of the runner to *4* on the **C** scale and read the
fourth power of *2* as *16* on the **LL3** scale.

Try cubing *7* on the **LL3** scale and see if you get *343.*

Now, check the other log log scales by using the reciprocals of simple numbers, so that when the hairline of the runner is set to a number on one log log scale, the reciprocal of that number is on another log log scale under the hairline, thus,

1.02 on **LL1** scale; *0.9804* on **LL/1** scale.
1.07 on **LL1** scale; *0.9346* on **LL/1** scale.
1.25 on **LL2** scale; *0.80* on **LL/2** scale.
2 on **LL2** scale; *0.50* on **LL/2** scale.
4 on **LL3** scale; *0.25* on **LL/3** scale.
200 on **LL3** scale; *0.005* on **LL/3** scale.

Conclusion. The satisfaction derived from the use of a precise and easily operated slide rule is well worth the small amount of time and effort required to select such a slide rule.

CHAPTER 18

FINAL SUGGESTIONS

If you have studied the earlier chapters carefully and practiced with a great many problems, you are now proficient in the use of the slide rule. You should be able to make any calculation in arithmetic with it. However, do not feel that you know all about the slide rule and that nothing more can be learned. Keep an open mind as you use it and try constantly to improve in speed and precision. Study the particular types of problems that you have to do and try to work out procedures for doing them more efficiently. The fundamental operations have been described in detail in this book and you should know them. However, it is for practical problems that you need the slide rule, and there is a great deal of difference between being able to do a problem and being able to do it quickly and precisely.

Good Judgment. You can save time and avoid errors by exercising good judgment in the use of the slide rule. It is a good practice to make a rough mental check of each calculation to see if the answer is reasonable. One common mistake, especially for the beginner, is to set 201 as 210, or 101 as 110. Another, in the use of the **C** and **D** scales, is to set 2 as 12. This sort of error can usually be detected if you make a mental estimate of the answer and compare it with the answer read from the slide rule.

Do not become such a slave to habit that you use the slide rule when you don't have to. For instance, don't use the slide rule to multiply 2 times 3, or 1.5 times 4, etc. Problems as easy as these can be done mentally.

Don't go through a procedure for locating the decimal point when the calculation is very simple. For instance, if you divide 31.7 by 6 and read the numerals of the answer as 528, you know that the decimal point must be located after the 5. The answer must be 5.28. It could not be 0.528 or 52.8. Save time where you can save it legitimately, and when it will not lead to errors.

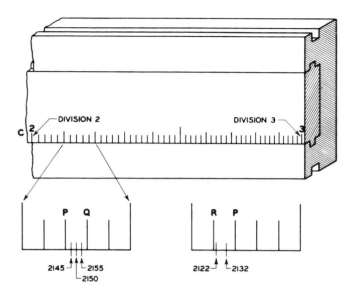

Fig. 18-1. Enlarged short portion of C scale, showing locations of 2145, 2150 and 2155 at lower left, and of 2122 and 2132 at lower right.

Greater Precision. It is possible to read portions of the **C** and **D** scales more accurately than was done in earlier chapters. Fig. 18-1 shows the portion of the **C** scale between divisions *2* and *3*. So far you have been reading only three digits of an answer when it is located here, and this has involved estimating one-half a space when the third digit is odd. However, you can estimate much closer than this. Fig. 18-1 also shows an enlarged short length of the **C** scale with correct locations for the numbers *2145, 2150* and *2155.* To locate these numbers requires estimating to one-fourth of a space. This can be done easily and enables you to obtain a more precise result. The mark designated by *P* represents *2140* and that designated by *Q* represents *2160.* The number *2150* is half-way between *2140* and *2160,* so it is located halfway from *P* to *Q*. The number *2145* is halfway between *2140* and *2150* so it is one-fourth of the way from *P* to *Q*. Also, since *2155* is halfway between *2150* and *2160,* it is located three-fourths of the way from *P* to *Q*.

Occasionally calculations will start with a number such as
2122. The correct location for this number is shown at the lower
right in Fig. 18-1. Note that this enlarged section shows the same
part of the scale that is shown in the enlarged section on the left;
namely, *2100* to *2200*. The mark designated by *R* represents *2120*
and that designated by *P* represents *2140*. The number *2122* is
one-tenth of the way from *2120* to *2140,* since the difference between 2120 and 2140 is 20 while the difference between 2120 and
2122 is 2 .Thus, on the slide rule you would locate *2122* by estimating one-tenth of the space from *2120* to *2140,* here one-tenth of
the space from *R* to *P.* This enlarged length also shows the correct
location for the number *2132.* This number is twelve greater than
2120 so it must be located at twelve-twentieths, or six-tenths, of the
space from *R* to *P.*

The type of marking between divisions *3* and *4* on the **C** scale
is the same as that between divisions 2 and 3. Hence, these remarks
also apply to it. Note that portions of the **A** and **B** scales are similar, so you can estimate more closely there.

**SUMMARY OF RULES FOR LOCATING THE DECIMAL
POINT.*** The most commonly used rules for locating the decimal
point in an answer are those for multiplication and division. Because of their importance, these rules are repeated here.

Multiplication with the C and D Scales.

1) *If the slide projects to the right of the stock during a multiplication with the* **C** *and* **D** *scales, the digit count for the product
is one less than the sum of the digit counts for the multiplicand and
multiplier.*

2) *If the slide projects to the left of the stock, the digit count
for the product is equal to the sum of the digit counts for the multiplicand and multiplier.*

Multiplication with the CI and D Scales.

1) *If the slide projects to the right of the stock during a multiplication with the* **CI** *and* **D** *scales, the digit count for the product
is equal to the sum of the digit counts for the multiplicand and
multiplier.*

**If you have learned to use the powers of 10 method for location of the
decimal point, as explained in Chapter 16, disregard all rules listed in this
section of Chapter 18.*

2) *If the slide projects to the left of the stock, the digit count for the product is one less than the sum of the digit counts for the multiplicand and multiplier.*

Division with the C and D Scales.

1) *If the slide projects to the right of the stock during a division with the C and D scales, the digit count for the quotient is one more than the digit count for the dividend minus the digit count for the divisor.*

2) *If the slide projects to the left of the stock, the digit count for the quotient is equal to the digit count for the dividend minus the digit count for the divisor.*

Division with the CI and D Scales.

1) *If the slide projects to the right of the stock during a division with the CI and D scales, the digit count for the quotient is equal to the digit count for the dividend minus the digit count for the divisor.*

2) *If the slide projects to the left of the stock, the digit count for the quotient is one more than the digit count for the dividend minus the digit count for the divisor.*

RULES FOR FUNDAMENTAL OPERATIONS ON THE SLIDE RULE

The rules for the fundamental operations of the slide rule are repeated below. They have been grouped together so that they will be convenient for reference and reviw. However, do not try to use this list of rules until you have studied the chapters in which they are explained and illustrated.

Rule 1. Multiplication. *Set one index of the C scale to the multiplicand on the D scale. Next, set the hairline of the runner to the multiplier on the C scale. Finally, read the answer on the D scale under the hairline.*

Rule 2. Division. *Set the hairline of the runner to the dividend on the D scale. Then slide the divisor on the C scale under the hairline. Finally, read the answer on the D scale under one index of the C scale.*

Rule 3. (a) The Square. *Set the hairline of the runner to the number on the D scale. Read the square of the number on the A scale under the hairline.*

(b) The Square Root. *Set the hairline of the runner to the number on the **A** scale. Read the square root of the number on the **D** scale under the hairline.*

Rule 4. (a) The Cube. *Set the hairline of the runner to the number on the **D** scale. Read the cube of the number on the **K** scale under the hairline.*

(b) The Cube Root. *Set the hairline of the runner to the number on the **K** scale. Read the cube root of the number on the **D** scale under the hairline.*

Rule 5. (a) The Sine. (Applies only to slide rules with both the S and ST scales.) *Set the hairline of the runner to the angle on the righthand markings of the **ST** or **S** scale. Read the sine of the angle on the **D** scale under the hairline.*

Rule 5. (b) The Arc Sine. (Applies only to slide rules with both the S and ST scales.) *Set the hairline of the runner to the number on the **D** scale. Read the angle which is the arc sine of the number on the righthand markings of the **ST** or **S** scale under the hairline.*

Rule 5, (c) The Sine. (Applies only to slide rules with the S scale but not the ST scale.) *Set the hairline of the runner to the angle on the **S** scale. Read the sine of the angle on the **A** or **B** scale.*

Rule 5. (d) The Arc Sine. (Applies only to slide rules with the S scale but not the ST scale.) *Set the hairline of the runner to the number on the **A** or **B** scale. Read the angle on the **S** scale.*

Rule 6. (a) The Tangent. (Applies only to slide rules with both T and ST scales.) For angles between 0.574° and 45°, *set the hairline of the runner to the angle on the righthand markings of the **ST** or **T** scale and read the tangent of the angle on the **D** scale.* **For angles between 45° and 84.26°,** *set the hairline of the runner to the angle on the lefthand markings of the **T** scale and read the tangent of the angle on the **CI** scale aligned with the **D** scale.* **For angles between 84.26° and 89.27°,** *set the hairline of the runner to the angle on the lefthand markings of the **ST** scale and read the tangent of the angle on the **CI** scale aligned with the **D** scale.*

Rule 6. (b) The Arc Tangent. (Applies only to slide rules with both T and ST scales.) If the number is less than 1, *set the hairline of the runner to the number on the **D** scale and read the arc tangent of the number on the righthand markings of the **ST** or **T** scale.* **If the**

number is greater than 1, *set the hairline of the runner to the number on the CI scale and read the arc tangent of the number on the lefthand markings of the T or ST scale.*

Rule 6 (c). The Tangent. (Applies only to slide rules with the T scale but no ST scale.) *Set the angle (from 5°43′ to 45°) on the T scale and read the tangent of the angle on the C or D scale. The tangent of an angle between 45° and 84°17′ is also found by using the T scale. In the case of these larger angles, first subtract the angle from 90°, then set the result on the T scale. Read the tangent on the CI scale lined up with the D scale on slide rules with the T scale on the front of the stock; on slide rules having the T scale on the back of the slide, read the tangent on the D scale under the lefthand index of the C scale.*

Rule 6 (d). The Arc Tangent. (Applies only to slide rules with the T scale but no ST scale.) *Set the number (between 0.1 and 1.0) in one of two ways. If your slide rule has the T scale on the front of the stock, set the number on the D scale and read the angle on the T scale. If your slide rule has the T scale on the back of the slide, bring the number on the C scale over the righthand index of the D scale and read the angle on the T scale against the mark.*

Numbers between 1 and 10 require a different procedure because the corresponding angles are between 45° and 84°17′. If your slide rule has the T scale on the front of the stock, set the hairline of the runner to the number on the CI scale, then read the angle on the T scale under the hairline. Then subtract this angle from 90°.

If your slide rule has the T scale on the back of the slide, set the lefthand index of the C scale over the number on the D scale. Then read the angle on the T scale against the mark, and subtract this angle from 90° to get the final result.

NEGATIVE NUMBERS

A negative number is a number that is less than zero—sometimes called a *minus* number. Such numbers are designated by a *minus sign* in front of the number. This is never omitted. An example is minus three, written as —3. Minus three is three less than zero. Negative numbers are encountered in many types of mathematical calculations. They are nothing to worry about if you will study a few facts and rules about them.

Fig. A shows a vertical scale that illustrates the relationship between positive and negative numbers. The long mark at the center represents zero. All numbers above zero are plus, or positive, numbers. Our limited space allows only a small part of the complete scale to be shown. The smallest possible number is negative and is at the very bottom of the complete scale. The largest possible number is positive and is at the very top of the complete scale. Look at Fig. A and note that any given number is less than any number above it, and is greater than any number below it. This is always true, regardless of the *numerical* or *absolute value** of the number. As examples of this, note by study of the scale that *5* is greater than —7; *0* is greater than —3; —2 is greater than —9; —7 is less than —5; —2 is less than 2; —9 is less than 9.

Fig. A

ADDITION AND SUBTRACTION – USING A
SCALE. To add to a number is always to increase its value. It follows then, that on the scale, Fig. A, *to add to a given number is to*

---

*The *numerical* or *absolute* value of a number is its distance from zero. Example: although —9 and 9 are not the same (see Fig. A), the absolute values of —9 and 9 are the same (9 units) because each is the same distance from zero.

count up from the number. Examples: *(1)* 5 + 6 = ? Starting at *5* we count up six spaces to stop on *11;* so 5 + 6 = 11. *(2)* −6 + 3 = ? Starting at −*6* we count up three spaces, to stop on −*3;* so −6 + 3 = −3.

To subtract from a number is always to decrease its value. Thus on the scale *to subtract from a given number is to count down from the number.* Examples: *(1)* 8 − 3 = ? Starting on *8,* we count down three spaces to stop on *5;* so 8 − 3 = 5. *(2)* 3 − *4* = ? Starting on *3* we count down four spaces. In doing this we pass zero and stop on −*1;* so 3 − 4 = − 1. *(3)* −6 − 4 = ? Starting on −*6* we count down four spaces to stop on −*10;* so −6 − 4 = −10.

ADDITION AND SUBTRACTION BY RULE.

RULE A. To find the sum of two or more numbers having the same sign, add the numbers arithmetically and prefix the common sign to the answer.

The following are examples of Rule A. Note that in each example both numbers have the same sign.

1. 6 + 3 = 9	**4.** −6 − 3 = −9
2. −4 − 7 = −11	**5.** 4 + 7 = 11
3. 2 + 5 = 7	**6.** −2 − 5 = −7

RULE B. To find the sum of two numbers having unlike signs, subtract the number having the smaller numerical value from the number having the greater numerical value and prefix the sign of the greater number to the answer.

The following are examples of Rule B. Note that the two numbers in each example have unlike signs.

1. −6 + 3 = −3	**4.** 6 − 3 = 3
2. −5 + 3 = −2	**5.** 5 − 3 = 2
3. −7 + 10 = 3	**6.** 7 − 10 = −3

Algebraic Sum. The answer obtained by following either of these two rules is called the *algebraic sum.* Note that adding two numbers in this way does not always give the sum of the numerical values. For exampe, −9 + 9 = 0, not 18. Or, −4 + 6 = 2, not 10.

Addition of a Negative Number. When it is desired to add a negative number, first remove the parenthesis marks and replace the two original signs (to the left and right of the first parenthesis) by a negative sign, then proceed to find the algebraic sum of the two numbers. As an example, $6 + (-3) = ?$ Remove the parentheses, substituting a minus sign for the two signs (the plus sign to the left of the parenthesis and the minus sign within the parentheses), and you have $6 - 3 = 3$. Note the following examples:

1. $9 + (-12) = -3$
2. $16 + (-3) = 13$
3. $14 + (-8) = 6$
4. $7 + (-12) = -5$

5. $-9 + (-7) = -16$
6. $-15 + (-4) = -19$
7. $-3 + (-6) = -9$
8. $-4 + (-10) = -14$

Multiplication of Positive and Negative Numbers.

RULE C. The product of two numbers having like signs is positive. The product of two numbers having unlike signs is negative.

Division of Positive and Negative Numbers.

Rule D. The quotient obtained by dividing two numbers having like signs is a positive number. The quotient obtained by dividing two numbers having unlike signs is a negative number.

METRIC MEASUREMENTS

A NOTE ON THE METRIC SYSTEM

At this time (1972), it appears likely that the United States will convert to the metric system of measurement during the next 20 years or so. A great deal of work is being done to make this conversion happen. International meetings are being held to advance it, agencies such as the National Bureau of Standards and the National Aeronautics and Space Administration are working on it, and many professional societies have committees studying it.

Actually, it will probably be called the International System of Units, rather than the metric system, and will be abbreviated as SI (Système International d'Unités).

The changes which will have the greatest meaning to most people will be in units of length, weight, and temperature.

The new basic length unit will be the meter, which is equivalent to 39.4 inches. This single unit will replace a whole set of length units now used in this country. Some of them are the inch, foot, yard, rod, furlong, and mile. All lengths can then be expressed as decimal fractions of a meter, although it is likely that there will be some use of the kilometer (1000 meters), the centimeter (1/100 of a meter), and the millimeter (1/1000 of a meter). The great advantage of adopting this single basic length unit is that it avoids having to multiply or divide by such factors as 12 (12 inches in a foot), 36 (36 inches in a yard), 16.5 (16.5 feet in a rod), and 5280 (5280 feet in a mile).

The new basic weight and force unit will be the newton, which is equivalent to 0.225 pounds. The use of this single unit for weight and force will avoid having to multiply or divide by such factors as 16 (16 ounces in a pound).

Temperature will be measured in degrees Centigrade (also called Celsius and abbreciated as °C) for most purposes. The Centigrade scale has its zero at the freezing point of water (32° Fahrenheit) and has a value of 100° at the boiling point of water (212° F). Scientists and some engineers will use the Kelvin (K) scale which starts at absolute zero (459.67° below zero on the Fahrenheit scale), but on which a 1° difference in temperature is the same as on the Centigrade scale. At any given temperature, the reading on the Kelvin scale is 273.15° greater than the reading on the Centigrade scale.

In the early part of this change to the SI system, there will be a lot of work in converting from the old units to the new, for example, from something like 1 pound 11 ounces to 7.506 newtons, or from 2 feet 6½ inches to 0.775 meters.

Then, when the conversion has been accomplished, new work will require calculation in the new system, for example, to calculate the area of a rectangle which is 3.4 meters long and 1.82 meters wide. The result, of course, will be in square metres.

The slide rule is a wonderful device for both types of calculation, either conversion from the old system to the new or computation in the new system. What you learn in this book will not become obsolete because of a change in the system of measurement.

CONVERSION OF LENGTHS TO AND FROM THE METRIC SYSTEM

Now that you know how to multiply and divide with the slide rule, you can easily learn to convert lengths from the old U.S. system of measurement to meters in the new SI system, or to convert back. There are conversion factors available. Thus,

(number of feet) $\times$ 0.3048 = number of meters,
(number of inches) $\times$ 0.0254 = number of meters,
(number of miles) $\times$ 1609 = number of meters,

or, you can write them in this way:

$$\frac{number\ of\ meters}{0.3048} = number\ of\ feet,$$

$$\frac{number\ of\ meters}{0.0254} = number\ of\ inches,$$

$$\frac{number\ of\ meters}{1609} = number\ of\ miles.$$

You should use your own slide rule now to verify that 17 feet is the equivalent of 5.18 meters, and that 9 inches is the equivalent of 0.238 meters.

One way to convert something like 3 feet 8¼ inches to meters is to multiply 3 by 0.3048 to get 0.915 meters, then multiply 8¼ by 0.0254 to get 0.21 meters, and add 5.18 to 0.21 to get 5.39 meters as the equivalent of 3 feet 8¼ inches. (This is not the only way to make this conversion)

A length of 5.35 miles would be converted to meters by multiplying 5.35 by 1609 to get 8600 meters.

On the other hand, if you wanted to know how many miles a kilometer (1000 meters) is, you could simply divide 1000 by 1609 to get 0.622 miles.

You might want to convert centimeters to inches. Now a centimeter is 1/100 of a meter, so 3.88 centimeters would be the same as 0.0388 meters. Then, you could convert to inches by dividing by 0.0254 and you would get 1.525 inches.

To convert 87.5 meters to feet, you could just divide 87.5 by 0.3048 and get a result of 287 feet.

CONVERSION OF VOLUME TO AND FROM THE METRIC SYSTEM

It is easy to convert volumes from the U.S. system to the metric system, and to convert volumes from the metric system to the U.S. system. You can do it simply by multiplying or dividing with the slide rule, since conversion factors are available. The new volume units will be the cubic meter, the liter, and the cubic centimeter. Just which one will be used in a particular case will depend on the size of the volume.

Very large volumes are often expressed in cubic yards now, for example, the volume of earth moved in constructing a highway. Such large volumes will probably be expressed in cubic meters. An actual cube which has a volume of one cubic meter is 39.37 inches on a side. You can convert from cubic yards to cubic meters with this conversion factor:

(number of cubic yards) × 0.7644 = number of cubic meters, or you can convert the other way with this,

$$\frac{(\text{number of cubic meters})}{0.7644} = \text{number of cubic yards.}$$

Thus, if you calculate that 3070 cubic yards of earth would have to be moved for a highway interchange, you could multiply 3070 by 0.7644 to get 2340 cubic meters. Or, if you wanted to know how many cubic yards were equivalent to 53 cubic meters, you could divide 53 by 0.7644 to get 69.3 cubic yards.

Volumes of intermediate magnitude are now expressed in such units as the bushel, gallon, quart, and pint. In the metric system, they will probably be expressed in liters. A liter is 1/1000 of a cubic meter. This is a little more than a quart. To convert from the U.S. system to the metric system, you could use these conversion factors,

(number of bushels) × 35.25 = number of liters,
(number of gallons) × 3.785 = number of liters,
(number of quarts) × 0.946 = number of liters,
(number of pints) × 0.473 = number of liters,

or, if you wanted to convert the other way, you could put these equations in the form,

$$\frac{\text{number of liters}}{35.25} = \text{number of bushels,}$$

$$\frac{\text{number of liters}}{3.785} = \text{number of gallons,}$$

$$\frac{\text{number of liters}}{0.946} = \text{number of quarts,}$$

$$\frac{\text{number of liters}}{0.473} = \text{number of pints.}$$

A volume of 60 bushels could be converted to liters by multiplying 60 by 35.25 to get 2110 liters.

If you wanted to know how many liters there are in 12 gallons, you could multiply 12 by 3.785 to get 45.4 liters.

Or, you could convert 3 quarts to liters by multiplying 3 by 0.946 to get 2.84.

A volume of 1.5 pints would be 1.5 × 0.473 = 0.71 liters.

It is just as easy to go the other way. If you have a known volume of 1360 liters, you can divide 1360 by 35.25 to get 38.6 bushels.

You could convert 22 liters to gallons by dividing 22 by 3.785 to get 5.82 gallons.

A volume of 3 liters would be converted to quarts by dividing 3 by 0.946 to get 3.18 quarts.

And, a volume of 1.7 liters could be converted to pints by dividing 1.7 by 0.473 to get 3.59 pints.

Very small volumes are often expressed in fluid ounces in the U.S. system, for example, quantities of cosmetics and extracts. In the metric system, the unit of volume for such small quantities will probably be the cubic centimeter. A centimeter is 1/100 of a meter, and a cubic centimeter is 1/1,000,000 of a cubic meter. A cube which is 0.3937 inches on a side has a volume of 1 cubic centimeter. Converting fluid ounces to the metric system is easy using this formula,

(number of fluid ounces) $\times$ 29.57 = number of cubic centimeters, or, you can convert the other way by rewriting the formula in this manner,

$$\frac{\text{number of cubic centimeters}}{29.57} = \text{number of fluid ounces.}$$

Thus, a half ounce of expensive perfume would be 0.5 $\times$ 29.57 = 14.78 cubic centimeters.

Or, 150 cubic centimeters of shaving lotion would be 150 divided by 29.57, which is 5.08 fluid ounces.

CONVERSION OF FORCE TO AND FROM THE METRIC SYSTEM

Anyone who can multiply and divide can easily learn to convert from forces and weights in pounds and ounces to forces in newtons in the metric, or SI system. These are the conversion factors,

(number of pounds) $\times$ 4.448 = number of newtons,
(number of ounces $\times$ 0.278 = number of newtons,

and, if you want to convert newtons back to pounds or ounces, you can express these equations as,

$$\frac{\text{number of newtons}}{4.448} = \text{number of pounds}$$

$$\frac{\text{number of newtons}}{0.278} = \text{number of ounces}$$

You can learn by following with your own slide rule that the way to convert 220 pounds to newtons is to multiply 220 by 4.448 and get 980 newtons. If you want to convert 6½ ounces to newtons, you can multiply 6.5 by 0.278 to get 1.81 newtons. And if the problem is to convert 5 pounds 9 ounces to newtons, you can convert 5 pounds to 22.24 newtons by multiplying 5 by 4.448, then convert 9 ounces to 2.51 newtons by multiplying 9 by 0.278, and add 22.24 to 2.51 to get 24.75 newtons as the final result. (This is not the only way to perform this conversion.)

Newtons can be converted to U.S. units by dividing. Thus, 183 newtons can be converted to 41.2 pounds by dividing 183 by 4.448. Or, 3.95 newtons can be converted to 14.2 ounces by dividing 3.95 by 0.278.

CONVERSIONS OF TEMPERATURE
TO AND FROM THE METRIC SYSTEM

Most of us are accustomed to using the Fahrenheit scale to measure temperature or to convey information about temperature. We know that water freezes at 32°F and boils at 212°F. We know that 75°F is comfortable for most people and 100°F is uncomfortably warm. It is easy to convert degrees Fahrenheit to degrees Centigrade by using this formula,

$$\frac{(\text{number of degrees Fahrenheit}) - 32}{1.8} = \text{number of degrees Centigrade},$$

or we can convert from Centigrade to Fahrenheit by rewriting the formula as,

number of degrees Fahrenheit = number of degrees Centigrade

$$\times \ 1.8 + 32$$

Thus, if you know that the temperature is 135°F in Death Valley, you can convert this to Centigrade by subtracting 32 from 135 to get 103, and then dividing 103 by 1.8 to get the temperature as 57.2°C. Try this for yourself with your own slide rule.

If you think that −20°F is pretty cold, you can see what it would be in degrees C by subtracting 32 from −20 to get −52, and then dividing −52 by 1.8 to get −28.9°C.

You might want to go the other way and convert the melting point of a certain alloy from 970°C to Fahrenheit. To do this, you would use the second formula and multiply 970 by 1.8 to get 1746, and then add 32 to 1746 to get 1778°F.

Or, if you wonder whether you would be comfortable in a room at 30°C, you could multiply 30 by 1.8 to get 54, and then add 32 to get 86°F. This is a bit too warm for most people.

ANSWERS TO PRACTICE PROBLEMS

Page 30

1. See examples 1-5.   2. 922.   3. 478.   4. 977.   5. 1,021.
6. 983.   7. 453.   8. 1,556 sq. ft.   9. 3480.   10. 255 mi.   11. 264.
12. 489 lb.   13. $8.   14. 1.256 lb.   15. 783 lb.

Page 32

1. 999.   2. 987.   3. 1,027.   4. 1,109.   5. 1,118.

Page 35

1. 0.000347.   2. 504.   3. 0.00526.   4. 14.87.   5. 2,240,000.
6. 0.0346.   7. 6,720 ft.   8. 1,925 cu. in.   9. 11,620 lb.   10. 63,300
in.   11. 790.16.   12. 2,625.

Page 36

1. 0.713.   2. 0.00889.   3. 94.2.   4. 0.00892.   5. 0.0000937.
6. 0.000903.   7. 5.36 gal.   8. 8,070 lb.   9. 740 sq. ft.   10. 9,590,000
sq. ft.

Page 38

1. 0.818; 0.727; 0.687; 0.593; 0.477.   2. 2,850; 6,490; 18,310;
27,300; 40,100; 68,200; 177,000; 230,000 cu. in.   3. $1.00; $1.15;
$1.30; $1.40; $1.62; $1.94.   4. 32.3; 42.5; 44; 66; 73.3; 88; 105.6;
124.8; 139.3 ft.   5. 110; 215; 328; 512; 678; 1,210 ft.   6. 2.65;
3.55; 7.37; 12.1; 17.76; 22.6; 27.9 lb.

Page 41

1. 0.0366   2. 7,820.   3. 1,900.   4. 5.14.   5. 6,880.   6. 1,877
cu. ft.   7. 2,990.   8. 125.6 gal.   9. 1.482.   10. 2,080 cu. yd.

Page 46

1. 22.8. 2. 43.3. 3. 0.585. 4. 0.858. 5. 84,000. 6. 0.189.
7. 28.7. 8. 72.5. 9. 150,000. 10. 9.54. 11. 71. 12. 1,015.
13. 35.4. 14. 671,000. 15. 20.3. 16. 3,240 lb. 17. 137.1 mi.
18. 6,050. 19. $22.10. 20. 1,069; 1,552; 490; 366; 62.8; 236.
21. 11,250 sq. ft. 22. 147,800 gal. 23. 14.7 lb. per sq. in. 24. 5,150.
25. 9.3. 26. 14.1. 27. 21.3. 28. 0.1036. 29. 63.1. 30. 213.
31. 23.3. 32. 63. 33. 568. 34. 70. 35. 16.3 36. 17,440.
37. 34,900. 38. 55.7. 39. 639. 40. 91,200.

Page 52

1. 557. 2. 173. 3. 866. 4. 136. 5. 746. 6. 72. 7. 69¢.
8. 361. 9. 86¢. 10. 798. 11. $32. 12. 679. 13. 768. 14. 234
in. 15. 12 ft.

Page 55

1. 1.203. 2. 0.1952. 3. 665. 4. 0.1822. 5. 15,750. 6. 12,710.
7. 153.3. 8. 0.01322. 9. 0.1141. 10. 11.31.

Page 56

1. 0.00394. 2. 9.22. 3. 0.839. 4. 0.0560. 5. 0.000629.
6. 17,680. 7. 0.00858. 8. 73.6. 9. 0.0001101. 10. 436.

Page 57

1. 0.636; 0.538; 0.467; 0.412; 0.368. 2. 0.1428; 0.0769; 0.0667;
0.0476; 0.0323. 3. 36.5; 27.2; 21.9; 15.48; 11.37.

Page 61

1. 0.1668; 0.257; 0.348; 0.469; 0.712; 0.864; 0.985. 2. 0.1169;
0.1661; 0.239; 0.326; 0.482 cu. ft. 3. 16; 29; 57; 69; 77; 97¢.
4. 1.95; 33.8; 51.5; 80.0; 106.1; 12.42; 1.369. 5. 13.65; 19.12; 26.7;
31.4; 43; 60; 75 m.p.h. 6. 161; 371; 795; 106.8; 1,248; 13.12.
7. 0.0321; 10.97; 0.723; 0.1046; 0.1249; 1.013. 8. 0.706; 0.294;
0.412; 0.471; 0.823; 0.941. 9. 11.6; 37.6; 20.6; 61.3; 9.25; 22.2.
10. 0.428; 0.157; 0.0672; 0.1142; 0.01285; 0.1315; 0.900; 0.714.

Page 63

1. 2.13. 2. 4.66. 3. 4.72. 4. 363. 5. 1.77.

Page 65

1. 377. **2.** 0.262. **3.** 1.208. **4.** 0.288. **5.** 0.1955. **6.** 0.01296.
7. 0.00218. **8.** 1.274. **9.** 5.02. **10.** 3.48.

Page 68

1. 2.52. **2.** 5.18. **3.** 0.0404. **4.** 3.71. **5.** 1.125. **6.** 94.3.
7. 80.6. **8.** 0.90. **9.** 64.8. **10.** 14.7. **11.** 0.0578. **12.** 5.65.
13. 5.66. **14.** 7,440. **15.** 12,920. **16.** 142.8. **17.** 2.93. **18.** 0.226.
19. 130.6. **20.** 19.08. **21.** 0.375; 0.231; 0.1762. **22.** 0.555; 0.455;
0.417. **23.** 0.1905; 0.238; 0.524. **24.** 0.1263; 0.276; 0.356.
25. 0.1285; 0.1745; 0.211. **26.** 9.73. **27.** 2.73. **28.** 0.203. **29.** 681.
30. 7.29.

Page 76

1. 47. **2.** 0.313. **3.** 1.235. **4.** 0.651. **5.** 0.00232. **6.** 75.5.
7. 0.234. **8.** 2.63. **9.** 31.3. **10.** 0.01193. **11.** 42,500. **12.** 1.
13. 0.0242. **14.** 3.67. **15.** 12.94.

Page 87

1. 20.2. **2.** 6,590. **3.** 51.6. **4.** 0.0259. **5.** 4,540. **6.** 13,980.
7. 23,700. **8.** 0.00108. **9.** 1.115. **10.** 6.38. **11.** 1.795. **12.** 3.87.
13. 392. **14.** 124.7. **15.** 194.8. **16.** 0.00241. **17.** .1822. **18.** 10.24.
19. 0.00383. **20.** 3. **21.** 0.685. **22.** 0.0963. **23.** 2.49. **24.** 0.53.
25. 0.1159. **26.** 141. **27.** 0.536. **28.** 11.84. **29.** 0.818. **30.** 25.3.

Page 93

1. 305 sq. ft. **2.** 132.9 sq. in. **3.** 6.42 sq. cm. **4.** 5.04. **5.** 31.8
lb. **6.** 0.00541. **7.** 38,500. **8.** 1,030. **9.** 0.097. **10.** 27,800,000.
11. 0.0000196. **12.** 75. **13.** 41,500. **14.** 0.00137. **15.** 400,000.

Page 95

1. right half. **2.** left half. **3.** center index. **4.** left half.
5. left index. **6.** left half. **7.** center index. **8.** right half. **9.** right
half. **10.** left index.

Page 97

1. 9.35 ft. **2.** 209 ft. **3.** 1.114 in. **4.** 0.259. **5.** 3.77 ft.
6. 4,740. **7.** 1,497. **8.** 0.01868. **9.** 28.2. **10.** 0.442. **11.** 3.16.
12. 0.0316. **13.** 761. **14.** 172. **15.** 0.00351.

Page 101

1. 529. 2. 3.81. 3. 38. 4. 147,000. 5. 0.77. 6. 28,800,000.
7. 1,740. 8. 0.00515. 9. 161. 10. 3,200. 11. 35.1. 12. 9.68.
13. 19.45. 14. 49.2. 15. 404. 16. 0.286. 17. 1.292. 18. 0.857.
19. 4.63. 20. 29.1. 21. 41.2. 22. 5.97. 23. 104.1. 24. 460.
25. 11.1.

Page 107

1. 930,000. 2. 0.000650. 3. 2,100,000. 4. 41.1. 5. 0.080.
6. 5,200. 7. 62,000. 8. 0.770. 9. 0.0084. 10. 7,550. 11. 379
cu. in. 12. 0.00816 cu. in. 13. 61.2 cu. in. 14. 990. 15. 106.

Page 110

1. 3.25. 2. 7.01. 3. 15.1. 4. 0.1954. 5. 31.8. 6. 125.
7. 17.4. 8. 6.6. 9. 0.755. 10. 19.7. 11. 4.73 in. 12. 12.4 ft.
13. 3.42. 14. 914. 15. 0.714 in.

Page 115

1. 60.5. 2. 1,950. 3. 0.357. 4. 9,800. 5. 0.150. 6. 439.
7. 104. 8. 7,400. 9. 5.45. 10. 23,600. 11. 3.27. 12. 0.875.
13. 5.33. 14. 21.3. 15. 1,398. 16. 7.52. 17. 4.46. 18. 0.38.
19. 1.212. 20. 26.

Page 120

1. 0.676; 2. 0.365; 3. 0.187; 4. 0.892; 5. 0.588; 6. 0.780;
7. 0.1348; 8. 0.553; 9. 0.319; 10. 0.462.

Page 122

1. 0.0108; 2. 0.0201; 3. 0.0611; 4. 0.0377; 5. 0.0890;
6. 0.0162; 7. 0.0728; 8. 0.0316; 9. 0.0515; 10. 0.0564.

Page 123

1. 0.382; 2. 0.938; 3. 0.755; 4. 0.957; 5. 0.0786;
6. 0.0314; 7. 0.769; 8. 0.574; 9. 0.1096; 10. 0.0628.

Page 124

1. 8.34°; 2. 42.3°; 3. 5.22°; 4. 46.3°; 5. 17.2°; 6. 2.48°;
7. 35.7°; 8. 3.54°; 9. 0.97°; 10. 21.5°.

Page 128

1. 0.920.   **2.** 0.800.   **3.** 0.1822.   **4.** 0.866.   **5.** 0.707.   **6.** 0.0779.
7. 0.447.   **8.** 0.264.   **9.** 0.0480.   **10.** 0.956.   **11.** 147.8 lb.   **12.** 147.8 lb.

Page 129

1. 0.827.   **2.** 0.903.   **3.** 0.620.   **4.** 0.676.   **5.** 0.940.   **6.** 0.0262.
7. 0.00436.   **8.** 0.513.   **9.** 0.233.   **10.** 0.412.

Page 130

1. 0.991.   **2.** 0.950.   **3.** 0.971.   **4.** 0.990.   **5.** 0.994.   **6.** 0.958.
7. 0.983.   **8.** 0.980.   **9.** 0.985.   **10.** 0.968.

Page 132

1. 48°25′.   **2.** 9°2′.   **3.** 3°15′.   **4.** 41°50′.   **5.** 25°30′.
6. 11°50′.   **7.** 4°48′.   **8.** 64°50′.   **9.** 20°30′.   **10.** 30°.

Page 134

1. −0.423.   **2.** −0.766.   **3.** 0.1765.   **4.** 0.836.   **5.** −0.887.
6. −0.5.   **7.** −0.152.   **8.** 0.152.   **9.** −0.625.   **10.** −0.542.

Page 136

1. −0.866.   **2.** −0.462.   **3.** 0.195.   **4.** 0.866.   **5.** −0.171.
6. −0.707.   **7.** −0.737.   **8.** −0.0987.   **9.** 0.707.   **10.** 0.924.

Page 137

1. 0.00940.   **2.** 0.00741.   **3.** 0.000348.   **4.** 0.00320.   **5.** 0.00577.
6. 0.00408.   **7.** 0.00240.   **8.** 0.001875.   **9.** 0.0001791.   **10.** 0.00618.
11. 10.1 lb.   **12.** 0.0852 mi. or 450 ft.   **13.** 11,440 ft.   **14.** 0.206 in.

Page 139

1. 33′42″.   **2.** 11′23″.   **3.** 2′29″.   **4.** 6′39″.   **5.** 18′36″.
6. 3′1″.   **7.** 13′17″.   **8.** 4′8″.   **9.** 23′30″.   **10.** 3′26″.

Page 140

1. 31°35′.   **2.** 72°18′.   **3.** 73°50′.   **4.** 79°13′.   **5.** 60°.
6. 44°35′.   **7.** 48°10′.   **8.** 84°16′.   **9.** 21°15′.   **10.** 65°22′.

Page 141

1. 73°57′. 2. 77°41′. 3. 79°44′. 4. 81°54′. 5. 71°48′.
6. 75°28′. 7. 75°56′. 8. 76°25′. 9. 84°16′. 10. 74°48′.

Page 148

1. 0.521; 2. 0.680; 3. 0.129; 4. 0.204; 5. 0.944; 6. 0.615;
7. 0.162; 8. 0.407; 9. 0.264; 10. 0.840.

Page 149-150

1. 0.0977; 2. 0.01308; 3. 0.0367; 4. 0.0825; 5. 0.0686;
6. 0.0497; 7. 0.0171; 8. 0.0279; 9. 0.0717; 10. 0.0913.

Page 150

1. 0.00873; 2. 0.00297; 3. 0.00646; 4. 0.00140; 5. 0.00838;
6. 0.00402; 7. 0.00742; 8. 0.00890; 9. 0.00201; 10. 0.00472.

Page 152

1. 1.234; 2. 9.50; 3. 3.37; 4. 1.079; 5. 2.66; 6. 1.14;
7. 1.568; 8. 7.38; 9. 1.934; 10. 3.84.

Page 153

1. 11.45; 2. 14.7; 3. 44; 4. 22; 5. 10.42; 6. 95.5;
7. 13.65; 8. 31.8; 9. 11.13; 10. 16.84.

Page 154

1. 71.7; 2. 85.4; 3. 130; 4. 104; 5. 205; 6. 573; 7. 286;
8. 179; 9. 80.7; 10. 260.

Page 155

1. 6.67°; 2. 42.7°; 3. 4.13°; 4. 27.96°; 5. 2.18°;
6. 23.16°; 7. 12.2°; 8. 1.06°; 9. 3.84°; 10. 21.56°.

Page 156

1. 53.5°; 2. 88.57°; 3. 80.86°; 4. 66.3°; 5. 76.7°
6. 85.78°; 7. 86.18°; 8. 82.3°; 9. 83.06°; 10. 87.51°.

Page 157

1. 0.535°;   2. 0.01146°;   3. 0.43°;   4. 0.309°;   5. 0.0975°;
6. 0.0378°;   7. 0.356°;   8. 0.249°;   9. 0.42°;   10. 0.0229°.

Page 157-158

1. 89.542°;   2. 89.776°;   3. 89.833°;   4. 89.454°;   5. 89.706°;
6. 89.748°;   7. 89.905°;   8. 89.692°;   9. 89.791°;   10. 89.510°.

Page 161

1. 0.667.   2. 0.498.   3. 0.313.   4. 0.915.   5. 0.1515.   6. 0.1036.
7. 0.368.   8. 0.227.   9. 0.766.   10. 0.339.   11. 57.8 ft.   12. 5.55 in.

Page 162

1. 0.0960.   2. 0.0323.   3. 0.0588.   4. 0.0698.   5. 0.0819.
6. 0.0421.   7. 0.0218.   8. 0.0888.   9. 0.0686.   10. 0.0381.   11. 136
ft.   12. 16.75 in.

Page 163

1. 0.00445.   2. 0.01621.   3. 0.00239.   4. 0.00675.   5. 0.01309.
6. 0.0000872.   7. 0.00361.   8. 0.0112.   9. 0.00504.   10. 0.01731.

Page 165

1. 1.055.   2. 3.13.   3. 9.17.   4. 1.192.   5. 1.693.   6. 4.61.
7. 2.01.   8. 1.00.   9. 6.06.   10. 10.00.

Page 166

1. 11.45.   2. 14.13.   3. 76.30.   4. 10.90.   5. 15.29.   6. 21.70.
7. 39.90.   8. 68.80.   9. 18.58.   10. 20.45.

Page 167

1. 6°44'.   2. 43°40'.   3. 40°55'.   4. 18°28'.   5. 35°20'
6. 34°45'.   7. 5°46'.   8. 25°5'.   9. 11°14'.   10. 16°44'.

Page 168

1. 45°20'.   2. 56°18'.   3. 73°51'.   4. 80°10'.   5. 75°59'.
6. 81°28'.   7. 61°37'.   8. 64°47'.   9. 71°55'.   10. 53°25'.

Page 170

1. 5°3'.   2. 9'40".   3. 5°34'.   4. 2°45'.   5. 38'0".   6. 3'37".
7. 6'38".   8. 3°47'.   9. 25'6".   10. 1°26'.

Page 171-172

1. 84°40′.   **2.** 88°39′.   **3.** 86°40′.   **4.** 87°9′.   **5.** 88°4′.
6. 84°50′.   **7.** 88°10′.   **8.** 87°23′.   **9.** 89°.   **10.** 89°14′.   **11.** 0.315.
12. 2.21.   **13.** 0.1028.   **14.** 0.943.   **15.** 4.39.   **16.** 0.543.   **17.** 0.0480.
18. 6.53.   **19.** 0.602.   **20.** 14.96.   **21.** 19°54′.   **22.** 74°33′.   **23.**
4°52′.   **24.** 36°45′.   **25.** 56°42′.   **26.** 87°20′.   **27.** 9°29′.   **28.**
69°48′.   **29.** 40°30′.   **30.** 3°10′.

Page 174

1. 1.086.   **2.** −1.102.   **3.** −0.148.   **4.** −0.245.   **5.** −1.634.
6. −0.698.   **7.** 1.000.   **8.** −5.77.   **9.** 0.519.   **10.** −1.000.

Page 181

1. 0.881;   **2.** 2.358;   **3.** 3.158;   **4.** 0.103;   **5.** 8.788-10;
6. 9.408-10;   **7.** 4.342;   **8.** 2.712;   **9.** 7.260-10;   **10.** 1.656.

Page 183

1. 23.7;   **2.** 269;   **3.** 5.54;   **4.** 0.152;   **5.** 3310;   **6.** 0.01883;
7. 42.4;   **8.** 1295;   **9.** 8.42;   **10.** 0.00468.

Page 185

1. 5.313.   **2.** 1.69.   **3.** 3.62.   **4.** −0.483.   **5.** 2.30 .   **6.** −2.87.
7. 4.92.   **8.** 9.90.   **9.** 0.583.   **10.** 6.77.

Page 187

1. 65.4.   **2.** 2.04.   **3.** 3.57.   **4.** 0.0369.   **5.** 10.00.   **6.** 0.100.
7. 19.13.   **8.** 5.98.   **9.** 0.514.   **10.** 41.3.

Page 192

1. 1056;   **2.** 1.334;   **3.** 0.848;   **4.** 4560;   **5.** 18.32;   **6.** 536000;
7. 0.0001638;   **8.** 471;   **9.** 27.35;   **10.** 0.0000381;   **11.** 299 sq. in.;
12. 16.93 sq. in.;   **13.** 104.1 cu. in.;   **14.** $5.54;   **15.** 0.00515 sq. in.

Page 194

1. 15.3;   **2.** 1.077;   **3.** 0.718;   **4.** 54.8;   **5.** 0.2733;   **6.** 12.41;
7. 0.0437;   **8.** 165.2;   **9.** 44.2;   **10.** 2.22;   **11.** 24.5 ft.;
12. 1.225 in.;   **13.** 173.2 ft.;   **14.** 0.798;   **15.** 0.1897 in.

Page 200

1. 10.58. 2. 773. 3. 41.0. 4. 150.9. 5. 10,310. 6. 0.361.
7. 750. 8. 112.6. 9. 32.5. 10. 0.0792. 11. 276,000. 12. 95,700.
13. 81,800. 14. 143.1. 15. 19,520.

Page 208

1. 233. 2. 11.60. 3. 0.141. 4. 210. 5. 0.0631. 6. 0.140.
7. 18.72. 8. 0.01093. 9. 13.87. 10. 3.03. 11. 1.208. 12.
0.000575. 13. 0.00439. 14. 2.58. 15. 2.18.

Page 215

1. 4,360. 2. 39.5. 3. 239. 4. 19,300. 5. 670,000. 6. 40.8.
7. 2.63. 8. 151.5. 9. 61.5. 10. 0.523. 11. 273. 12. 190.5.
13. 7,240. 14. 12. 15. 0.548.

Page 219-220

1. 0.376. 2. 2.46. 3. 1.127. 4. 3.52. 5. 35.9. 6. 0.348.
7. 2,420. 8. 0.336. 9. 8.51. 10. 10.6. 11. 3,980. 12. 0.0001028.
13. 0.77. 14. 2.54. 15. 152.6.

Page 220-221

1. 941. 2. 6.47. 3. 32,500. 4. 89,800. 5. 57. 6. 592.
7. 0.253. 8. 19.7. 9. 169.7. 10. 3.23. 11. 1.777. 12. 183.
13. 159.2. 14. 9.53. 15. 1.4. 16. 0.917. 17. 0.323. 18. 12.52.
19. 0.00762. 20. 69.8.

Page 228

1. 13.4; 2. 222; 3. 17.84; 4. 262; 5. 21; 6. 204;
7. 302,000; 8. 343; 9. 1080; 10. 4450; 11. 23800; 12. 602 mi.;
13. 28.7 sq. in.; 14. $3.05; 15. 3270.

Page 235

1. 17.8; 2. 3.56; 3. 0.715; 4. 0.0243; 5. 24.9; 6. 0.0385;
7. 12.4; 8. 0.0673; 9. 0.141; 10. 0.402; 11. 0.0361 lb.; 12. 55
cents; 13. 477 lb.; 14. 54; 15. 14.2 in.

Page 241-242

1. 131; 2. 11.28; 3. 12.53; 4. 4.94; 5. 0.0815; 6. 175;
7. 0.323; 8. 0.213; 9. 189; 10. 0.0514.

Page 243

1. 449; **2.** 58.9; **3.** 1068; **4.** 55.8; **5.** 1775; **6.** 42; **7.** 6720; **8.** 93.8; **9.** 15.9; **10.** 17; **11.** 1408 lb.; **12.** 3240; **13.** 338 sq. in.; **14.** 8780; **15.** 56500 lb.

Page 245

1. 40300; **2.** 1673; **3.** 82.3; **4.** 732; **5.** 1760; **6.** 116.2; **7.** 153.2; **8.** 129.2; **9.** 89; **10.** 6550; **11.** 680 cu. in.; **12.** 2320 cu. ft.; **13.** $15.65; **14.** 6180 lb.; **15.** 77800.

Page 246

1. 32.8; **2.** 202; **3.** 278; **4.** 176000; **5.** 83.6; **6.** 123; **7.** 69700; **8.** 323; **9.** 4020; **10.** 797.

Page 247

1. 3.30; **2.** 1.023; **3.** 0.474; **4.** 4.62; **5.** 2.13; **6.** 0.121; **7.** 30.5; **8.** 54.8; **9.** 0.260; **10.** 7.52; **11.** 18.4; **12.** 6.24; **13.** 2.70 cents; **14.** 5.71 ft.; **15.** 111.2 ft./sec.

Page 249

1. 0.0172; **2.** 17.55; **3.** 2.48; **4.** 0.141; **5.** 0.0444; **6.** 0.191; **7.** 0.0913; **8.** 1.745; **9.** 0.121; **10.** 0.1068.

Page 250

1. 0.510; **2.** 1.185; **3.** 222; **4.** 1.188; **5.** 0.0563; **6.** 1.995; **7.** 0.572; **8.** 2.11; **9.** 3.75; **10.** 0.821.

Page 265

1. 6.45. **2.** 2.25. **3.** 1.598. **4.** 4.44. **5.** 1.0319. **6.** 4.65. **7.** 1.1192. **8.** 43. **9.** 1.076. **10.** 1.01063.

Page 267

1. 0.0727. **2.** 0.9625. **3.** 0.719. **4.** 0.785. **5.** 0.099. **6.** 0.913. **7.** 0.0294. **8.** 0.971. **9.** 0.410. **10.** 0.9105.

Page 269

1. 260,000; **2.** 113,500; **3.** 1,495,000; **4.** 0.00000105; **5.** 0.0001562; **6.** 13,020,000; **7.** 254; **8.** 31.3; **9.** 0.000241; **10.** 0.00089.

Page 272

1. 5.76. **2.** 0.532. **3.** 9.03. **4.** 0.0665. **5.** 363. **6.** 2400.
7. 1,258. **8.** 0.0056. **9.** 0.853. **10.** 0.9715.

Page 273

1. 5.45. **2.** −1.785. **3.** 4.29. **4.** 0.418. **5.** −1.533. **6.** 4.65.
7. −2.51. **8.** −0.0835. **9.** 1.87. **10.** −0.588.

Page 280

1. 2.56×10^2; **2.** 8.93×10^1; **3.** 5.88×10^{-1}; **4.** 2.80×10^3;
5. 1.34×10^5; **6.** 7.22×10^{-2}; **7.** 3.73×10^4; **8.** 3.47×10^{-4};
9. 9.80×10^3; **10.** 6.54×10^{-2}.

Page 281

1. 945; **2.** 0.00987; **3.** 842000; **4.** 21300; **5.** 1.435; **6.** 2.46;
7. 11,900,000; **8.** 5820; **9.** 72.3; **10.** 0.178.

Page 282

1. 159; **2.** 3830; **3.** 0.01863; **4.** 357; **5.** 672; **6.** 0.00242;
7. 0.01696; **8.** 0.000148; **9.** 56.8; **10.** 33100.

Page 284

1. 9.48; **2.** 167; **3.** 692; **4.** 0.00203; **5.** 3190; **6.** 0.738;
7. 33600; **8.** 238000; **9.** 8.02; **10.** 253.

Page 285-286

1. 550; **2.** 14200; **3.** 23,400,000; **4.** 8400; **5.** 1.62;
6. 0.0280; **7.** 0.0069; **8.** 0.000725; **9.** 0.0000179; **10.** 0.00127.

Page 287

1. 25.6; **2.** 18.08; **3.** 86.4; **4.** 42.8; **5.** 0.44; **6.** 0.133;
7. 2830; **8.** 0.0730; **9.** 0.0384; **10.** 0.0149.

Page 288

1. 18700; **2.** 2,100,000; **3.** 0.77; **4.** 0.000258; **5.** 33,800,000;
6. 0.00567; **7.** 72,000,000,000; **8.** 577; **9.** 0.000417; **10.**
0.0000335.

Page 289

1. 11.14; **2.** 32; **3.** 63.2; **4.** 0.430; **5.** 0.266; **6.** 0.722;
7. 152.5; **8.** 0.183; **9.** 18.1; **10.** 0.127.

INDEX

J

K

L